MW00930550

The Essentials
of
Chemical Dependency

Toward a Unified Theory
of Addiction

by

Robert M. McAuliffe, Ph.D., S.T.Lr.

Mary Boesen McAuliffe, Ph.D.

The American Chemical Dependency Foundation
Minneapolis, MN

Bloomington, IN   Milton Keynes, UK
authorHOUSE®

AuthorHouse™
1663 Liberty Drive, Suite 200
Bloomington, IN 47403
www.authorhouse.com
Phone: 1-800-839-8640

AuthorHouse™ UK Ltd.
500 Avebury Boulevard
Central Milton Keynes, MK9 2BE
www.authorhouse.co.uk
Phone: 08001974150

© 2007 Mary Boesen McAuliffe. All rights reserved.

No part of this book may be reproduced, stored in a retrieval system, or transmitted by any means without the written permission of the author.

First published by AuthorHouse 2/11/2008

ISBN: 978-1-4343-0953-2 (sc)

Library of Congress Control Number: 2007903002
Printed in the United States of America
Bloomington, Indiana

This book is printed on acid-free paper.

A publication of the American Chemical Dependency Foundation

Cover Art: "The Fire of Desire"

The art represents the consuming dynamism of the fires of love, attraction, desire, expectation, passion, committed pathological love, pandemonium, and whole person disintegration inherent in addiction.

Acknowledgments:

The authors wish to thank John Hansen for his assistance in developing and editing this new edition, and Scot Adams and Jean Sassatelli for their suggestions, review, and encouragement.

I dedicate this book to my beloved husband, Robert, whose entire life gave witness to his commitment to the pursuit of Truth. I have been gifted over the past forty years to collaborate with him in probing to the essence of addiction and its healing, which is what this book is all about. It has been a labor of Love for both of us. It is our hope that the wisdom and knowledge of addiction contained herein will serve to set free from bondage addicted persons and families everywhere, that they may have fullness of Life in all its dimensions.

Mary

Table of Contents

PART FOUR
Chemical Dependency Diagnosis and Evaluation

Toward a Unified Theory of Addiction

Much has changed in the field of chemical dependency research and treatment in the more than 30 years that have passed since the first publication of *The Essentials of Chemical Dependency* in 1975.

On the positive side, we have seen some significant growth in both the number and effectiveness of preventive education, counseling, and treatment programs for chemically dependent persons and those closest to them. Chemical dependency counselors and workers, who were members of a still somewhat fledgling occupation when we first wrote, have gained in professional recognition both among those in the helping professions and among those seeking help. We have also seen an immeasurably important growth in society's understanding of addiction as a serious disease, one that affects people of all ages and from every walk of life. This view has encouraged more people to seek help and treatment than in the not-so-distant past, when addiction was too often seen as a problem to be hidden or denied, often until it was too late.

Some notable advances have also been made in the areas of medical and scientific research. These advances may help to more accurately diagnose the stage of the disease's advancement in an individual so that appropriate and effective treatment can be provided. For example, the American Society of Addictive Medicine (ASAM) recently published a second edition of its Patient Placement Criteria. This detailed document, based on data gathered at hospitals and treatment centers across the country, closely matches the symptoms and stages of chemical dependency described in our original book, which are presented here again in this revised, updated, and expanded edition. We arrived at our conclusions through a mix of personal experience, philosophy, theology, psychology, and, we believe, rigorous induction based on extensive clinical experience. It is gratifying for us to find the medical sciences arriving at a strikingly similar description of the symptoms and stages of chemical dependency.

Another notable advance in the field has been in the area of co-occurring disorders. While chemical dependency is a disease in itself, and should be diagnosed as such, it frequently occurs in people who are also suffering from diagnosable mental health disorders. The Substance Abuse and Mental Health Service Administration (SAMHSA) has been working with ASAM and many other organizations and individuals in the addiction field to document research and collect data that will improve the diagnosis, placement, and treatment of persons with co-occurring disorders.

An Addiction Crisis of Pandemic Proportions

While there has been much good news to be thankful for, the decades have had their dark sides as well. For example, the availability and abuse of illegal drugs was certainly widespread in the 1970s. Today, however, we clearly face an alcohol and drug addiction crisis of pandemic proportions. The massive amounts of psychoactive substances currently available and easily accessible to everyone, youngsters included, far surpasses that of the '70s. Also, many of the drugs ingested today are of such potency in inducing dramatic, intoxicating "highs" that they have the potential to draw those who ingest them into addiction and ultimately self-destruction at even more alarming rates than before. For example, in the past, people might abusively ingest drugs for some time, even years, before hitting the maintenance or escape stages of addiction. Today, a relatively few encounters with a drug like crystal meth can be enough to send a person into rapid physical, mental, and emotional decline.

The challenges to workers in the chemical dependency field today are greater than ever before as they seek to guide people suffering from addiction — whether it is to alcohol, pharmaceuticals, or illegal drugs — to a state of recovery, health, and happiness. Accomplishing this vital task takes a deep knowledge of the disease of addiction and its essential symptoms and of proven methods of treatment. It also requires great love and compassion for those who are suffering and for the loved ones who suffer with them.

The Need for a Unified Theory of Addiction

For all the time that has gone by since the first edition of *The Essentials*, and all that has happened since then, there is one extraordinarily fundamental thing that has *not* changed, and that is this: there is still no general agreement in the field about what addiction *is*. The comments and debates about the nature of addiction have taken many forms over the years, but the general view still seems to be that we do not know what addiction is. Here, we think, is one of the clearest and strongest expressions of this problem made in recent times:

> "Over the years there has been much data generated from addiction research. We continue however to lack a unified theory of what addiction is, despite the knowledge from biology, psychiatry, psychology, sociology, and criminology."
>
> — Robert Morse, R.M., M.D., from "The Nature of Drug Addiction" in *Addiction and Compulsive Behaviors* (p. 165), published by the National Catholic Bioethics Center, 2000.

Probably no contemporary addiction professional is better qualified to make that statement than Dr. Morse, who, at the time of this writing, is Professor

Emeritus, Department of Psychiatry, at the Mayo Medical School. Dr. Morse is also the former director of Addiction Disorders Services at Mayo. In the early 1990s, he served as co-chairperson of a committee organized by the American Psychiatric Association to develop a definition of drug and alcohol addiction, or "substance dependency," for the Diagnostic and Statistical Manual of Mental Disease, fourth edition (DSM-IV).

Dr. Morse made the above statement in a presentation on "The Nature of Drug Addiction," which was given at a workshop on "Addiction and Compulsive Behaviors" in Dallas, Texas in 1999. The workshop was hosted by the National Catholic Bioethics Center for the bishops of the United States and Canada.

Given his extraordinary credentials and experience in the field, Dr. Morse's speech is well worth a close look. In the course of his talk, he provides a concise description of five basic characteristics of addiction. In his talk, he also offers this summary definition of alcohol/drug addiction: "If you had to boil down a definition of substance dependence to its very essentials, it probably would be 'continued use of the substance (drugs, alcohol) despite the adverse consequences suffered from its use (continued use despite adverse consequences).'"

In his definition, Dr. Morse zeroes in on the inevitable compulsion that accompanies an addiction to mood-altering chemicals. Compulsion is certainly an *essential* symptom of the disease, one that affects everyone suffering from chemical dependency. Addicted persons compulsively keep using their drugs of choice no matter how adverse the consequences suffered from their use. This symptomatic irrational behavior manifested by the addict is caused by, produced by, and flows out of something very powerful, something that comes from very deep within the person of the addict. As Dr. Morse notes, the search for that "something" has motivated a lot of good work in addiction research in so many fields, and yet the essential nature of the disease entity, in most accounts, still appears elusive.

The Main Question Is Still Asked: What Is Addiction?

Dr. Howard J. Shaffer, Ph.D., C.A.S., addresses the question of the nature of addiction in a recent article titled "What is Addiction? A Perspective," which appeared in the Harvard Medical School Division on Addictions website (January 2005). In his essay, Dr. Shaffer discusses the difficulties of arriving at a clear definition of addiction when our understanding of it is influenced by so many different disciplines (including medicine, psychology, chemistry, biology, and sociology, to name a few) and by various forms of addiction, including chemical dependency, of course, but also such behaviors as compulsive gambling, eating disorders, and sexual addictions. Taken as a whole, the attempts to arrive at a clear definition has resulted in a state of affairs that he refers to as "the contemporary conceptual chaos surrounding addiction."

Dr. Shaffer discusses with considerable clarity why an accurate definition of addiction must be based in "the necessary and sufficient cause of addiction." What he is after is what we have always sought to do, and that is to define addiction on the basis of its *essential* cause, and not its complications and effects. For example, while ingesting drugs is certainly a prerequisite of every chemical addiction, we have long argued that it is not the *ultimate cause* of addiction. Dr. Shaffer supports this view when he writes that "simply using drugs or engaging in certain activities do not cause addiction." He then has this to say: "Now let me be explicit: from a logical perspective, the objects of addiction are not the sole cause of addictive behavior patterns."

From our point of view, this approaches the truth about the complex nature of addiction, which affects the whole human person and which, in the case of chemical dependency, certainly cannot be reduced to a physical dependence on a drug.

If the object of addiction is ultimately not the essential cause of the addictive behavior, then what is? In addressing this vital question, Dr. Shaffer writes of the need to develop a new model of addiction. He states: "One strategy for developing a new model is to emphasize the relationship instead of either the attributes of the person struggling with addiction or the object of their addiction."

It was emphatically clear to us by the late 1960s that a unifying theory or organizing principle of some sort was missing from our society's descriptions and definitions of addiction. We had a pressing need to know what *is* this disease. We resolved to pursue this burning question until we could arrive at an answer.

An Organizing Principle for Understanding Addiction

As readers of the original edition of *The Essentials of Chemical Dependency* already know, we have done precisely that. We have long proposed that the key to understanding addiction is the person's committed *relationship* to mood-altering chemicals, the object of addiction. We defined addiction as a *relational* disease. We have been putting forth that theory and exploring its potential as an organizing principle for understanding chemical dependency and other addictions for more than 30 years. From a practical standpoint, workers in the field of chemical dependency treatment have found this approach extraordinarily successful in both diagnosing and treating chemically dependent persons. If anything, *The Essentials of Chemical Dependency* represents an organized effort to clearly define the complex relationship between a chemically dependent person and the object of his or her addiction.

Those scientists who today seek a "unified theory of what addiction is" encounter formidable limitations in their search. As scientists, a major limitation — imposed almost by definition — is their reliance on modern empirical science as their exclusive method of inquiry. This science is concerned with matter, the material world of material things. Scientists concentrating on material dimensions systematically ignore or devalue those powers, activities, and relationships that transcend matter and defy measurement or quantification. These transcendental aspects of human experience (and of being itself) have long been the province of philosophy and theology. There is a long overdue critical need to integrate the application of these disciplines into the study of addiction in order to effectively address all aspects of the human person. If the ultimate cause of addiction rests in a love relationship between a person and the object of his or her addiction, as we will show it does, then the study of this relationship, it seems to us, might greatly benefit from the perspectives of these other disciplines.

Defining an Essentially Relational Illness

Our "theory" initially grew out of a personal experience of alcoholism addiction and treatment for it. Subsequently, in our professional work as clinicians in the addiction field, we gathered actual data about addiction by observing on a daily basis the reality of chemical addiction as it exists in addicted persons. Our theory was and is one arrived at inductively, moving from observed effects to their underlying causes, from essential symptoms produced directly by addiction to the essential nature of addiction itself and to its roots in the various faculties or functional power centers of the human person. In this way, we arrived at our first essential definition of the "disease" entity, the pathology of chemical dependency.

In effect, we defined chemical dependency as a *relational* illness that put addiction into a new disease category. This definition was as follows.

> *"Chemical dependency is essentially a pathological relationship of a person to a mood-altering chemical substance, a psychoactive drug, in expectation of a rewarding experience."*

Over the years, as we learned more about the nature of the disease and how it affects individuals, we continued to refine this definition in an effort to arrive at the most accurate description possible. These efforts have led us, in this current edition, to put forth the following definition, which adds the critical words "committed" and "love" to the original definition:

> *"Chemical dependency is essentially a committed pathological love relationship of a person to a mood-altering chemical substance, a psychoactive drug, in expectation of a rewarding experience."*

In both the original *The Essentials of Chemical Dependency,* published by the American Chemical Dependency Foundation in 1975, and in this revised and expanded edition in 2007, we have sought to penetrate beyond the behavioral manifestations of the disease. These manifestations are, at best, only symptoms of a massive pathology that constitutes the internal nature of the disease — that is, its structure and content. From the start, we have wanted to reach down into the sick sources of the sick behavior within the human person who is the subject of the disease of addiction.

Early on, it was clear to us that faculty psychology, an outgrowth of the philosophical principles of Aristotle, might be a useful approach in our examination. We know of no other model, past or current, that takes into account the *whole person* as thoroughly and completely as this model does. It provided us with a structure for examining the nature and function of the whole person, *soma* and *psyche*, body and soul. In other words, we took into account *both* the material and the spiritual or transcendental nature of the human person wherein addiction exists.

In this new revised edition of *The Essentials of Chemical Dependency*, we address the following points:

- We identify and define more precisely the essential nature of addiction, with a specific focus upon chemical dependency.
- We present a unifying theory of what constitutes the "disease" of addiction.
- We support this theory by identifying essential properties or elements of addiction pathology.
- We apply this theory in a systematic analysis of chemical addiction.
- We point out some implications of this theory in regard to essential requirements for successful prevention, diagnosis, treatment, healing, and recovery from addiction.

In accomplishing these objectives, we offer far more than a unified theory of what addiction is. We define and describe the actual *existential reality*, that is, the actual existence of the disease entity of addiction as opposed to the conceptual possibility. Our description might be called a *phenomenological approach* because it focuses on a central phenomenon, the pathological love relationship with mood-altering chemicals, and identifies the actual particular phenomena that lead to this relationship and to addiction. These particular phenomena indicate the various elements of the pathology that constitute the disease entity itself. This disease entity is the one and only unifier that can possibly bring together all addiction data of whatever kind and garnered by whatever means. In naming this disease entity, readers will note in the course of the book that while we generally use the term "chemical dependency," we also, in some contexts, use the terms "illness," "alcoholism," "addiction," "substance abuse," "chemical dependent," "alcoholic," and "addict."

The Essentials Approach

We offer our work not as a final word but as a definition of chemical dependency that identifies the relational "unifying factor" that will help integrate all that has been and is yet to be discovered or known about alcohol and other drug addictions.

The "essentials approach" employed throughout this book is both *specific* and *definitive*. It is specific in that it focuses on those key characteristics that are constant in chemical dependency and that are therefore found to some degree in every instance of the illness without exception. In this, it differs from *individualistic* approaches that focus exclusively or excessively on the unique and widely variable aspects of each individual case or of each particular drug of preference. It differs, too, from generic approaches that lump together in a general and abstract way all the common elements that can be found among drug dependencies without distinguishing between what is constant or variable, essential or accidental, central or peripheral, either in chemical dependency itself or in chemically dependent persons. Both individualistic and generic approaches leave chemical dependency essentially unspecified and therefore without a proper object for scientific inquiry and without a definite object of therapeutic practice.

The essentials approach is *definitive*, but not in the sense that the last "definitive" word has been uttered on the subject. It is definitive in the sense that its goal is to *define* perceived realities by naming them as precisely and objectively as possible. This is done within the limits of ordinary dictionary language. Each essential definition describes the specific nature, characteristics, and causes of the realities defined. In this, it differs on the one hand from broad descriptive approaches and on the other hand from single-factor causality approaches, from metaphorical model approaches, and from speculative approaches that begin with theoretical assumptions or hypotheses and proceed to test these under artificially constructed and controlled conditions.

All of these approaches are useful, of course, depending on the goals one has in view. Our goal of analyzing, synthesizing, and articulating the essential characteristics and causes of chemical dependency is best served, we have found, by using a definitive approach.

To All Who May Benefit from this Book

We originally wrote this book in the hope of helping individuals who, for a variety of reasons, find themselves dealing directly with the realities, problems, and basic questions of chemical dependency. That purpose has not changed over the years.

This book is addressed first and foremost to everyone who is genuinely concerned about drug problems, and especially to those professionals, students, and trainees in the chemical dependency field and in other fields who must be prepared to recognize and deal with chemical dependency, with its victims, and with the enormous range of problems that drug involvement spawns.

In the second place, the book is addressed to all those front-line workers, both full-time and volunteer, who deal daily with the victims of alcoholism and the other drug dependencies and who feel the need for a clearer statement of what it is they are dealing with in order to know why what they are doing works and how they might improve their helping skills.

This book is also addressed to the millions of men, women, and children who find themselves the unexpected victims of chemical dependency, either through their personal drug involvement or through that of loved ones and associates, and who wonder about the nature of this destructive force that they seek to recover from.

Finally, the book is meant to speak to those with an interest in knowing what chemical dependency is in order to avoid it personally and to prevent it from happening to others.

We know that chemical dependency affects people from every walk of life, without exception, and that therefore the persons who might benefit from this book will inevitably represent the widest range of philosophical, religious, and spiritual beliefs one could imagine. While we would not expect every single reader to share our personal beliefs, we know these beliefs have greatly influenced our approach to our work. At the same time, we are certain that all who have suffered from chemical dependency, or who have sought to help others fighting addiction, will find in these pages accurate and comprehensive descriptions of the causes, symptoms, pathology, and stages of chemical dependency that are firmly based in concrete reality, in the lives and experiences of chemically dependent persons.

We believe that each human being is created unique and irreplaceable, a one-time, no-repeat, never duplicated, individual person who is intended and equipped by God to contribute some particular good to the human family. The good may be great or small; the person may be well-known or little known or unknown; but the contribution is always a special gift of God transmitted to the human family by this unique, irreplaceable person. The exploration, analysis, identification, definition, and articulation of chemical dependency as a "committed pathological love relationship of a person to a mood-altering chemical substance" may be our miniscule contribution to our sisters and brothers who suffer the excruciating experience of personal addiction and its disastrous, destructive effects and consequences upon themselves and others. We wish them all a return to freedom, health, and true happiness.

Robert M. McAuliffe
Mary Boesen McAuliffe

Robert passed away in November 2005 before he could complete this revision of the original The Essentials of Chemical Dependency. *I promised him that I would bring it to completion. The publication of this work fulfills his wish and my promise.*

Mary

What Is Addiction?
My Search for an Answer

By Robert M. McAuliffe

The first edition of *The Essentials of Chemical Dependency* grew directly out of my own experience of alcohol addiction and the treatment I so gratefully and fortunately received for it. In preparing this new edition of *The Essentials*, I felt it might be helpful to describe these experiences and the thoughts and events that followed. My purpose in relating this story is to give readers some sense for the personal, practical, professional, and philosophical bases that contributed to the ideas in this book.

Misery, Then Crisis

It was September 14, 1967. I was on a flight from Chicago heading toward Hazelden Alcoholism Treatment Center in Center City, Minnesota, north of the Minneapolis–St. Paul metropolitan area. Details of the flight and how I came to be on it were blurry to me. So were the events in my life leading up to this day. I felt utterly defeated, confused, guilty, depressed, scared, and very lonely. I asked myself over and over how this could be happening to me. After all, I told myself, I've always been a person of integrity, dedicated and committed to my work. By most standards, I was very well educated. For almost 30 years, I had held highly responsible positions as a priest, philosopher, theologian, professor, writer, counselor, and director of several ministerial programs.

What had gone wrong on that awful night a mere week ago? It was a question that had preoccupied my mind to the point of obsession. I found myself replaying the events of that night again and again, hoping desperately to dredge up the answer from the black hole I imagined in my memory.

I recalled that I had been on my way to visit a friend in a western suburb of Chicago. I had stopped to pick up a bottle of blackberry brandy to bring along as a gift to share with him during my stay. But neither I, nor the bottle, ever reached our destination.

I remembered sampling the brandy just to make sure it was a high-quality gift fitting for my host. The next thing I remembered was growing very tired. I had pulled into a forest preserve along the way to rest. I sincerely thought this was a responsible thing to do. Next, I could vaguely recall someone, either a park guard or police officer, shining a flashlight in my face and knocking on the car window. He told me in no uncertain terms that I was to move out at once, as no one was allowed to stay overnight in the park. I felt rather indignant about the rough manner in which I was awakened and ordered about, but I complied at once without any resistance.

Try as I might, I could not recall a thing from that point until the next morning, when I found myself in a suburban police station, miles from my destination, standing before a court official who was reading a list of charges against me: driving while intoxicated, having an open and empty bottle in the car, reckless driving, which included side-swiping and ramming cars parked on a street in a residential neighborhood, and, finally, fleeing the scene of an accident.

I was in a state of shock — bewildered and unbelieving. How could these charges be true? I had no recollection of any of the things they were accusing me of. As the seriousness of the charges settled in, I was struck by the fear that I had perhaps injured, maimed, or even killed someone. When I was told that I had not done so, that no one had been injured, I broke down in tears of relief.

Fortunately, the judge agreed to delay sentencing (later reduced to fines) if I would enter a residential treatment program for alcoholism and successfully complete the program. I suddenly became — as I later learned through AA — "willing to be willing."

I had to admit to myself that for six years I had prayed for help — not for the grace to stop drinking, but for the grace to learn how to drink in a way that would give me some peace. Drinking was no longer the great pleasure it once was, nor did it bring me any relief from the unnamed, perpetual misery I suffered. I had been so miserable for the previous six years, I couldn't deny I needed help — not for alcoholism, I thought then, but for whatever would take away this dark and painful condition I suffered day and night.

Highlights of My Treatment Experience

My first four days in treatment at Hazelden were mind-blowing, heart-breaking, and life-changing. Mind-blowing because I discovered that I was unquestionably an alcoholic, and that I had much to learn about the disease. Heart-breaking because I realized how much of my life had forever passed me by and how much unintentional hurt I had obliviously inflicted on others. Life-changing because I experienced a providential point of conversion, a "turning around," from a drug-centered life to freedom and a new life. I had no clue then what this new path might require of me.

On my second day in treatment, I read a little book by Dr. Marty Mann called *A Primer on Alcoholism*. Alcoholism was described as a "disease" with many symptoms, a couple dozen of which were presented in a checklist to be completed by the reader. I started to work my way through the checklist and before I got to number twenty, I had checked "Yes" eighteen times. I was stunned. I felt like eighteen tons of bricks had just been dropped on me. I kept repeating to myself, "I'm an alcoholic. I can't drink. Ever!" This sudden realization of my being sick with alcohol addiction drove a conviction to get better so deep into my guts that it has never left. Not even wavered. I believed then, and still do, that it was Providence that put that little book in my hand, opened my eyes to the truth, and gave me the grace of acceptance. But I was still miles away from "letting go" and "letting God," as I heard repeatedly in lectures and AA meetings.

The greater my intellectual insights into this awful disease, the greater were my misery, self-loathing, fear, anger, depression, and despair. In addition to the deep, persistent suffering that arose from my new knowledge and awareness, I found myself suffering greatly for what I did not know — or more precisely, could not remember. I felt continually plagued by the specific fact that I had blacked out under the influence the night of the accident. That had been a shattering experience for me. I felt especially tormented by not knowing what else I might have done that night. My greatest fear and concern was that I might have injured someone in a hit-and-run accident prior to my arrest. I feared that I might have unknowingly committed any of a number of crimes yet to be discovered. I did not even know what they might be because I remembered absolutely nothing. I lived with the gnawing fear that any day a police officer would show up at my door, that I might yet be apprehended for and charged with offenses I would have no memory at all of committing. While on the one hand I was doing my best to follow my treatment program with an open and positive attitude, on the other hand, I was still a wreck from guilt, worry, and anxiety.

My counselor said I was in a state of "smiling depression," which only made me more depressed. I was told I had been placed on "open-ended treatment status." I felt worse than ever. The God of my understanding, at this point, was nothing more than a gray glob. I desperately decided to take things into my own hands by embarking on a Fourth Step Inventory to figure out what was really wrong with me. Then, I thought, I'd fix it myself. For days, I probed the deep, dark, dank well within me. The weaknesses, wrongs, and failures always seemed to outweigh my strengths. I tried to scratch and claw my way out of the well into light and freedom, but it wasn't working.

Late one sleepless night, I was at the point of exhaustion when I experienced a powerful gestalt-like insight: "Surrender to the reality of my addiction and of my entire life. Let go — fall through the bottom of the well into freedom." I felt a rush of inspiration compelling me to say "Yes" to this realization. At once, the oppressive fear I felt seemed to dissipate. I experienced a sensation of a free-floating fall, relaxed, gentle, and incredibly peaceful. I fell into a sound sleep, the first I had experienced in many years. In the morning, I awoke rested, refreshed, and with a sure knowledge that I had indeed hit bottom — not the harsh, devastating bottom I expected, but the gentle hands of Love.

In pajamas and robe, I hurried to the nurses' station in the unit to share my experience with them. As I approached the head nurse, Dee Smith, R.N., she took one look at me and her face lit up. She said, "It happened, didn't it, Bob?" She could clearly see what I so deeply felt, which was immense relief and profound gratitude. Apparently, my whole demeanor had changed dramatically from the figure of a man lost in depression, fear, hopelessness, and desperation to one informed by relief, joy, peace, and hope. As she reached out in compassion and hugged me, I realized tears were pouring from my eyes, and that they were tears of thankfulness and hope. I saw how clearly I had "hit bottom." I saw, too, that I was completely powerless over alcohol. And yet there I was, with a new life opening up to me, and I was eager and unafraid to enter it.

"We Don't Know What Alcoholism Is"

In one of the early lectures I attended, Hazelden director and psychologist Dr. Daniel J. Anderson, Ph.D., said, "We don't know what alcoholism is. But if you do what we tell you, you can get well." I could hardly believe my ears. How could this well-known, highly respected director of this very reputable treatment center not know exactly what was being treated here? If he didn't know, how would I ever know? And if I didn't know, when would this monstrous disease and all its misery strike me again? I was shaken to my roots. Suddenly, I felt a lot of fear and anxiety.

Fortunately, I had also heard Dr. Anderson say, "If you do what we tell you, you can get well." This I believed, and so I became determined to follow their advice. I did what they said, and they were right: it was working. I was on my way to being well again. I guessed at the time that Dr. Anderson's claim to ignorance was thrown out to us to discourage us from getting "into our heads" and speculating about the disease, rather than picking up the tools we needed to recover from it. As it turned out, however, he was stating a simple truth. He *did not know* exactly what alcoholism was. Despite the fact that he was one of the leading pioneers in the multi-disciplinary treatment of alcoholics, commonly referred to as the "Minnesota experience" or "Minnesota model," Dr. Anderson was unable to define the disease for us.

Throughout treatment, I attended the daily lectures faithfully — and there were a lot of them. Over the course of nine weeks, I attended 162 lectures on a great variety of topics. The lecturers included medical doctors, psychiatrists, psychologists, nurses, clergy, educators, sociologists, alcoholism counselors, social workers, and an assortment of recovering alcoholics. I was surprised at how often the lecturers disclaimed knowledge of the nature of alcohol addiction. In fact, most of them would say something along the lines of, "I don't know what the disease is, but I know a lot about it." Or they might say, "It's probably a symptom of some underlying disease or disorder, but we don't know what that underlying problem is."

Near the end of my stay in treatment, I made two very firm resolutions. First, I resolved to make every possible effort to discover, define, and articulate the essential nature and pathology of the disease of alcoholism. I was determined to do this because of the apparent confusion in the field, because of the anxiety I felt at not knowing the essential nature of my disease, and because I had witnessed the confusion and fears of my fellow patients on this same account. Second, having been blessed in receiving so much knowledge about alcoholism, its symptoms, and its healing, I resolved to spend a major part of the rest of my life sharing this information with others and spreading the message.

On November 19, 1967, I completed nine weeks of treatment for chronic alcoholism. I accepted the diagnosis and the recommendations for aftercare. I had been deadly sick. Now I was alive and on the road to recovery. I was willing to go to any length to maintain abstinence, gain a comfortable sobriety, and advance in my recovery. And I must emphasize here again that I was very grateful.

My Search for the Essential Nature of Alcoholism Begins

Upon completion of inpatient treatment, I applied to my religious order for a two-year leave of absence from active ministry, which was generously granted. (As it turned out, at the end of that period I was granted permission to leave the order and later married my wife, Mary, in the early 70s.) Thus in my first year after treatment, I was privileged to have the time and resources to devote myself primarily both to recovery and to my search for answers about the essential nature of alcoholism. Clearly, I first needed to review the available literature to find out what professionals in this field were saying it was.

I began with the work of E. M. Jellinek, the most prominent authority at that time on the subject of alcoholism as a disease. Jellinek was the author of the 1960 classic, *The Disease Concept of Alcoholism*. In his book, he described some forty formulations of alcoholism in physiopathological and physical terms. He included himself as favoring the view that alcoholism is likely "an allergic disease" and writes that a "physiological X factor accounts for a disease condition outwardly manifested through loss of control."

This view didn't get me any closer to defining alcoholism as a disease since an "X factor," by definition, names an unknown. Overall, I found Jellinek's work to be of little help toward achieving an essential definition. This was mainly because the information he presented to support and clarify his claims involved symptoms that are mostly complications and consequences of drinking. While these symptoms may possibly point to a disease that causes them, they say nothing about the nature of the disease entity.

After studying Jellinek's work, I then began a review of literature on alcoholism published by academic and professional sources. I gained some new information about the disease, but I was puzzled that so little of use could be added to what I had already learned at Hazelden and from Alcoholics Anonymous (AA) literature, and so my search continued.

Personal Insights

From my personal experience with alcoholism, I had no doubt that an intense, complex *psycho-physiological* pathological process was at the heart of alcoholism. It followed that any formal definition would have to include implicitly, if not explicitly, both the psychological and physiological elements of the disease.

My own reflections on the existential nature of the human person provided a fundamental insight for me at this point in my search. The human *psyche* (soul) and *soma* (body) are the two substantial parts of the composite human substance, the *whole human person*. Whatever the nature of the disease entity/pathology of alcoholism as it exists within the alcoholic, it affects the whole person. It extends itself throughout both substantial parts of the person. It cannot be otherwise. This insight into the nature of alcoholism as a "whole person disease" was personally freeing and reassuring. It gave me a deeper understanding and acceptance of how totally I had been affected by my own alcoholism.

These realizations served to support the theories I had already started to form from my personal experience of the disease, from observations and conversations with other alcoholics, and from my Hazelden education.

Two conclusions stood out at this stage of exploration:

1. Alcoholism is a complex, multi-factorial disease that does not fit into any one of the "standard" categories of physical, mental, or emotional diseases.

2. Alcoholism is a "whole person" disease that affects in some way all of the physical, mental, emotional, and spiritual parts and aspects of a person.

Insights from Alcoholics Anonymous Literature

At this stage, I turned to a thorough study of standard AA literature, which I had been introduced to while in treatment at Hazelden. I found both *Alcoholics Anonymous*, commonly referred to as "The Big Book," and *The Twelve Steps and Twelve Traditions* of AA to be very insightful with regard to the "whole person" condition of addicts in their sickness, treatment, and recovery.

The first thirteen chapters of The Big Book contained the best presentation on the disease of alcoholism that I had ever seen. As I studied it, I came to realize that Bill Wilson, co-founder of AA, had articulated a whole pathology of addiction. It was not all put together in one tidy package, but it was all there, either in exact words or in descriptions that could be summed up and labeled in one or a few words. Wilson spoke either explicitly or implicitly about such topics as obsession, compulsion, denial, low self-esteem, negative attitudes, delusion, powerlessness, pleasure, relief, maintenance, and escape. The list made from his insights could go on and on.

Most of these terms could be found in the literature of academics and professionals, but when they appeared, they seemed to be scattered fragments or tag ends of some other central topic, rather than key words describing or explaining a pathology of addiction. I began to explore words such as "obsession," "compulsion," and "delusion" to see how well they might serve to put names on particular aspects or elements of addiction pathology. After much sifting, sorting, and matching, I was able to identify what seemed to be eight pathological elements in a single disease entity that extends into every part of the subject, the human person.

As I restudied the first part of The Big Book, the greatest eye-opener for me was how often Wilson spoke of "God." From beginning to end, the central theme of Wilson's Big Book is that one's sick relationship with alcohol can be healed by replacing it with a healthy relationship to a Higher Power, or God.

During my own treatment at Hazelden in 1967, I personally put this simple AA formula into practice. I have practiced it continuously ever since and have been blessed with a full and joyful recovery. I have also applied it consistently and successfully in clinical practice and have placed it at the heart of all my education, training, and consulting work in the addiction field.

To my knowledge, Bill Wilson never explicitly identified the AA Twelve Steps recovery program as "love relationship exchange" or "replacement therapy." Nor to my knowledge has AA leadership or anyone else ever done so. However, anyone who has been in the program or is familiar with it, or anyone who has studied The Big Book, is keenly aware that the AA program's core dynamic is this exchange/replacement of personal love relationships.

A Turning Point in My Search

The thought that opening oneself to a personal relationship with God brings about the healing of addiction led me to a further thought, which was this: *Perhaps being in a personal love relationship with alcohol, with mood-altering chemicals, somehow causes the disease.* This was a turning point in my search for the nature, the pathology, and the causes of this disease. And ultimately, it led to a formal definition of the disease's essential nature and properties.

I became preoccupied with pursuing this idea that addiction was based in a "relationship." It seemed in some way to hint at an answer to the question of what addiction is as a disease. I thought, Could it *be a relational disease*? I hadn't run across this concept of disease in the literature of academicians and professionals. No insights along these lines were mentioned in their writing. There was a huge gap between the academic-professional camp and the camp of Bill Wilson, his close associates, and "the AA crowd." In fact, they were worlds apart. I was struck with the realization of a pressing need to bridge this gap. I was both frustrated and challenged by this realization. I decided to let go the frustration and take up the challenge of exploring the idea of *relationship*, thinking that this, perhaps, *is* the bridge over the gap.

Relationship as the Ultimate Line of Reality

In reflecting upon the essential nature of relationship and, specifically, upon the possibility of the essential nature of an addictive relationship to alcohol, I drew upon my years of philosophical study. Since a *relationship* is a *transcendental reality*, I wanted to see if I could use metaphysical first principles to identify it and describe it as a possible key factor in the disease of alcoholism/chemical dependency. I had learned from my years of study that a *relation* or *relationship* is the *ultimate line of reality*. That is, it is as far as one can go in probing to the essence, or *esse*, of any particular thing, which is what I was after with regard to chemical dependency. Exploring this line of reasoning was certainly a new realm for me. Through my years of intense study in pursuit of a doctorate in philosophy, and in my subsequent years as a professor of philosophy in a number of colleges and universities, I never imagined that one day I would rely on the knowledge and methods of that discipline to explore the essential nature of a disease I had unwittingly fallen prey to. I was not aware of anyone before who had attempted to do so.

Before I get into the steps I took to probe the nature of the disease of alcoholism, I ask you to bear in mind that the thought processes I engaged in to arrive at the conclusions that follow did not take place in a matter of the few moments it takes one to read this section of the book. Perhaps it is the nature of the "philosophical beast" to ask a hundred questions about each aspect under deliberation, to look at things from both sides and up and down, to read, review, reflect, and engage in long discussions with like-minded "beasts" before arriving at definitive answers. Believe me, that is how the process went. For the sake of brevity, however, I present in summary form only selected key aspects within the first stage of my search.

I began by grounding my search on the basic metaphysical principle that all particular, finite beings exist in relation to other finite beings. There is a fine passage in Louis de Raeymaeker's book *The Philosophy of Being* that describes this: " . . . every particular being possesses in itself its existence; it is an 'in itself,' but it is finite and therefore it is related to a reality situated outside of its own limits. This relationship with something outside itself does not suppress its own subsistent reality, its 'in itselfness'; on the contrary, it is necessarily connected with it. The particular being is wholly marked with this relativity since it is wholly finite, and its activity bears witness to this by its whole structure. Finite reality is characterized, therefore, by its relativity." (De Raeymaeker, *The Philosophy of Being*, 1966, p. 201)

As wholly finite beings, we can exist only in relationship to the great wide realm of other finite beings, both living and inanimate, in existence around us. This is what is meant by the idea that relationship is the *ultimate* line of reality. Our reality is composed of the interrelationship of finite beings. As individuals, we are who we are largely because of our relationships with that "something outside" ourselves.

A Phenomenological Approach

Although I could not say at the start of my studies exactly what alcoholism was, I knew all too well from personal experience that it was real. My evidence for its existence (and for that of chemical dependency) was of the phenomenological variety: I had experienced the phenomena in myself and clearly witnessed it in those around me. Something had happened to us in the course of our encounters with alcohol and other drugs, something that produced a specific, generally identifiable — yet somehow indefinable — disease. From a logical perspective then, it made sense that whatever alcoholism was, it must in some way be "marked with relativity." In this way, I settled on a field for my investigations. What I needed to do next was narrow the path into that field.

As De Raeymaeker notes, *being* itself is a transcendental reality "which never reveals itself without a question mark." Thus, the philosopher asks, "What question can I formulate?" I began with the question, *"What is the ultimate cause or causal factor that accounts for this disease in every single case of alcoholism/addiction?"*

I looked for the answer first in existential reality, "the here and now," beginning with my own addiction experience and that of others whom I knew so intimately from treatment and AA fellowship. I spent hours listening to histories and stories of recovering alcoholics at the AA club on First Avenue South in Minneapolis hoping to find a clue or a new lead to follow in my search for an answer. It wasn't long before this approach exhausted me. I felt like a swimmer drowning, not in a sea of water, but in a massive flood of symptoms, complications, and life histories that swept me away from, rather than toward, an answer.

Frustrated, I put the question to myself in another way: *"What is the ultimate factor, which if absent, prevents the disease from existing in even one person and which is necessarily present in every person who has the disease?"* Then I formulated the same question in another way, positing a conditional negative question: *"If we had never used, never ingested mood-altering chemicals, is it conceivable that we would be addicted?"* Clearly, the answer is "no." No relationship → no ingestion → no possibility of disease or addiction. To ingest mood-altering chemicals, we had to relate to them. We had to be united to them by means of ingestion. Therefore, relationship → ingestion → possibility of disease/addiction.

Having established that some kind of relationship is necessary for even the possibility of addiction to exist, I asked the next question: *"Given the ingestion of mood-altering chemicals, what kind of relationship is it?"* In philosophical terms, every relationship has a point of *origin*, a *foundation*, and a point of *termination*, its *term* or *end point*. Applying this language to alcoholism, I identified the person as the point of origin, the subject of the relationship, the one in whom the relationship originates and resides. The point of termination or end point of the relationship is the mood-altering chemical. In metaphysical terminology, this kind of relationship would properly be called a *personal* relationship.

This realization, simple as it may seem, was profound for me. It struck me forcefully. I had come to realize that my life was disordered in many ways, and that many of my relationships were sorely damaged and in need of repair, and that some of these relationships were even in need of full restoration, if that were possible. While I had often considered the effect alcohol had had on my personal relationships, I had never fully considered that I had a personal relationship with alcohol. I had always thought that it was the drug that was wreaking havoc upon me. I was uncomfortable with the realization that the source of havoc actually came back to me seeking the drug, wanting it, committing to it. It was a strange notion, and yet somehow, it seemed to fit me. I thought about this relationship for days.

Then I formulated a final question: *"Granted that a personal relationship most likely is a factor, is it absolutely the ultimate factor?"* Even as I asked the question, I intuitively knew the answer was "yes." I knew all relationships tend toward some good that is highly prized for the rewards it promises to give. Certainly mood-altering chemicals held out to me, and all the other alcoholics I knew, a promise of welcome, pleasurable experiences: physical, mental, and emotional. I told myself the obvious: I'm a person, and I tended toward — related to — mood-altering chemicals for years. They were the object I sought out, even when they failed to deliver on the promise of pleasure. The relationship was mine. It was in me, it resided in me.

Although the dynamics of this relationship and its far reaching effects within my person and in my life relationships were not clear to me at this point, I was convinced that the ultimate factor in the disease entity of my alcoholism was, somehow, my personal relationship to alcohol and pills. This was the point I had reached in my thinking when my year of study ended. I would continue the exploration as I moved into professional work in the field of alcoholism treatment.

The Johnson Institute Experience

A little over a year after my discharge from treatment, I received a totally unexpected opportunity to fulfill both of the firm resolutions I had made upon leaving Hazelden. Rev. Dr. Vernon Johnson invited me to become the second full-time professional staff person employed by the Johnson Institute, which he was organizing to carry on applied research and to offer a variety of services in the alcohol/addictions field.

I had been very impressed with Dr. Johnson's Hazelden lectures and greatly appreciated the private conversations I had with him while in treatment there. During the year following treatment, I lived in the Twin Cities and made it a point to visit with him periodically in order to explore some of the many unsolved "mysteries" of alcoholism and its treatment. These sessions were enlightening and refreshing. Dr. Johnson and I came to see eye to eye on many aspects of the disease and its treatment. My avid perusal of "the literature" raised many questions that found possible answers in his applied research and daily work with recovering addicts.

St. Mary's Hospital Alcoholism Treatment Program

About a month after I came onto the staff of the Johnson Institute, Dr. Johnson accepted an invitation to develop a residential treatment program at St. Mary's Hospital in Minneapolis. He assigned his staff psychologist and me to research existing hospital programs in North America and, with his involvement, to design a treatment program suitable for St. Mary's.

Subsequently, Dr. Johnson appointed me as director of the treatment program. I could not have imagined a better opportunity to pursue my burning resolves to define the essential nature of chemical dependency and to share with others the insights I received about the disease and its symptoms, its diagnosis, treatment, healing, and prevention. I was also very interested in "data testing" my growing conviction that this was not a physical, mental, or psychological disease that could be fitted into any customary categories, but instead was some other kind of a disease altogether, a relational disease of the whole person.

The Problem of Definition

By far the greatest difficulty the St. Mary's program experienced was the lack of an adequate definition of the disease we were dealing with. This is undoubtedly the greatest problem faced by every addiction service ever attempted. It will no doubt continue to be a problem until a definition is formulated and accepted by addiction professionals.

At St. Mary's, several complications flowed directly from this deficiency. Physicians from almost every specialty referred patients. With few exceptions, they had their own opinions about what the disease was and how it might be better or differently treated, compared to what we were then doing. Some physicians could not understand why their addictive prescription medications could not be continued while their referred patients were in treatment for their alcoholism. Others insisted that the diseases they had diagnosed in their patients should be given primacy over the alcoholism/chemical dependency diagnosis.

Efforts to form a unified multi-disciplinary team were badly hampered by having no united focus for our therapy, our therapists, and our patients. Some patients and some team members used this to justify their own biased opinions and to manipulate for the acceptance of their views in opposition to the consensus of the team. We learned some important lessons about the differences between "consensus" and "definitions," and the value of everyone knowing precisely what our target was.

Without definitive knowledge of the disease, any therapy for it is bound to be tentative, uncertain, and, at best, experimental. At worst, such attempts at therapy were very confused, even counterproductive. Of course, we will always be faced with some diseases that are undefined, but nonetheless urgently in need of treatment. In such cases, we do the best we know how for the good of the patients — which is what we did at St. Mary's. Even without a defined disease entity, we could and did address its symptoms, hoping to thereby reduce elements of its pathology.

Dr. Johnson gave an excellent example of this by focusing on the rigid, locked-in feelings of alcoholics. He referred to alcoholism as a "feeling disease," as, in fact, it is in part. He therefore employed a group therapy process designed to help patients get in touch with and learn to express their feelings appropriately. This greatly enhanced both the quality of treatment and of patient recoveries.

The Origin and Development of *The Essentials of Chemical Dependency*

St. Mary's treatment program was immediately successful. In two years, it expanded rapidly. This, of course, created an urgent need for more trained alcoholism specialists. From the start, we had undertaken a small, on-site, in-service training program. Our first students were a few recovering outpatients who showed promise, some hospital personnel, and some potential staff for other new hospital-based programs that had called on the Institute for help. But now, with the expansion of the St. Mary's program, and with other hospitals looking to the Institute for start-up assistance, Dr. Johnson, George Mann, MD, our medical director, and I agreed that a college-level training program was urgently needed to develop adequate numbers of quality staff.

There were no chemical dependency manuals or textbooks available at the time that seemed appropriate for student or teacher use in such a program, so one had to be produced — and soon. Because much of my professional background was in university and college teaching, which included some curriculum development, I was asked to put together a college-level curriculum for training chemical dependency specialists. Along with my responsibilities as program director, I worked for two years to produce a "bare-bones" text that might be used for drug education, training, and clinical practice. In it, I proposed a first version of an essential definition of chemical dependency as a relational disease. This definition was stated in the very first sentence of the text:

> *"The essence of chemical dependency is a pathological relationship of a person to a mood-altering chemical substance, a drug, in expectation of a rewarding experience."*

The entire content of the curriculum was built around this core definition, which included implicitly or explicitly all that is or can be known about the essence of chemical dependency. Obviously, much more than this is known about many particular aspects of the disease. But as far as I could see, none of these were essential. They might or might not be present, and the disease would still be chemical dependency. They were not core factors, like the essentials.

The next step was for me to persuade one of the half dozen universities or colleges in the Twin Cities area to offer this training to its students. I designed a curriculum that the Metropolitan Community College in Minneapolis agreed to offer as a two-year degree program for training chemical dependency specialists.

Along with my wife, Mary Boesen McAuliffe, Ph.D., we selected and put together some of the now considerable chemical dependency/addiction materials we had collected or created. In 1971, we then had this document printed and bound as a manual and made it available to the college as the textbook for the core course around which we built the curriculum. Mary taught this course at the college for four years. The manual we had developed, *The Essentials of Chemical Dependency (Alcoholism and other Drug Dependencies)*, was the first version of what, with numerous additions, was published under the same title in 1975.

For the next three years, I continued my daily work in the addictions field, gathering deeper insights into the nature of chemical dependency and other addictions. At the same time, I worked toward publishing a more complete edition of *The Essentials of Chemical Dependency*.

When the new edition came out in 1975, it was basically a fleshing out of the bare-bones version. The original formal definition was slightly reworded to read as follows:

> *"Chemical dependency is essentially a pathological or sick relationship of a person to a mood-altering chemical substance, a psychoactive drug, in expectation of a rewarding experience."*

The addition of the words "or sick" was intended to clarify somewhat the meaning of the word "pathological." The word "psychoactive" was added so that everyone would understand it was a synonym for "mood-altering chemical substance" and that this described a central nervous system drug.

Over the years since 1975, through continued work with addicts and their professional caregivers, and through continual scrutiny of the published literature on the subject, I gained some further insights, which have led to a deeper understanding of the nature of this relational disease.

In this new edition of *The Essentials of Chemical Dependency*, we have added two very significant words to our essential definition of addiction: the word "committed" and the word "love." The definition now reads:

> *"Chemical dependency is essentially a committed pathological love relationship of a person to a mood-altering chemical substance, a psychoactive drug, in expectation of a rewarding experience."*

The word "committed" is included because it describes the state of being bound emotionally, and/or intellectually, to some course of action; in this instance, to the pursuit of a bonded, permanent relationship with drugs for the sake of an expected reward which drugs hold out in promise, the psychoactive "high." "Commitment" is the distinguishing factor in the progression from the casual pre-dependency "use" relationship to early pleasure-stage chemical dependency, that is, to a pathological love relationship of the person to drugs.

The word "love" is included because it tells us exactly what *kind* of a personal relationship we are talking about and dealing with. While love is the key emotion that drives all action toward a real or perceived "good," it is *pathological love* that drives one into and along the path of addiction. The core of addiction consists in a committed, pathological love relationship. It *is* love run wild.

One might think that this marked the end of my search, but it was an idea whose exploration, in philosophical and practical terms, has filled a lifetime with work, study, and an effort to help others. If you are new to the ideas in this book, or perhaps somewhat new to understanding this disease in yourself or in others, you will soon see what I mean. While the greatest truths may be unchanging, our efforts to understand them never cease.

PART ONE

The
Essential Nature
of
Chemical Dependency

Chemical dependency is essentially a
committed pathological
love relationship
of a person to a mood-altering chemical
substance, a psychoactive drug, in
expectation of a rewarding experience.

CHAPTER ONE

The Essentials Approach

Chemical dependency is a complex disease in the way it affects the whole person and every aspect of his or her life and being. It is no wonder then that when people speak or write about alcoholism and the other drug dependencies, they display a tendency to address themselves to unknowns and to focus attention on uncertainties. Even a matter as basic as defining the nature of addiction, as we have seen, raises a cloud of questions and concerns. This leaves readers and listeners with the impression that little of value or use has been discovered in the field and that what is known is highly uncertain, mere guesswork, doubtful assumption, and subjective opinion.

The opposite, of course, is true. Much has been discovered about addiction by experts in the field. The fact that there is more to be learned does not diminish in any way either the amount or the value of what is already known. It seems to us that the body of knowledge that exists should be shared with a wider audience. This knowledge should become the common property of the general public, while exploration of unknowns and uncertainties remains a responsibility and a proper task of experts.

A major purpose of this book is to present an orderly summary and synthesis of essential matters that are known about alcoholism and the other drug dependencies. What do we mean by an "essentials approach" to chemical dependency?

By an **essentials approach,** we mean the following:

- A rational, inductive, reality-based method of dealing with chemical dependency, both conceptually and practically.

- A method that focuses directly and primarily on the specific nature and characteristics of personal drug relationships, that is, on those key constant aspects that are always and necessarily present in every individual case of chemical dependency.

Existential reality is the starting place for this approach. The reality is that there are millions of people who actually ingest mood-altering chemicals and who are personally related to them in some way. There are millions more who are negatively affected by such personal drug relationships.

This same existential reality is the ongoing checkpoint and the ultimate testing ground for verifying, confirming, and validating (or invalidating) any conclusions that are drawn. Whatever the approach employed in examining drug involvement, the existential base must remain the same: actual drug relationships in real live persons. And the ultimate objective, too, remains the same: to clarify our understanding of the essential nature and characteristics of drug involvement.

Content, Structure, and Process

In this book, we are concerned with content, structure, and process. An essentials approach necessarily involves all three. But above all, our concern is to present a *chemical dependency content*. This content can be modified as to structure and process by educators, trainers, researchers, and therapists to meet the needs of their specialized disciplines and the particular clientele they serve.

We believe the content of this book provides a sound base for defining the essential nature, characteristics, and causes of chemical dependency as a *phenomenon in itself*. This may close the door, partially at least, to misconceptions of it as merely a result or symptom of "some other" problem. In other words, chemical dependency is a primary disorder in and of itself.

The most common misconception about alcoholism and the other drug dependencies is that these conditions are results or symptoms caused by some other preexisting problem.

Theories about what that "other problem" is differ widely and even contradict each other. Some popular labels are "psychological," "psychiatric," "medical," "social," "behavioral," etc. The consequences of this error are many and grave. Two of them are especially harmful.

First, persons who are chemically dependent, and their families and associates, are harmed when the focus of diagnosis and therapy is directed to some other problem. The chemical dependency problem remains undiagnosed and unattended. Clients are left to pursue their drug involvement, and they grow progressively worse.

Second, dependents whose drug problems have been identified and treated, and who are enjoying good recoveries, sometimes find themselves under continuing clouds of suspicion because both they and others keep looking for some mysterious "other problem" to suddenly show up. It is a waiting-for-the-other-shoe-to-drop anxiety that is founded in fantasy, not in reality.

Most of the so-called other problems that accompany and are alleged to cause chemical dependency are in fact caused by chemical dependency itself. Rarely do they continue unresolved once chemical dependency is properly treated and recovery is under way.

Granted, other problems may precede, accompany, and follow drug involvement. But there exists no present evidence to demonstrate causation. The most that can be validly affirmed is correlation. Failure to pinpoint exactly what chemical dependency is and what its essential causes are leaves the way open for erroneous assumptions about other preexisting or underlying problems as its cause.

Toward Early Diagnosis, Intervention, and Treatment

Many people are still diagnosed as chemically dependent on the basis of social, physical, psychological, and moral problems. These diagnostic criteria are actually late-stage complications of a drug involvement that has existed for some time, perhaps for years. Such complications are accidentals, not essentials. They may or may not appear in individual cases, and they are often present in the lives of persons who never ingest mood-altering chemicals at all. In other words, there is *no essential cause-and-effect relationship* between such complications and chemical dependency.

Essential characteristics, on the other hand, are present from the beginning and continue with increasing intensity throughout the entire progression of the drug involvement. These characteristics include essential symptoms and pathology. Essential symptoms involve direct cause-and-effect relationships, which are the proper criteria for chemical dependency diagnosis. They are the basis for the early identification, evaluation, and diagnosis of chemical dependency that opens the way to the development of effective intervention and therapeutic strategies to assist chemically dependent persons and their family members before their lives are in shambles.

Toward Preventive Education

By focusing on essentials, it is possible to lay a firm foundation for preventive education. Without a clear understanding of the essential nature of chemical dependency, there is no definite target for prevention. Lack of a target reduces efforts to scattershot approaches with the hope of accidentally hitting on something relevant to prevention.

The goal of preventive chemical dependency and drug abuse education is to help individuals develop a sense of *personal responsibility for their own relationships to mood-altering chemicals.* This applies first to those whose purpose is to offer preventive education. In other words, the first responsibility of drug educators is for their own drug relationships.

The common denominator of many such programs appears to be that they do not focus direct attention on the essential nature and characteristics of chemical dependency or of drug use, misuse, and abuse. Instead, they focus on something else: on drugs themselves; on scare tactics; on law and law enforcement; on environmental factors; on socio-cultural conditions and influences; on effecting change in society or in some of its institutions; on personal and social values and their clarification; on personal growth and development; on interpersonal relations and communication; on alternative highs or life styles; on human health and well-being as such; on skills for living. In short, the focus is anywhere except on the central problem of the personal relationship to mood-altering chemicals and its direct effects on a person and his or her close associates.

Unquestionably, the "something elses" deserve attention in and of themselves. No one doubts the desirability of any or all of them. Moreover, they may be useful supplements not only to prevention but also to treatment programs, and they are indispensable elements in recovery and rehabilitation programs. But in and of themselves, they are not chemical dependency or drug abuse prevention because they are without a specific chemical dependency focus and content. To assume that they are prevention is to misread or to mislabel the particular phenomenon of chemical dependency.

The Importance of Clear Definitions

The hit-and-miss prevention efforts that we have witnessed over many years in the field provide clear evidence of a lack of focus on the part of many educators. This lack of focus demonstrates a want of understanding or a misunderstanding about what chemical dependency is.

Enormous expenditures of time and money are poured into ambitious prevention programs without the organizers first defining what they mean to prevent. Elaborate structures and processes are set up, experts from various disciplines are brought in, participants are enrolled, and programs are carried out. Although the programs may be well planned and skillfully implemented, results are often poor. Unless the objective of preventing drug abuse and chemical dependency is focused on the essential nature of the disease, these programs run the risk of being counterproductive.

In making application of content, drug educators, like other helping professionals, must be aware of and sensitive to where their clients are. They must not only know what it is they are educating to prevent, they must also organize their material and adapt their processes to the existential condition and needs of their clients.

It is unrealistic to assume, for example, that typical groups of preschool or early elementary school children are not seriously affected by the drug involvements of their parents, siblings, peers, and teachers. It is even less realistic to assume that other, older groups of children are unaffected by personal drug involvement and/or the involvement of their family members, friends, and peers.

Although they themselves may not be using drugs, they are nevertheless often suffering drug-related disabilities: hurt and bewilderment; preoccupation; negative attitudes of fear, resentment, anger, hatred, loneliness, rejection, and feelings of parental abandonment; a steady build-up of defenses; low self-image; and deep feelings of guilt, shame, insecurity, and inadequacy. They are also drawn into the manipulation and counter-manipulation that always go along with drug abuse and chemical dependency. In other words, they are being forced into the enabler role and are already in the process of developing the sick attitudes and behaviors of a corelative dependency that characterize the enabler role.

Chemical dependency and drug abuse are always more than individual affairs. They are family and group matters, with all members inevitably involved. The codependent enabler role — and the sickness that goes with it — is every bit as essential to this illness as any other aspect of it. Education to prevent it must take this into account. Therefore, educators cannot ignore the harmful effects chemical dependency is likely having here and now on those who are being educated. To do so is to launch preventive education into a vacuum.

This is not to minimize in any way the possibility or need of preventive education, but only to emphasize that its focus and objectives must be clear, its contents well defined and organized, and its audiences realistically perceived. Finally, there is a critical need for everyone engaged in preventive drug education to have a firm grasp of the categories of causation.

Drug educators familiar with previous editions of this book have found its focus, content, and structure helpful in designing both special courses and programs and more generalized preventive education. And the book itself, in the hands of those being educated, provides for them a ready means of continuing self-education on this vital subject.

CHAPTER TWO

Drug Ingestion,
Use, Misuse, and Abuse

We have all felt the frustration of not having the proper tools with which to do a job or of trying to do a precision job with dull, crude tools. We all know, too, how frustrated we feel when we do not have the proper words to express our ideas exactly or when we struggle to express them with crude or clumsy words. And we have all found ourselves confused when words are shifting about in their meaning. I use words in one sense, you use them in another sense, and others use them in still other senses. We may all end up not knowing what the conversation is about.

Words are meant to express ideas. To be useful, they must have agreed-upon meanings. When key words are not defined, all parties to discussions come away frustrated and confused. There are few places, perhaps, where we find a clearer case of this than in the field of alcohol and other drug problems.

Defining Terms to Avoid Confusion

For example, many reports and studies have been publicized about "drug use" among high school students. In a typical report, we might learn that the number of eighth graders who used marijuana doubled from one in ten to one in five between 1991 and 2001. The increase in marijuana use may be read to mean that there is a growing "drug problem" among these students. In a very general way, this would probably be true simply because increased marijuana smoking usually leads to more marijuana-related problems.

Before we can draw any more definite conclusions, we have to ask some basic questions. A first question has to be: What is meant by marijuana "use"? Does it mean taking an occasional puff? Does it mean one joint a week? Or three or four or more? Does it mean getting a slight high or totally spaced out? Is the marijuana used with alcohol or other drugs? Actually, we have no way of knowing whether there is any student drug problem at all unless the term "use" is clearly defined.

We would have to ask, too, what is meant by a "drug problem." Does it mean trouble with schoolwork or teachers or other students? Does it mean legal troubles? Does it mean loss of interest in activities or sports? Or apathy to life in general?

We have no way of knowing anything very definite about a "drug problem" until the term "problem" has been defined.

In an effort to avoid any confusion here, we begin by defining our terms. Our definitions are largely those found in any standard dictionary of the English language. You may wish to define these terms in other ways, of course, or to use other words to describe the same realities. But at least you will know what we mean when we use these terms.

DRUG INGESTION

The first word to be defined is "ingestion." It is the physical act of taking a substance into one's body. Eating food is ingestion. Drinking liquids is ingestion. Inhaling tobacco smoke is ingestion.

Drug ingestion is the physical act of taking a drug into one's body. Alcohol and pills are usually ingested orally, that is, by mouth. Marijuana and some other drugs are ordinarily ingested by inhaling or "sniffing." Heroin and certain other drugs are commonly ingested by injection, or "shooting." However it is accomplished, ingestion always refers to drug intake, to any physical act of getting the drug into one's body.

When the terms "drug-taking" or "drug use" are employed, they usually mean drug ingestion — but not always. In lectures and literature about drug problems, for instance, it is not always clear how these terms are being used, and they are seldom defined for us. The burden of giving meanings to the terms is placed on the audience, which means, practically, that it is left to guesswork or conjecture. This is clearly unsatisfactory, although it does point up the need for developing critical listening skills.

DRUG USE

Beyond drug ingestion is drug use. While these two terms are often used interchangeably, there is considerable difference in their meanings.

"Use" means to put into service or to employ for a purpose, as soap is used for washing. "Drug use," therefore, means to ingest drugs for a purpose. Note that the mere of taking drugs — ingestion — refers only to the physical act, whereas *use* implies an action of the total person for a *purpose*. Drug use involves a personal decision and a personal choice; it is a fully human act, not just the physical act of drug-taking.

We define **drug use** as a reasonable ingestion of a mood-altering chemical substance or drug, for a clearly defined, beneficial purpose, and in a manner or mode that is regulated by that purpose. How ingestion takes place is the *mode* or *manner* of ingestion. It is a *reasonable* mode of ingestion when it is determined, controlled, and limited by the beneficial *purpose* of ingestion.

The purpose also governs all of the circumstances that pertain to the ingestion. Morphine, for example, may be reasonably ingested at times for the beneficial purpose of relieving pain. The manner or mode of ingestion is governed by the purpose. Thus morphine ingestion is regulated as to quantity and frequency of dosages. It is also regulated with regard to other circumstances, such as time, place, situation, and company. This is all done in order to achieve that definite beneficial purpose — relieving pain — while at the same time avoiding any harmful consequences or side effects either to the drug-taker or to others.

Examples of Drug Use

Drug use or reasonable drug ingestion, as here defined, includes ingestion for a variety of purposes. The following are examples:

- *Ritual use* is ingestion for the purpose of sharing in a religious rite, such as in Native American religious rituals, the Lord's Supper, or a Passover service.

- *Ceremonial use* is ingestion for the purpose of participating in a social event or act prescribed by custom or etiquette, such as offering a toast or celebrating a wedding, a birthday, or some other festive occasion.

- *Utilitarian use* is ingestion for a practical or pragmatic purpose, such as adding flavor to food.

- *Medicinal use* is ingestion for the purpose of healing an organism, curing a disease, or controlling disease symptoms. Examples would be use for the relief of pain, for anesthesia, to relieve panic attacks, or for the treatment of common colds.

- *Social or convivial use* is ingestion for the purpose of mildly enhancing the pleasure of interpersonal relations and mutual communication in a social situation.

- *Private or personal use* is ingestion for the purpose of obtaining a mild, subjective effect or a mildly rewarding experience, usually pleasure in the form of physical sensations or pleasant changes of feelings, moods, or mind.

Drug use is essentially reasonable if ingestion takes place for a defined, beneficial purpose. Reasonable drug use contributes to a person's well being. It is therefore both appropriate and healthy. If, on the contrary, ingestion takes place with no defined, beneficial purpose, it is no longer "use" in the sense of our definition. It is unreasonable because it is without proper regulation. It is then misuse or abuse.

DRUG MISUSE

"Misuse" means a misapplication, an incorrect or inappropriate use of something or of someone. A knife intended for carving meat, for example, is misused when it is applied to whittling wood. A table knife is misused when it is applied as a screwdriver. A human being is misused when he or she is treated as a thing instead of as a person. Drug misuse, therefore, is a *misapplication* of drugs: it involves incorrect or inappropriate ingestion.

We define **drug misuse** as an unreasonable ingestion of mood-altering chemical substances that is always *potentially* harmful to the drug misuser and to others. Such ingestion is unreasonable because it is not for a well-defined beneficial purpose. It is for some other arbitrary purpose or perhaps for no particular purpose at all — simply a random act. The ingestion is essentially unregulated, uncontrolled. It is not limited in regard to quantity, potency, or frequency of dosages. It is not governed with regard to other circumstances, such as time, place, occasion, and situation. And because it lacks a purpose, it is always *potentially* harmful.

Examples of Drug Misuse

Examples of drug misuse are common. Pills prescribed for one purpose are misused for other purposes. Pills prescribed for one person are misused by others. Parents share drugs prescribed for themselves with their children and with each other. Neighbors and friends share each other's prescriptions. Alcoholic beverages intended for social use are misused as medicines to relieve pain, tension, anxiety, and discomforts. In every such case, the potential for harm is present whether or not actual harm results from the misuse.

Among the most serious current forms of misuse is the prescription of drugs whose effects are not completely known. In some cases, drugs are prescribed without knowledge of their possible side effects or without knowledge of how a particular person will react. And it is not uncommon for physicians to rely on the pitches of drug salesmen and the marketing literature of drug manufacturers for their "professional" knowledge about the drugs they prescribe.

DRUG ABUSE

Beyond drug misuse is drug abuse.

"Abuse" in one sense can mean the same as misuse, namely, to misapply or to use inappropriately or improperly. Misuse, however, stresses incorrect handling that carries with it a *potential* for harm, while abuse puts the emphasis on *actual* harm or injury.

We define **drug abuse** as an unreasonable ingestion of a mood-altering chemical substance that causes harm or injury to the drug abuser and in some instances to other persons. There is no beneficial purpose in drug abuse; it is essentially harmful. It makes no contribution to the health or well-being of a human person. On the contrary, it is unhealthy and detrimental to human well-being. Lacking positive purpose, drug abuse is essentially uncontrolled, without limitations as to quantity, potency, or frequency of ingestion. It is also without regulation in regard to time, place, occasion, or other circumstances of ingestion. Of its nature, therefore, it is destructive, and it typically produces actual harm.

In particular instances of drug abuse, of course, the harm may be relatively slight. But harm does not necessarily mean disaster. The fact that drug abuse tends to be recognized only when it approaches disaster may blind one to the lesser harm produced in every instance. The harmfulness of drug abuse is sometimes denied unless people are visibly injured. This view tends to obscure the physical and psychological harm done by the drug abuser to him- or herself.

Examples of Drug Abuse

Getting drunk or stoned is a common example of drug abuse. Quite apart from any resulting physical damage, all of the drug abuser's functional powers are seriously impaired by intoxication. His or her mental, emotional, physical, volitional, spiritual, and social powers all become dysfunctional under the influence of the toxic or poisonous substances. In no way is this condition beneficial and in no sense is it reasonable. Note that not all abusive ingestion is chemical dependency; however, frequent abusive ingestion may lead to chemical dependency.

Another common example of drug abuse is the ingestion of pills to get high. The original medical purpose of the pills is set aside, except perhaps as an excuse for obtaining further supplies. The directly intended goal of ingestion is to get high. This is clearly drug abuse.

One of the more sophisticated forms of drug abuse, and one of the most destructive, occurs when medications are prescribed indiscriminately for the purpose of controlling the minds, emotions and behaviors of men, women, and children who are labeled "deviant," "defective," "maladjusted," "disturbed," "hyperkinetic," and so on. Not only does such abuse frequently lead to chronic chemical dependency, it also deprives many innocent people of their freedom and of the ordinary use of their natural life powers. In doing so, it effectively destroys the possibility of full human growth, development, and integrity for those persons who are its victims.

CHAPTER THREE

Chemical Dependency
in
Focus

Beyond drug abuse, or more frequently right along with it, is drug dependency or **chemical dependency.** The line between abuse and dependency, if it exists at all, is very fine indeed.

To take a common example, consider the act of getting drunk or stoned. Unquestionably, this is drug abuse. It is unreasonable ingestion. It is unregulated ingestion. It is harmful ingestion. A reasonable person, having had the experience once, will take every precaution not to repeat it. Even a reasonable person, of course, may get drunk on very rare occasions in spite of all safeguards. But if it happens, it is unexpected and accidental, and it is clearly regarded as a miserable, unreasonable experience not to be repeated.

A reasonable person does not repeat unreasonable, harmful experiences. Repeated drug abuse to the state of intoxication is a clear sign of chemical dependency. It shows that the drug abuser is acting by compulsion, not by reason and choice. It shows that he or she has an unhealthy need to ingest drugs in an irrational, unregulated, and harmful manner. In other words, it demonstrates an unhealthy or sick personal relationship to mood-altering chemicals.

Distinctions Made Between Users

Take another example. For many years, attempts were made to draw lines of distinction between "heavy drinkers" and "alcoholics" and between "problem drinkers" and "alcoholics." More recently, similar attempts have been made to distinguish between "heavy drug users" and "drug addicts." Such efforts have never been successful. And when we understand chemical dependency, we can see why. These distinctions between one drinker and another were based on accidental complications and the circumstances of particular cases. They were not based on essential symptoms. No meaningful distinctions between one drinker or drug user and another can be drawn from complications and circumstances.

Physical and/or social complications vary with each case. So do circumstances. Frequency, quantities, and occasions of ingestion, for example, are never identical.

The essential reality is that heavy use and problem use are drug abuse. Repeated abuse is both a product and a symptom of alcoholism or drug addiction — that is, of chemical dependency.

Some alleged differences are also made between "social use" and "abuse" and between "social use" and "dependency." The phrase "recreational use" is also often employed in an effort to make a distinction between drug behaviors that are freely chosen (presumably just for fun, in this case) and behaviors that are compulsively abusive or dependent. The delusion persists in some quarters that getting drunk or stoned in the company of others or for supposedly recreational purposes somehow changes the essential nature of drug abuse and of chemical dependency. With this view, it is as if social approval or custom makes drug abuse less irrational and harmful and chemical dependency less pathological. The fact is that both abuse and dependency remain essentially the same objective realities, whatever the social setting or professed intention. If you are drunk, you are drunk. If you are stoned, you are stoned. There may be a hundred people around you, or you may be all alone. It makes no significant difference. You are abusing chemicals, and if you do so repeatedly, you are certainly chemically dependent.

There are legitimate social uses of mood-altering chemicals, as already noted. They are controlled by the social situation. The primary source of pleasure and good feelings in a truly social gathering lies in person-to-person relationships, not in person-to-drug relationships. Drug use is incidental: its purpose is to mildly enhance the pleasure of social interchange. This sets limits on the manner of ingestion, so that drug use does not interfere with person-to-person relationships.

To get drunk or stoned or even to get mildly intoxicated is antisocial in the proper sense of the word. These conditions interfere with person-to-person or social relationships. Those who get high are enjoying their person-to-drug relationships first of all and their interpersonal relationships only secondarily, if at all. Their good feelings are drug-centered and drug-induced, not other-person-centered or other-person-induced.

In our culture, so-called social or recreational use covers a multitude of abuses and dependencies. Social defenses are so firmly implanted in our minds that many people seriously refer to cocktail parties, beer parties, pot parties, or raves as "social events." And many who are otherwise quite rational are unable to see that what goes on around them is not social at all. It is instead a kind of pooling of drug-abuse experiences and a mutual protecting of individual chemical dependencies. Whatever the labels used to cover it up, drug abuse remains essentially an unreasonable, unregulated, harmful ingestion. And repeated drug abuse demonstrates a sick relationship to mood-altering chemicals. It is a product and a symptom of chemical dependency.

14

The Term "Chemical Dependency"

When the first edition of this book was published, the term "chemical dependency" was still a fairly recent addition to the language of alcohol and other drug problems. It was practically unheard of until the mid-sixties. By the mid-seventies, it already seemed destined to become one of the most significant terms in the drug/alcohol vocabulary. Today, it is widely used in discussions, lectures, and literature. It has been institutionalized in treatment and training programs, in information and referral centers, in government bureaucracies, and in private businesses, societies, and associations.

We believe the term caught on mainly because "chemical dependency" brings together in appropriate terms the essential realities that we deal with in this illness. The term is highly effective in keeping the focus of attention on the one most essential problem: a chemically dependent person's unhealthy or pathological relationship to mood-altering chemicals.

Many Meanings

Over the years, "chemical dependency" has meant many things to many people, and to some it still means little or nothing. It is sometimes used, for example, as a general catch phrase to lump together in a vague way any and all the problems growing out of the use, misuse, and abuse of alcohol and other drugs. Or, it is used merely as a substitute or synonym to avoid monotonous repetitions of such words as "alcoholism" or "drug addiction." It is also used at times by the victims of alcohol and other drugs to soften the moralistic overtones and the negative stereotypes implied in such words as "alcoholism" and "alcoholic" or "drug addiction" and "drug addict." Finally, it is used by some dependents in an extremely vague sense as a cop-out — to give the appearance of admitting to a personal drug problem, but at the same time to avoid identifying themselves as having a definite alcohol or other drug dependency.

The wide variety of applications has not reduced "chemical dependency" to meaningless verbiage. On the contrary, it appears to have established a common ground for clarifying meaning and giving deeper insights into alcohol and other drug problems at the essentials level. It seems to appeal to a basic human instinct for using accurate words to define commonly perceived facts and aspects of reality.

Essential Realities

We began using the term as soon as it became clear to us through clinical experience and applied research that we were dealing with the same essential realities in every drug problem case. In each client, the same basic characteristics were present. In every case, the same typical elements and symptoms appeared.

We were struck by the fact that all bore a remarkable likeness to one another. We were equally struck by the wide variety of persons and the great differences in their case histories.

For example, an elderly male client might have an alcohol problem, a 50-year history of problem drinking, and a dozen or more major physical and social complications. A 12-year-old female client might have an alcohol problem, a six-month history of drinking, and no major physical or social complications. Another adolescent client might have a marijuana problem, a five-year history of pot-smoking, and a host of severe complications. A 45-year-old suburban father might have been on heroin for 10, 20, or 30 years and exhibit practically no complications. And a 35-year-old inner-city mother might have a polydrug problem with a long track record of complications. In spite of these differences, we have found a constant pattern of close similarities in all cases.

Each person appeared to have the same fixed commitment to taking drugs for his or her own subjective purposes — each, that is, was seeking to get high on drugs. Each appeared to be rigidly set in a drug relationship. This relationship held a place of high priority among other relationships. It gave a definite drug orientation to the person's life, and in fact often dominated and determined his or her entire life style. Each person seemed to relate to drugs obsessively and compulsively and with many destructive effects. We observed other constants, too, along with many variables.

Differences and Similarities

Here in outline form are the main differences and similarities that we observe in persons with drug problems:

1. Individual case histories and complications vary almost infinitely in particular details.

2. All persons have an identical core problem, namely, an unhealthy relationship to mood-altering chemical substances.

3. All clients manifest certain identical characteristics: a psychological need for drugs; preoccupation with them and impulsive ingestion of them; a loss of self-esteem and self-respect along with feelings of guilt due to drug-induced and drug-related behaviors; locked-in negative-feeling postures or attitudes; a rigid defense system protecting the drug relationship and rejecting outside intervention and assistance; an inability to recognize the drug-involved condition; and powerlessness to help himself or herself.

4. Clients are a true cross section of humanity. They include young and old, male and female, persons of every race and ethnic origin, brilliant and dull, weak and strong, dependent and independent, extroverted and introverted, dominant and submissive. They are as remarkable for their wide variety and diversity of basic personality types and personal characteristics as they are remarkable for their rigid uniformity of personality and personal characteristics once their drug relationship has taken over.

5. In each case, "personality changes" occur, and clients usually have strong impressions that something is the matter with them, that they "must be going crazy."

6. Clients represent the entire spectrum of socio-cultural environments: inner city, outer city, suburban and rural; metropolitan, town, and village; poverty and affluence; privilege and underprivilege; upper, middle, and lower classes; highly educated and uneducated; devoutly religious and irreligious; every kind of position and profession. Yet whatever their geographical and socio-cultural environments, their common denominator is identical: they are all hooked on drugs — in every case the basic elements of the sickness are the same.

7. Clients ingest the whole range of mood-altering drugs: sedatives, stimulants, narcotics, hallucinogens, etc. Many clients are on more than one drug and some are literally "on everything." But the particular drug or drugs of individual preference make no significant difference so far as the core realities are concerned. Regardless of the various drugs of preference, each client manifests the same unhealthy drug relationship with its typical pathological elements and symptoms.

A Drug Relationship Syndrome

What emerges is a pattern of common characteristics, a drug relationship **syndrome**. This syndrome indicates an unhealthy, abnormal condition within the person, a condition centered in and growing out of that person's committed relationship to psychoactive drugs. The appearance of this syndrome is clear evidence of an *underlying pathology* or *disease entity* within the person.

When this became clear, we began using "chemical dependency" as our term of preference for the drug relationship syndrome. We then made summaries of the common or constant aspects of drug involvement. We worked from outlines in presenting, on a trial basis, an "essentials of chemical dependency" approach to individual clients and patients, to community and professional audiences, to student trainees, to Alcoholics Anonymous groups, and to other peer-support groups.

We also checked out this "essentials" content and approach with other professionals in the field. At the same time, we continued to sift and sort our own and others' clinical experience and observation for further insights that might confirm or contradict the validity of this approach. Positive feedback from professionals, clients, students, and community groups indicated that the approach was valid. Practical confirmation came, too, when invariably several persons in an audience identified themselves as chemically dependent after hearing this description of the syndrome.

Up to this point, we had identified a personal committed relationship to drugs as the essential constant factor in chemical dependency. We had also identified a pattern of symptoms as the chemical dependency syndrome. We were still faced with two major tasks. One was to formulate an essential definition of chemical dependency. This definition needed to state exactly what this illness is and distinguish it from any and all other illnesses. Such a definition would go to the essence of the illness and would be objective, exact, and universally applicable. It would include the personal relationship to mood-altering chemicals and the pathology that is caused by this relationship. It would also take into account the essential causal factors that produce the illness.

The second task remaining was to identify the *essential pathology* of chemical dependency. This is the pathology caused by the drug relationship that in turn causes the essential symptoms and the syndrome. But before we go on to formulate definitions and give descriptions, we need to clarify how chemical dependency can be called an illness or a disease in a proper sense of the term.

CHEMICAL DEPENDENCY AS AN ILLNESS

The subject continues to generate confusion and controversy. Those of us who have been through the experience personally have absolutely no doubt that chemical dependency is an unhealthy condition, a state of ill-health, a departure from natural, normal human well-being. Call it "illness," "disease," "disorder" or "x-y-zilch" — we were sick. Whatever else we were, we were certainly not in a state of normal good health by any standards. And those of us who deal on a day-to-day basis with chemically dependent persons and families have this hammered home to us again and again. Working with so many clients who are so desperately sick, we have little time or energy for controversial discussions about whether or not this is an illness. It is. And call it what you will, it is deadly.

Sources of Doubt

Doubts about the matter appear to come from five main sources:

- *First*, from persons who are not in immediate, ongoing contact with the reality of chemical dependency as it actually exists here and now in sick persons and families.

- *Second*, from persons whose outlooks are clouded by preconceptions about what chemical dependency ought to be to fit into their established and familiar classifications and categories.

- *Third*, from persons who are themselves in fact chemically dependent but who have not yet been identified as such. The latter group still comprises the vast majority of chemical dependents, including many helping professionals who are frequently faced with the problem in the exercise of their professional duties. Their persistent quibbling about whether or not this is an illness stems largely, of course, from their personal and compulsive need to protect their own pathological drug relationships.

- *Fourth*, doubts come from a large group, including many academicians, who bring into their views of chemical dependency attitudes that prevent their coming to grips with this reality — or any other reality, for that matter. These are people who never seem to come to any definite, objective conclusions. They are intellectually positioned in chronic doubt and skepticism. Their supreme norm of knowledge is subjective opinion. Chemical dependency — along with everything else — becomes whatever any individual says it is. And one individual's opinion is as valid as any other's, so that all opinions are equally invalid. This view is commonly rationalized and misrepresented as "open-mindedness."

- *Fifth*, and finally, some people become so exasperated by the confusion and controversies that they prefer to ignore the question of whether or not chemical dependency is an illness and get on with their work.

Yes-No Positions

Leaving chronic doubt positions behind, and turning to firm answers given to the question of whether or not chemical dependency is an illness, we find two extreme positions: "yes" and "no." The extreme "yes" position holds that it is essentially and exclusively a *physical* disease. The extreme "no" position maintains that it is not a disease or illness in any proper sense, either (1) because there is no such thing as a disease; or (2) because it is only a symptom of some other disease (as yet undiscovered or undetermined); or (3) because it is only maladaptive behavior; or (4) because it is essentially moral degeneration, a result of weakness of character and lack of will power; or (5) because it is stupidity, due to personal intellectual deficiencies, inept learning, or defective education.

The "no" camp includes a small fringe of extremists, who are more or less appalled by the ignorance of health professionals. These people feel deep resentment and antagonism toward the wealth, status, and oppressive power of the "medical establishment." They would reject altogether any term that has become a part of the medical vocabulary — words such as "illness," "disease," "pathology," "symptoms" — on the grounds that these words are already too contaminated by "medical model" interpretations to be useful in describing chemical dependency.

Debate at the "yes-no" extremes will no doubt continue for some time. Meanwhile, the consensus of those who hold a middle position is that chemical dependency is in fact an illness and that it is not exclusively a physical disease. For them, the really pertinent question is: "What *kind* of an illness or disease is it?" Wrestling with this question are all the "in-betweens." These are people who recognize that chemical dependency is indeed an illness but who have difficulty defining it in terms of existing illness/disease classifications and categories.

Chief among these are some who believe it is a mental or emotional disorder, some who think it is a personality or character disorder, others who see it as a behavioral disorder, and still others who view it as a social or psychosocial disorder. In each of these views, there is some considerable grain of truth. Because of this, there are still others who adopt a more general position, calling it simply a psychophysical disorder, a multifactorial illness, a complex illness, and so on.

The latter position, although more general than others, holds much promise. This is because it implies certain attitudes and recognitions that the more limited viewpoints do not. It implies, for example, the following:

1. an attitude of open-mindedness and humility, a readiness to accept whatever further data the phenomenon of chemical dependency itself may present;

2. an exploratory attitude, a willingness to venture into this relatively new field with openness to new approaches and new perspectives;

3. a recognition that existing disease classifications do not in fact adequately accommodate chemical dependency;

4. a recognition that attempts to force this illness into existing molds impede investigation and distort conclusions;

5. an attitude that looks to chemical dependency itself for answers rather than to preconceived notions, popular (or personal) prejudgments, or misconceptions about it;

6. a recognition that this illness involves whole persons, not just aspects or parts of persons; and

7. a recognition that all disciplines and sciences having to do with human beings may make valuable contributions to our knowledge of chemical dependency.

A Relational Illness

To the question, "Is chemical dependency an illness?" our answer is emphatically, "Yes." It is unquestionably an unhealthy condition, a departure from natural, normal good health and well-being by any reasonable standards of measurement.

To the question, "What kind of an illness is it?" our answer is, "A relational illness." It is essentially an unhealthy *personal relationship* to mood-altering chemical substances. It involves the whole human person and the whole human organism — all psychic powers, all internal personal activity, all external personal behavior, and all personal relations. It is, in other words, a "whole-person" or "total-person" illness growing out of a committed personal relationship to drugs. It can be adequately defined, described, and treated only in reference to the whole human person.

To the further question, "How does this fit into existing disease/illness classifications?" our answer is, "It does not essentially." Existing concepts and categories are too limited, too specialized, to accommodate chemical dependency. Ironically, the very thing that has resulted in so many spectacular breakthroughs in the field of human health (and in other fields) — namely, specialization — now stands as an obstacle in the way of similar breakthroughs with chemical dependency.

Definition of Terms

When we affirm that chemical dependency is an illness or disease, we are employing those terms in a proper sense. To help readers get a better appreciation of this, we include at this point some dictionary definitions of "disease," "illness," and other related terms that we employ throughout this book in reference to chemical dependency.

    Disease, in one sense, is an abnormal condition of an organism or part, especially as a consequence of infection, inherent weakness, or environmental stress that impairs normal physiological functioning. Disease also is any condition or tendency regarded as abnormal or pernicious, that is, destructive and tending to cause death, serious injury, or great harm. To be diseased means to be affected with disease, to be unhealthy, unsound, or disordered. While chemical dependency is not essentially a consequence of physical infection, inherent weakness, or environmental stress, it is certainly an abnormal condition that impairs functioning; and it is destructive to the point of death. A chemically dependent person is unhealthy, unsound, disordered by reason of the drug involvement.

    Illness is sickness of body or mind, or a sick *condition*, that is, an unhealthy, unsound, or abnormal state resulting in suffering, distress, harm, and death. "Illness" and "sickness" also mean "disease," and we use them interchangeably with reference to chemical dependency.

    Pathology, in one sense, means the scientific study of the nature of disease, its causes, processes, development, and consequences. It also means a disease entity with its anatomic or functional manifestations. In this sense, "pathology," "disease," "illness," and "sickness" are synonyms; they all concur in their meaning of an entity within an organism, an entity that has its own identity, characteristics, and manifestations. We use "pathology" in the sense of "disease entity" or "illness entity" in reference to chemical dependency.

    Pathological means something that pertains to or is related to, or that causes or is caused by, a pathology or disease entity. Thus, in regard to chemical dependency, we speak of a pathological condition, a pathological relationship to drugs, a pathological element or aspect of a total pathology, pathological behavior, etc.

    Symptom means any circumstance or phenomenon regarded as an indicator or characteristic of a condition or event. In medicine, it means any phenomenon experienced by an individual as a departure from normal function, sensation, or appearance, generally indicating disorder or disease. In chemical dependency, we use "symptom" to mean an observable sign or indication, caused directly by the underlying pathology, that manifests the presence of chemical dependency within a person.

Syndrome means a group of signs and symptoms that collectively indicate or characterize a disease, psychological disorder, or other abnormal condition. It also means any complex of symptoms indicating the existence of an undesirable condition or quality. The "chemical dependency syndrome" means the group or pattern of symptoms caused directly by the underlying pathological entity (the disease/illness/sickness of chemical dependency) and therefore collectively manifesting the presence of the underlying chemical dependency pathology within a person.

Essential symptoms, in our meaning of the term, are those signs that are intrinsically related to the pathology and hence necessarily follow from it; the syndrome is the collective pattern of these symptoms. Because they are essential signs or indications, whenever a particular illness or pathological entity is present these signs are present, too. A direct *cause-and-effect* relationship exists between the pathology and the symptoms; hence the symptoms are *natural* signs, as smoke is a natural sign of fire. Fire directly causes smoke; smoke is a direct effect of fire. Such a direct cause-and-effect relationship is the basis for all essential symptoms. We reserve the term "symptoms" to this meaning, and the term "syndrome" to the collection of essential symptoms.

Complications are any secondary, more remote, nonessential consequences that may or may not occur. They are not necessarily present when the disease is present, as essential symptoms are. They are other signs or indications that are not intrinsically related to the pathology and hence do not necessarily follow from it. These we refer to as accidental complications or consequences of an illness rather than as symptoms.

From the foregoing definitions, it is evident that chemical dependency is an illness or disease in a proper sense of the terms. As we proceed to examine the nature of chemical dependency and to explore its pathology, symptoms, and causes, each of the terms defined above will be further clarified.

CHAPTER FOUR

Essential Definition
of
Chemical Dependency

Chemical dependency is essentially a committed pathological love relationship of a person to a mood-altering chemical substance, a psychoactive drug, in expectation of a rewarding experience.

What do we mean when we define chemical dependency in terms of what it *essentially* is? *Essence* identifies what a thing is in itself. *Essence* is what makes a thing — anything — exactly what it is and different from every other thing.

An essential definition must include the following: (1) *all* that is essential; (2) *only* what is essential; (3) what has been found to be true in every *known* instance; (4) what is and can be objectively verified in every *present* and *subsequent* instance; and (5) the essential causes of the phenomenon that is defined.

Our definition of chemical dependency fulfills all five requirements. Nothing essential is omitted, and nothing but essentials is included. We arrived at the definition inductively, through long experience. We examined many particular instances of chemical dependency over long periods of time and in varying circumstances. This process included intense and systematic clinical observation and experiment, along with careful reality-testing and evaluation. Over time, we were gradually able to eliminate nonessentials and isolate and identify the essentials of chemical dependency.

By means of this inductive process, evidence was collected that made it possible to present a definition that can be objectively verified in every known instance of chemical dependency. As we examine this illness in its essential nature, it will become apparent that every aspect we explore is in some way incorporated into the essential definition. The first step in this examination is a clarification of each term and phrase used in the definition.

ESSENTIAL

To understand better what an essential definition is, it is necessary to grasp the distinction between "essence" and "accidents." *Essence* refers to the inner, specific elements in a thing. *Accident* refers to other elements or aspects that are present or that may be present. Some of these accidents are so closely related to the essence itself that they are always present. Others are more remote — they may or may not be present. In either case, they refer to something in *addition to* the essential nature.

For example, the essence of a human being is rational animality. The essential nature of a human person includes two absolutely necessary elements: (1) an intellectual power or rationality, and (2) sense power or animality. Both must be present or there is no human person. Impairment or dysfunction of either a person's natural intellectual or sense powers, or of both (such as occurs, for example, when a person is in a coma following a serious accident or illness) does not change the essence of personhood. In the briefest of terms, it might be said, "Once a person, always a person." By contrast, eyes and ears or legs and arms are accidental in the sense in which we use the term "accident." These organs and limbs are integral parts of a human being, it is true. But it is also true that they may be lacking or removed in an individual without destroying the essence of that human being.

Similarly, certain elements in chemical dependency are essential — without them there is no chemical dependency. Other elements are accidental — they may or may not be present in a chemically dependent person, but the dependency remains. Liver damage is one example of an accidental. With or without liver damage, a person may be chemically dependent. Some other accidentals are the frequency of drug use and the quantities of drugs ingested. One person may use alcohol or other drugs in large quantities every day. Another may use them only periodically or occasionally and in small quantities. Yet both may be chemically dependent to the same degree. It is accidental how much and how often drugs are ingested.

Accidentals also include the various complications that frequently accompany chemical dependency but are not always present in every case of chemical dependency. These include some psychological and physical problems, family difficulties, involvement with the law, loss of employment, or even driving while intoxicated. A person may be dependent *essentially* without ever experiencing such accidental complications.

PATHOLOGICAL

In Chapter Three, we defined "pathology" and "pathological." Now we take another look at these terms to clarify the meaning of the word "pathological" as it is used in the definition.

> **Pathology** in this definition means the primary set of harmful effects within a person caused directly by that person's relationship to mood-altering chemical substances. "Pathology," in other words, means the illness entity itself.

Pathological means sick, ill, diseased, that is, deviating or departing from normal health.

The pathology of chemical dependency is characterized by the following:

1. a typical pattern of particular elements that are always present and objectively identifiable by their symptoms in a person suffering from this illness;

2. a process of development or a progression that the pathology (and its elements) typically follows; and

3. various destructive effects or resulting conditions that these elements produce within the victim.

The set or pattern of elements always found present in the pathology of chemical dependency are as follows:

1. psychological dependency or need;

2. powerlessness to recognize one's condition, to freely and comfortably control ingestion within reasonable limits or to terminate ingestion and effect recovery without outside help.

3. mental obsession with drugs and their rewards;

4. emotional compulsion to ingest drugs in order to experience their rewards;

5. diminished ego strength with a low self-image;

6. rigid, negative feeling states or attitudes;

7. a rigid defense system surrounding the drug relationship and its consequences; and

8. delusion, that is, impaired and distorted awareness, insight, reasoning, and judgment regarding reality.

It should be noted that we are speaking here about a pathological *state* or *condition*. Hence, "pathology," as used in the definition, does not refer to those immediate physical, pharmacological, psychological, or social effects that may occur even with occasional use of mood-altering drugs. Intoxication, for example, or headache, or destruction of brain cells, or impaired speech and motor control, or social misbehavior, or even death may result from a single ingestion of drugs by a person who is not pathologically related to drugs.

Furthermore, everyone who uses drugs at all is dependent on them on each occasion of use for the effects the drugs produce on that occasion. Hence, there are many persons who are dependent on drugs in some sense but who are not necessarily *pathologically* dependent. They are able to maintain such reasonable limits that the pathology of which we speak does not develop. They are drug users in the proper sense, not drug abusers or chemical dependents, and their person-to-drugs relationship is casual, not committed.

RELATIONSHIP

Relationship is the key concept in our definition of chemical dependency. A firm grasp of this concept is necessary in order to understand the illness. The basic definition of a *relationship* or *relation* is a *tendency toward another*. The graphic below depicts the essential nature of all relationships, both transcendental and material. The point of origin is the *subject* in which the relationship exists or resides. The point of termination is the *object* toward which the relationship is directed and in which it comes to rest.

Essential Nature of Relationship
"Tendency Toward Another"

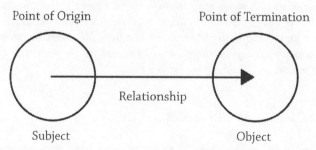

Point of Origin   Point of Termination

Relationship

Subject   Object

A careful look at our experience of relationships makes clear what is meant by "subject" and "object." In my own relationships, for example, I, a person, am the subject. My relationships are in me: they originate in me and they exist in me; they reside or are rooted in me. Another person or thing is the object of my relationships, that is, my relationships tend toward and terminate or end up in a person or a thing.

Types of Relationships

Foremost among our human relationships are person-to-persons relationships. These involve ourselves and people who are close to us and with whom we have meaningful association.

Examples of such relationships are those that we have with our parents, our husband or wife, our children, our blood relatives, and our in-laws. Included also are friends and companions, peers, neighbors, fellow workers, business and professional associates, and those with whom we share recreation, hobbies, pastimes, politics, and religion. In each case, we share some special bond of common interest that draws us together, gives rise to the relationship, and keeps it going. And in each case, there is some kind of love at work to build and to firm up the bond.

In addition to our person-to-persons relationships, we all have many person-to-things relationships: person to home, person to job, person to animals, person to recreation, hobbies, pastimes, nature, place, time, community, and so on.

We all have a perfectly natural desire to experience new pleasures and joys, to expand our states of consciousness, and to want new adventures. This desire leads us to seek new and varied relationships both to people and to things. Normal human beings relish this variety, so every healthy person has a host of wholesome relationships.

All of us are immersed in our many relationships; they are literally all over the place. Perhaps because they are so commonplace, we seldom consider them directly. Usually, we take them for granted and leave them unexamined until a crisis forces us to look at them more closely: a marriage heading for the rocks, a job in jeopardy, a parent-child conflict, a friendship that is breaking up. Then we discover that relationships are *realities*, that they do indeed exist and that some of them are very meaningful to us. We begin to probe the nature of our relationships, their various kinds, and their influence in our lives. We become more attentive to our relationships and grow more aware of where we are with the persons and things with whom and to which we are related.

Casual and Committed Relationships

Some relationships are casual; they come and go without making any significant difference to us one way or another. They are passing because we make no commitment to the object of such relationships. Take, for example, our person-to-persons relationships. We have casual acquaintances of many kinds: the butcher, the baker, the mail carrier, the gas station attendant. We relate to them on a temporary basis, which is pretty much determined by our need for their products or services. We respect and value them as persons, of course, but there is no deep bond between us. Other kinds of casual relationships are with neighbors, classmates, work associates, and so on. These relationships may last for some months or even a few years. Some develop into satisfying and beneficial committed relationships. Others lose their attractiveness and fade away.

Other relationships are firm and deep; they contribute to our well-being and are of great significance to us. They are lasting and even permanent because we make a commitment to the object of such relationships. Again, take our person-to-persons relationships as an example. We have parents, children, spouses, and friends. We relate to them on a continuing basis because of some deep bond between us. In some cases, a bond is already established in nature, like the blood bond between parents and children. In other instances, the bond is established by our personal decisions and choices, as with spouses and friends. In the latter cases, we make a commitment to the object of our relationship, and this sets up a lasting bond between us.

The same can be said of person-to-things relationships. We have some that are casual and some that are lasting. The difference is that in some cases we make a commitment to the thing that is the object of our relationship and in other cases we do not. Committed relationships contribute to the health and well-being of a person provided these relationships are regulated by a clearly defined, beneficial purpose and maintained in a manner or mode that is regulated by that purpose. The relationship may be with another person, or with a thing, or even with an activity.

To the degree that you desire and value a particular relationship, you will *cultivate* your relationship to the object and maintain it, foster it, nourish it. It will become an increasingly important part of your life, a center around which many of your thoughts, fantasies, words, feelings, and actions revolve. More of your time will become devoted to it. Your relationship will develop from a transient, passing encounter with its object, to frequent but casual unions, to a permanent but bonded commitment.

As you cultivate your relationship, it will intensify. Prompted at first by slight inclinations to pursue its object, you will find the promptings growing stronger until you have developed a firm habit of repeatedly pursuing the object to obtain its rewards. To repeat again, as long as you regulate your commitment by a clearly defined beneficial purpose and maintain it in a manner that is regulated by that purpose, it will grow stronger and deeper and prove more beneficial to you, especially in the case of mutually reciprocal person-to-person relationships.

We all have tendencies toward excess. From time to time, everyone is likely to go beyond the parameters of the beneficial purpose that regulates a relationship. Gradually — or sometimes quickly — you may find yourself seeking those rewards more frequently and more excessively. At this point on the possible road to addiction, in any relationship, you have become burdened with a bad habit, a vice. At this point, too, you still remain free to choose either to pursue or not to pursue the union with the object of your relationship. But the powerful promptings to pursue become very difficult to resist. You are now on the brink of addiction. You must make a decision whether or not to continue or to break off your relationship. And you must make a choice based on your decision.

Making a commitment to remain in the relationship in order to repeatedly experience the special rewards of union with the object marks the transition from habitual actions that are excessive but freely chosen (willed) to excessive actions that are no longer free, but compulsive. In effect, the commitment is a self-surrender to the power of the object, a letting go of freedom and entering into the first stage of enslavement to compulsion.

A Chemically Dependent Love Relationship

We now move from examining the general nature of relationships to focusing specifically on the nature of the chemically dependent relationship. As we have just seen, the committed self-surrender of a person to the power of an object — in this case, a psychoactive or mood-altering substance, a drug — signals a letting go of personal freedom and an entering into the first stage of enslavement to the bondage of compulsion.

Chemical dependency is essentially a love relationship that originates in one's personal commitment to drugs for the sake of the rewards — the highs or euphoria expected from ingesting them. Some people make a conscious decision along the way in the development of their pathological love relationship to pursue drugs no matter what, but for the most part the commitment is subconscious, pushed out of conscious awareness by the power of expectation and the rational defense system that darkens reason with clouds of denial. Conscious or subconscious, the commitment forms a lasting, bonded relationship, and this relationship continues until the person, through whatever means, comes to revoke the commitment and thereby dissolve the bond of pathological love. In other words, chemical dependency is a committed love relationship with a person as its subject and a mood-altering chemical substance as its object.

Chemically Dependent Love Relationship

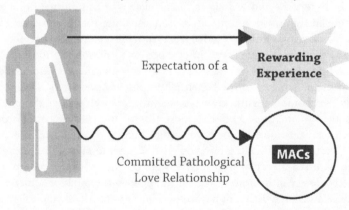

In the diagram above, we use a wavy line to indicate the disease entity residing in the person and terminating in the drug object. The line also indicates that the relationship is no longer casual but committed — a committed, lasting love relationship that sets up a deep bond between the person and mood-altering chemicals for the sake of the expected psychoactive "high" experience.

On one end of these relationships are individual human persons: you and I. On the other end are powerful drugs that can change significantly the way we feel and perceive and act. To the uninitiated, these drugs are mysterious and thus attractive, in the sense that they hold out a promise of unimagined altered states of consciousness. This promise makes these drugs very desirable. They have a natural appeal to our appetite for new adventures, new experiences, and new pleasures. We tend toward them in relationship because every normal human being likes to feel better and to perceive and act differently at times. Hence, every normal person is a natural candidate for drug use, for setting up drug relationships, and for the drug problems that addictive drug relationships can spawn.

As in any relationship, we can rely on and value these relationships so much that we become sick — certainly in a mental sense, but often in a physical way, too — if one of our relationships becomes so overpowering that it damages or destroys the others. In the process, disordered relationships eventually lead to the destruction of the human person. This is what happens in all disordered relationships. It is what happens in pathological gambling or watching endless hours of TV, for example. It is what happens in a disordered relationship to food, to money, to possessions that one will kill for to have and keep. It certainly happens in sick, pathological romantic relationships. And this is what happens in sick, pathological drug relationships.

The Appetitive Faculty

But how, exactly, does this happen? To answer that question, we need to explore the nature and dynamics of a key faculty, a transcendental power of the human person. That power is the *appetitive power*. The foundation of every human relationship is in appetite, specifically an appetite *directed by love* toward an object that is perceived by the person as good or beneficial, as shown in the following diagram.

Essential Lover-Beloved Relationship

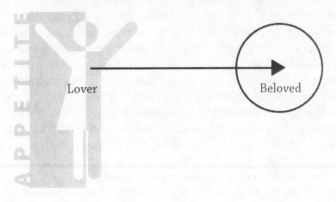

Appetites are based in a physical or transcendental foundation. For example, if we are speaking of a personal physical relationship, we search for a physical foundation, as in the case of the appetite for sex, or food or water, or material things.

If we are speaking of a transcendental or spiritual relationship, we look for a transcendental or spiritual foundation for the appetite, as in the case of spiritual hunger or thirst for the Other, for More, for Mystery, for a Higher Power, for God, or for such values as beauty, truth, or virtue. If the relationship has elements of both the physical and the transcendental, we look for both in the foundation, because the spiritual appetite is proportioned to a spiritual object perceived as good, and a physical appetite is proportioned to a physical or material good.

All five of our senses — sight, hearing, taste, touch, smell — have appetites for good. Each of our numerous appetites relates to or tends toward a proportionate good. *Love* is the first action/response that appetites have to an object perceived as good, be it a material or transcendental good. We can say that love of the good is the first act of appetite that stirs or triggers *attraction* toward a "proper" object. Love arouses *desire*, which is the second movement of the appetite. Desire, in turn, triggers *pursuit of the good* in expectation of achieving union with the good and experiencing the rewards the beloved object holds out in promise.

Dynamics of the Appetitive Faculty

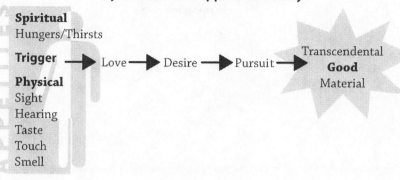

Three Clarifications

Whatever else alcoholism and the other drug dependencies may be, they are always and in every case *personal pathological love relationships to drugs*. This is the foundation, the essential constant factor that is always present, without exception, in every instance of chemical dependency.

To bring this personal pathological relationship into sharper focus, three clarifications must be made.

- First, chemical dependency is a *specific* dependency relationship, one of many possible sick dependencies.

- Second, since all human beings are essentially the same, all such relational dependencies will closely resemble one another in essential aspects. But these *similarities do not make different dependencies identical*.

- Third, dependencies differ in the object of dependency and in how that object affects the person.

PERSON

We define **person** in the definition as an individual substance of a rational nature — a rational animal — composed of two substantial parts, a transcendental spiritual soul and a material, physical body.

Composite Spirit-Matter Nature
of the Human Person

Spirit/Soul
Matter/Body

Chemical dependency adversely affects the *whole person*, body and soul. For this reason, some acquaintance with the basic human psychic or life powers and their areas of activity is necessary in order to understand chemical dependency and to diagnose and treat it properly.

The human soul, a direct, immediate spiritual creation of God, is the principle of human life, the energy source enlivening the material body. The human person as a whole exists as the principal source or chief cause of human activity in all areas of life. However, the person acts through specific psychological or psychic powers, also called *faculties*, that produce all the human activities of the person, both internal and external.

For example, I, a whole human person, think; but I think by means of my psychic thinking power or my "thinking life power," which is my intellect. I, a whole human person, feel emotions; but I feel by means of my psychic "feeling life powers," namely, my emotions. My person, in other words, is the originating source, like a spring or a fountain; my particular psychological powers are like channels or riverbeds through which my personal activities flow. The outward flow of these activities is directed by our appetitive faculty, the will, which acts with love or hate in response to the goods or evils perceived and presented to it by a mental faculty, the intellect, and exercises free choice in pursuing the good or avoiding evil.

Use of the terms *good* and *evil*

We would like to add a note about our use of the words *good* and *evil* here and in various places later on in this text. We know that to many people these words are highly charged with religious and ethical meanings and associations. We are aware, too, that there are a great many philosophical positions and debates about the meaning of these terms. To simplify this, we need to focus on what we mean when we use the terms good and evil.

Our definitions derive from metaphysics and classical philosophy. George Klubertanz, S.J., in his *Introduction to the Philosophy of Being*, defines the "good" as "that which is perfect according to its kind" and "at the same time an object of appetite, or tendency." Conversely, the word "evil" designates "something which is without (deprived of) some particular good which it should have according to its kind." In short, "evil" is a lack or negation or privation in something. To offer a simple example, a bowl of rice or a piece of bread is an obvious and natural object of appetite and unquestionable good to a hungry person. When a starving person goes without food, he or she is deprived of a good they *must* have, by reason of being human, and consequently suffers the "evil" of starvation.

These ideas are important to the overall themes of this book. Every one of us has a natural appetite or tendency to pursue what is "good," and to do so in all manner of complicated scenarios involving our reason, emotions, and spirit, as well as our body. When we "avoid evil," what we are avoiding is something that diminishes, damages, or threatens to destroy our pursuit or possession of the good. While it may not always seem so, our actions are predominately motivated by a natural appetite for what we *perceive* to be "the good."

The Psychic or Life Powers

The human person acts through or by means of the powers below to carry on activities in various areas of life:

> *Spiritual life powers,* which enable a person to function in the area of ethics and religion. These powers allow a person to develop personal, moral, and religious values or guiding principles and to apply these in evaluating his or her behavior and judging it as good and right or as evil and wrong.

Mental life powers, which enable a person to function in the area of mental life. Three specific mental powers are included:

>*Intellect*, which enables a person to experience awareness, insight, and understanding of reality and to carry on reasoning about it. These powers allow a person to form judgments and opinions, to draw conclusions, and to deliberate, evaluate, and make practical decisions.

>*Imagination*, which enables a person to fantasize. These powers allow a person to form and manipulate images taken from or suggested by reality and to elaborate these images.

>*Memory*, which enables a person to receive, to retain, and to recall experiences, ideas, and images.

Volitional life powers, or will powers, which enable a person to freely accept reality, to freely choose among action alternatives, to freely select means to goals, and to freely direct and control actions through which the means are applied to achieve goals.

Emotional life powers, which enable a person to experience feelings. These include pursuit feelings in reference to attractive goods and avoidance feelings in reference to repugnant evils.

Social life powers, which enable a person to function in relationships with other individuals and with groups and communities of various kinds.

Physical life powers, which enable a person to function as a physical organism. These include experiencing sensations of pleasure and pain, comfort and discomfort, tension and relaxation, etc.

These psychic, transcendental life powers are displayed graphically in the "Life Powers Wheel."

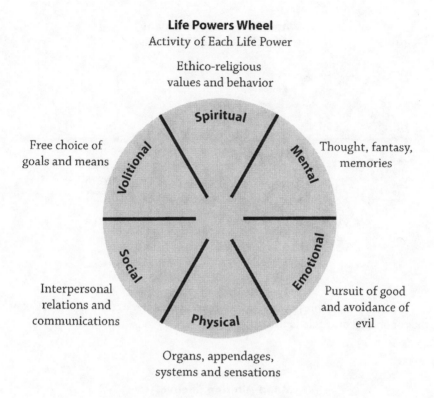

Life Powers Wheel
Activity of Each Life Power

Chemical dependency is a complex illness affecting the whole person. It is a total-person illness because the drug relationship involves both the person as a whole and all of the person's life powers.

The whole person and each of his or her psychic powers are engaged in making the initial drug commitment:

**Whole Person Commitment
to Mood-Altering Chemicals**

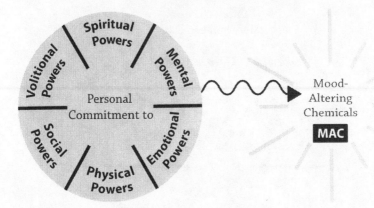

Each of the psychic powers remains fixed upon drugs as the beloved object of the committed drug relationship:

**All Life Powers Fixed on
Mood-Altering Chemicals**

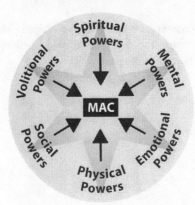

Each of the psychic powers in turn is adversely affected, impaired, and rendered dysfunctional as the drug relationship continues and deepens:

**Progressive Impairment
of All Life Powers**

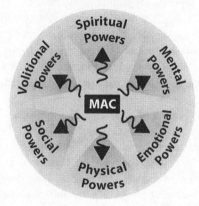

It is the disorientation, distortion, and ultimately the devastation of all the psychic powers that constitute the essential pathology of chemical dependency and produce the total personality disintegration of those who are its victims:

Personality Disintegration

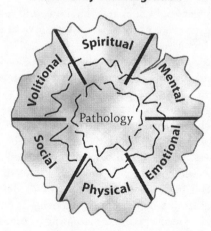

MOOD-ALTERING CHEMICAL SUBSTANCE

Mood-altering chemical substance, in the definition, refers to psychoactive substances that directly affect the central nervous system and in turn produce significant and welcome changes of psychological states or mood. Hence the labels "psychoactive" or "mood-altering" drugs. Both the common denominator and the essential aspect of all dependency-inducing psychoactive drugs is their intrinsic power to significantly change the way one feels. Psychoactive substances directly affect the central nervous system. Once ingested by whatever means, the substance travels through the blood stream to a cell receptor site in the brain where the drug action takes place. The pharmacological effects are then transmitted throughout the central nervous system, resulting in significantly altered physical, mental, and emotional states.

Psychoactive drugs are toxic substances — poisons. When they enter the human organism, both their presence and the battle to be rid of them impair normal functioning. The name "psychoactive" indicates that their principal effects are on the actions of the psyche, that is, their poisonous powers bear directly on the psychic or life powers of the human person. These drugs are variously called "mood-altering," "mind-altering," "mood- and mind-changing," "mind-expanding," "hallucinogenic," "sedative," "stimulant," "narcotic," and so on — all names that point to psychic action as their chief effect and that imply modifications of natural, normal functioning. Without going into details about the psychopharmacological effects of particular drugs or classes of drugs, the essential point is clear: the natural balance of the human organism is upset when these chemicals are ingested so that the various psychic or life powers cannot function normally.

Such chemicals are the objects of the person-to-drug relationship that we have defined. Whatever the particular drug may be, the common characteristic of all these chemicals is their intrinsic power to alter moods. It is in this characteristic that their inherent danger (and value) lies. The simple and central fact that certain drugs have the power to make us feel good or better, or at least different, is the reason why they can "hook" us.

By **mood** we mean a state involving physical sensations, emotional feelings, mental activities, and behaviors. The term is used to denote a condition of the whole person, not merely to indicate feeling states limited to emotions.

A mood-altering chemical or drug is often referred to as the *agent.* The agent is the means by which the person expects to achieve a rewarding experience. In order to produce its immediate effects, the agent must be actually ingested by the person in some way. The fixed pathological relationship to the drug however, remains in the person and continuously produces its destructive effects whether the drug is actually being ingested at the moment or not. Merely taking or keeping the drug supply away from a dependent by removing it or hiding it leaves the pathology untouched. For recovery to take place, drug ingestion must be completely terminated. A process of therapy must then be applied to reduce and ultimately to remove the pathology.

IN EXPECTATION OF A REWARDING EXPERIENCE

One phrase remains to be clarified, namely, **in expectation of a rewarding experience**. This means in the hope of, out of a desire for, or in anticipation of receiving a welcome change in psychological state or mood. This state is often referred to as a "high," a word with obviously positive connotations. We ingest the drugs for the purpose of achieving this mood change. Dependency develops through a continuing reliance on these chemicals not simply to feel different, but to feel better, to experience the sought-after high.

The word "high" is sometimes taken to mean drunk, stoned, or intoxicated. In our usage, it means the subjective, singularly rewarding experience that is expected and/or enjoyed by the drug abuser. Abusers seldom intend to get intoxicated because intoxication goes beyond — and therefore spoils — the desired high. "Mildly intoxicated" would correspond to what we mean by "high," but not "drunk" or "stoned," or "out of it." Again, "high" is sometimes taken to mean stimulated as a result of ingesting "uppers." In our usage, "high" means the euphoria or the good feelings expected and/or achieved by the drug abuser, whether the euphoric experience results from "uppers," "downers," "mind-expanders," or other mood-altering chemicals. Essentially, it is a change from a subjectively less desirable to a more desirable state produced by any psychoactive drug.

Hence, to one who is chemically dependent, it matters little or not at all what chemical or physiological processes bring about a mood change. What is all-important is "what drugs do for me," the welcome effects they produce. And it is the expectation of achieving repeated highs that motivates the commitment to drugs as the means to those highs. This is a personal drug commitment that sets up a lasting bond between the person and drugs. This commitment establishes the person's relationship to chemicals as pathological. It also marks the point of transition from predependency into the initial or pleasure stage of chemical dependency.

The Power of Expectation

The significance of expectation can hardly be exaggerated. This expectation comes from many sources. All the pressures and examples from one's environment go into the making of it. So do all the influences operating within oneself: thoughts, memories, fantasies, feelings and attitudes, physical conditions, social relations, personal values, and habits. All of these factors influence a person's first response to the question, "Should I try drugs?" When the answer is "yes" and drugs are chosen, it is in the hope of enjoying the goods that drugs hold out in promise.

If a first-time actual drug experience does not match the expectation, then the expectation is not discarded or even discouraged. It remains in force to motivate further quests of drug highs.

Marijuana smoking is a good example. Initial ingestion is often disappointing and sometimes quite uncomfortable. But built-up expectation does not quit easily.

It prompts additional experiments until the desired rewarding high is achieved. And even if expectations are not being realized, we find dependents subjectively continuing to expect that somehow, sometime, their currently desired rewards will be achieved. This expectation is so powerful that taking placebos may produce desired highs.

Classification of Mood-Altering Chemicals

In the chart below, we present a common classification based on certain pharmacological effects along with selected drug examples in each category:

Category	Examples
Depressants	alcohol, including liquor, wine, and beer
	pharmaceutical tranquilizers, anti-anxiety drugs, and sedatives, such as Valium®, Librium®, Xanax®, Ativan®, and Ambien®
	GHB, liquid ecstasy
Stimulants	cocaine, crack
	amphetamines and methamphetamines (speed), such as crystal meth, crank, and pharmaceutical stimulants, such as Dexedrine®, Benzedrine®
Hallucinogens	LSD, DMT, STP, PCP, ecstasy, ketamine, psilocybin, mushrooms, mescaline, peyote, marijuana, hashish, hash oil
Narcotics	opium, morphine, heroin, methadone, and pharmaceutical analgesics, such as codeine, Demerol®, Dilaudid®, Vicodan®, Percodan®
Inhalants	amyl and butyl nitrates
	nitrous oxide (laughing gas)
	commercial solvents such as glue, gasoline, paint thinner, lighter fluids
	aerosols such as hair spray, spray paint, insecticides

CHAPTER FIVE

Essential Progression of Chemical Dependency

Chemical dependency is commonly recognized as a **progressive** illness. This means it is a pathological condition that has a definite start and a continuing process of development. As the illness passes through successive stages, it becomes increasingly destructive to its victims. Left untreated, it is terminal.

While all of this is generally agreed upon in principle, it is often disregarded in practice. More often than not, chemical dependency is seen as suddenly coming into being fully developed, like Athena springing full-blown from the head of Zeus.

The arrival of complications and problems is often mistaken for the beginning of chemical dependency. Dependents often confuse their own first awareness of a drug problem with the start of complications. So do their families and other concerned persons, including some professionals. Some see the illness as starting when a notable change occurs in the manner of use or in the personality or behavior of the dependent. What they may not see is that these changes are themselves effects and signs of an illness that has been present for some time. Chemical dependency does not come into existence only when someone notices it for the first time.

Measuring Progression

Before attempting to unlock a door, you want to have the proper key in hand. So before describing the progression of chemical dependency, we must be clear about its measure.

A measure of progression must fulfill at least four conditions:

1. The measure must be an *essential aspect* of the illness; that is, it must be present from beginning to end.

2. The measure must be *constant*; that is, it must remain present throughout the course of the illness.

3. The measure must also be *variable*; that is, it must change with the successive stages of the illness.

4. The measure must be *observable*; that is, it must be sufficiently apparent (at least to trained observers) to serve as a principle for tracing the progression.

The expectation of a rewarding experience is what keeps a dependent tied to drugs through the entire course of the illness. It is therefore a *constant* factor. The rewarding experience that is expected *varies* as the illness advances. This variation provides the principal clue for measuring the progression of the illness.

Both the constancy and the variations of this motivation are observable. In the chart below, the constancy can be seen in the dependent's non-stop pursuit of chemical highs. The variations can be seen in the changes that take place from time to time in the kinds of highs that are sought.

Constant and Variable Factors of Chemical Dependency

Constants	Variables
• Commitment to drug highs • Pathological love relationship to drugs • Drug abuse as the mode of ingestion • Expectation of a rewarding experience • Four stages of progression	• The kind of reward expected • The predominant motivation at each stage of the illness: 1. Pleasure 2. Relief 3. Maintenance 4. Escape • The rate of progression through the four stages

The Four Predominant Motivational Expectations

It is not surprising that the power of expectation should get people into drugs and keep them hooked as long as expectations are rewarded. It is harder for people to understand how dependents continue in their self-destructive drug ingestion even in the face of great and constant misery. We sometimes see people astonished and amazed by this as they ask, "Don't they ever learn from their bad experiences?"

One would expect that the intense pain of this devastating downward spiral would make them stop. But, no, they continue abusive ingestion even in the face of death. Instead of retracting their drug commitment and reordering their motivation, they simply shift their expectation from one reward to another. By the time their quest for *pleasure* is no longer yielding the hoped-for highs, the quest for *relief* is already under way. And even while seeking relief as their main motivation, dependents are steadily shifting toward an expectation of *maintenance*. Then, when the maintenance motive is running out, a final, fatal expectation is ready to replace it. It is to *escape to oblivion* through drug ingestion.

Beginning in predependency, the pleasure motive is at work in moderation. With the onset of dependency, and through the initial stage, pleasure remains the dominant motive. But now it operates on the strength of a drug relationship that is no longer casual but committed and pathological. The sick committed relationship is in force. Drug abuse remains the mode of ingestion throughout the progression of the illness. We use the four motivational expectations of pleasure, relief, maintenance, and escape to oblivion to identify each of the four successive stages of chemical dependency.

Diagnostic Evaluation

Diagnosticians identify the presence of illness in their clients. They have the further function of evaluating the stage of its progression.

Motives are dynamic and usually mixed. They change back and forth very quickly from one expectation to another. Diagnosticians therefore need more than "snapshots"; they need "moving pictures" of motivation over a period of time to determine the typical expectation at this point in the client's illness. This must be distinguished from the shorter-term shifts that are continually taking place. It is important to note here that these stages of predominant motivation are not discrete, and that a dependent will shift back and forth between stages very quickly from one motivation to another so that at any one time the most obvious present motive may not be the one that is predominant. This shift is often due to the dependent's exercise of "marginal control." Having some degree of awareness that the drug ingestion is getting out of control and either spoiling or preventing the desired "high," the dependent attempts to prove to himself and usually to others that he is "in control" and "really can handle it." Marginal control will generally work for a time, but it is ultimately destined to give out. It is also worth noting that some kind and degree of pleasure can be experienced at all stages of the illness. For example, a dependent who has moved well into the relief stage will still experience and desire pleasure, even after the predominant motivation for use has shifted. In each case, the diagnostician must examine various symptoms for evidence that can confirm the diagnosis and support the evaluation.

As the following diagram shows, once the disease begins progressing through the various stages, the highs are never as high as they once were, and the lows are always lower. All the while, the sick relationship to drugs steadily and directly descends through each successive stage. In the absence of effective intervention, the disease will ultimately end in insanity or early untimely death, either through accident, injury, drug-induced physical complications, overdose, or suicide.

A Moving Picture of Motivation in Chemical Dependency Progression

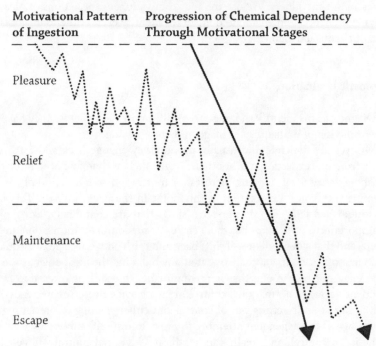

Motivational Pattern of Ingestion

Progression of Chemical Dependency Through Motivational Stages

Pleasure

Relief

Maintenance

Escape

PASSAGE FROM CASUAL USE THROUGH STAGES OF CHEMICAL DEPENDENCY PROGRESSION

In predependency, a person has many person-to-persons and person-to-things relationships. Among these is a casual relationship to mood-altering chemicals. Ingestion is reasonable. It is drug use in the proper sense. It does not interfere with or impair other relationships.

Later on, as the person repeats ingestion, he or she may start to look forward to the welcome effects produced by mood-altering chemicals and to view these pleasant highs as significantly rewarding experiences. After several such experiences (or, in some cases, one particularly rewarding one), the person makes a commitment to getting high on drugs. This commitment is not necessarily a conscious, deliberate, articulated choice, and the process of commitment may vary considerably from person to person. Some people, looking back at the beginnings of their chemical dependency, can name the moment they made that commitment, however unaware they might have been of it at the actual time. For others, the commitment process is subtler and may take place over a period of time. But however the commitment begins — suddenly or subtly — all dependents enter and at some point firmly establish an ongoing love relationship with mood-altering chemicals. Their motivation for pursuing and cultivating this relationship comes from their expectation of repeatedly receiving the rewards of ingestion. This motivation marks the transition from predependency into the initial, pleasure stage of dependency.

Once a person has entered this first stage, it is as if he or she has passed into the open mouth of a funnel, as illustrated in the diagram that follows. We have found that the image of the funnel provides an apt metaphor for the progression of the illness. As labeled below, the funnel also provides a relatively simple frame of reference for tracing the progression of the particular elements in the pathology, which will be discussed in succeeding chapters. For now, let us note that as the committed drug relationship continues, other relationships grow less and less important. The dependent eliminates these relationships altogether if they threaten the drug relationship in any way. As the dependent becomes an increasingly rigid, drug-centered person, the funnel grows narrower and narrower. Ultimately, there is no way out but untimely death.

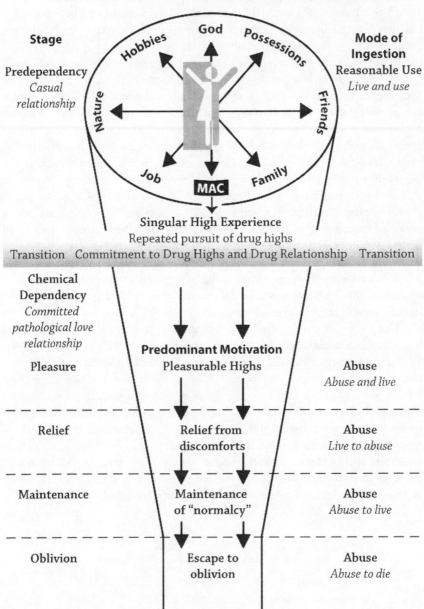

Funnel Chart of Chemical Dependency Progression

Pleasure Stage

The pleasure motive in pre-dependency is moderated by reason, in expectation of a mild mood change through the ingestion of mood-altering chemicals. With the onset of dependency, and through the initial stage, the predominant motive is pleasure, or more accurately, a highly pleasurable change of mood or psychological state. This welcome mood swing is enough in itself to lead a person into a pathological relationship with the drug. No mysterious psychological or social problems need to be behind it. Every normal, healthy human person enjoys a pleasant mood. Psychoactive highs are extremely pleasurable to many people. The highs experienced by some persons who ingest drugs are all that is needed to hook them. The pleasure motive now *operates on the strength of a drug relationship that is no longer casual but committed and pathological.* The sick committed relationship is in force. The typical ingestion is now drug abuse in expectation of highly rewarding, drug-induced highs. Drug abuse remains the mode of ingestion as the predominant pleasure motive gives way to the motive of relief, then, to maintenance, and finally, to escape to oblivion.

For the sake of example, we might take ten perfectly normal, healthy, well-adjusted persons who have their first drink of alcohol or smoke their first joint of marijuana at the same time and in the same circumstances. For purposes of this illustration, let's say their socio-cultural environments are identical in every respect. Of the ten "first timers," some few may get sick, become sleepy, or perhaps panic. For them, this is an experience they will likely avoid in the future. Others will receive a neutral experience. Their reward is mildly pleasant, perhaps, but only "so-so"— for the moment at least, it leaves them indifferent to the drug. They may (or they may not) repeat their ingestion of it.

But for some few, perhaps two or three of the ten, the pleasant mood will be "something else." Their first drug ingestion turns out to be a highly rewarding experience. Later on, they will reflect upon it with pleasure, and in fantasy they will look forward to its repetition. That "extra something," that special high, is the hooker. It is the springboard for their commitment to continued drug use. Their reflection on the experience is the beginning of a preoccupation that leads to obsession. Their fleeting fantasies of future experiences bring tugs of anticipation that will lead to compulsion. Repeated drug abuse is now under way. The first stage of dependency is now established, with pleasure as its predominant motive.

Relief Stage

Once we discover that a certain drug will "do something for us," we are set up for further experimentation. We can try it out on various occasions as a remedy to medicate our tensions, emotional upsets, sorrows and pains, conflicts and disappointments. If we discover through some of our experiments what seems to be "instant relief," we move on into the second stage of dependency. In this stage, relief is our predominant motive.

In the pleasure stage, of course, relief is sometimes our motive. And in the relief and later stages, the pleasure motive is seldom abandoned altogether. Recall that this is a matter of *predominant* motive rather than of *exclusive* motive. Hence, as one stage passes into another, the earlier motivations are not altogether abandoned. Even the dependent who has advanced into the terminal, escape-to-oblivion stage usually continues to hope for pleasant moods and/or relief.

It sometimes happens, of course, that one is introduced to drugs by medical prescription for the purpose of relief. With such prescription drugs, the initial experience may be so rewarding to the particular user that chronic dependency based in relief develops very quickly. Thousands of drug ads repeated daily through mass media propose relief as the primary motive for taking drugs. Undoubtedly, many persons come into the drug scene with relief as their initial motivation. They either bypass the initial stage of the illness altogether or pass through it so quickly that it is of little or no practical significance.

Maintenance Stage

The third stage of the illness is characterized by the predominance of still another motive — the maintenance of "normalcy." Psychological adjustments or adaptations to continued drug abuse create a demand for the continued presence of drugs in the system for functioning at minimal levels of effectiveness. While the illness is primarily and essentially "psychological," it is still a whole person illness, involving both *soma* and *psyche* by virtue of the composite nature of the human person. The maintenance stage of the illness, therefore, is ordinarily characterized by the onset of *physical addiction* for some dependents. Not all psychoactive substances have the power to induce physical addiction. But for those who engage in abusive ingestion of addictive substances over time, physical addiction is a reality they cannot escape.

The development of physical addiction adds strength to the dependent's predominant motive, maintenance. Physical addiction frequently becomes significant enough to create the danger of acute withdrawal symptoms if a dependent's accustomed drug dosages are greatly reduced or terminated abruptly and without adequate supervision or proper supportive therapy. In such cases, avoidance of acute withdrawal symptoms reinforces in a secondary way the motivation to keep things going as usual. If addiction is severe, the withdrawal symptoms will be acute, and the dependent will not survive.

We are not speaking here of instances of "acute intoxication." A chemically dependent person may become acutely intoxicated at any stage of dependency, and even persons who are not dependent may occasionally ingest sufficient quantities of drugs to produce acute toxicity. We are referring to an acute *continuing condition* in which the person has reached a stage of dependency where the human organism requires constant or frequent dosages of drugs in order to maintain a normalcy that has been drug induced.

In summary, in this third or maintenance stage of chemical dependency, the predominant motivation of drug abusers is to maintain themselves in a "drug-normal state," that is, in a state of continuous or intermittent intoxication appropriate to what has become each one's personal "normal" level of need. Reinforcing this motivation in a secondary way is fear of the prospect of the possible acute withdrawal symptoms that may follow upon termination of drug ingestion.

Escape Stage

Like the three preceding stages, the fourth and final stage of chemical dependency exhibits its own predominant motivation — escape to oblivion. We might also call this stage "terminal" because in it the rewarding experience that is expected and directly sought after is terminal: an escape from and end to experience. The dependent seeks to blot out his or her consciousness of existential reality first through frequent or constant intoxication and, finally, through death.

In some respects, of course, all drug abuse is a form of escape — escape from one mood to another by means of drug ingestion. Thus we escape from a less pleasant to a more pleasant feeling state. We escape from discomfort to comfort by taking drugs for relief. We escape total dysfunction and/or the suffering of acute withdrawal by taking drugs for maintenance.

The escape motivation that characterizes this stage is significantly different from the escape aspects of earlier stages. In the first three stages, *hope* is a major element in the motivation. Some aspect of life remains an object of hope, and escape is secondary. Addicts hope for pleasure to enhance their lives. They hope for relief to make their lives more comfortable. They hope to maintain their lives at some minimal level of functioning. In doing so, they escape, at least temporarily, from mere natural pleasures. They escape from pain and discomfort. They escape from total dysfunction.

But in the final, terminal stage, they replace hope with *despair*. Life — at least in some of its aspects — is no longer an object of their hope. They seek final escape, total escape from life itself. Their goal is escape to final and total oblivion. That death can be and is sought as a rewarding experience reemphasizes the fact that chemical dependency is a fatal illness, essentially suicidal. In the escape stage, the personality is so disorganized, the self-image is so low, the moral anxiety is so massive, the attitudes toward self and others are so negative, and the misery is so intense that the most appealing reward is oblivion. At this point, the person suffers total personality disintegration. In the end, the ultimate driving motive of drug abuse is self-destruction.

The
Essential Pathology
of
Chemical Dependency

Chemical dependency is essentially a
commited pathological love relationship
of a person to a mood-altering chemical
substance, a psychoactive drug, in
expectation of a rewarding experience.

Locating Elements of Pathology

The focus of Part Two is the pathology of the disease as it is rooted in and resides in the whole person and in his or her two substantial parts, the *psyche* (mind, soul, or spirit) and the *soma* (body). Just as the human person is a psycho-somatic (soul-body) composite, so also is chemical dependency a psycho-somatic (soul-body) disease.

Some of the identified elements of addiction pathology are rooted in and appropriately assigned to the whole person of the addict rather than to particular faculties. The elements of psychological and physical dependence, for example, are rooted not in particular faculties but in the two substantial parts of the human composite, the soul and the body. Since the whole soul is in the whole body and whole soul is in every part of the body, we have a psycho-physiological dependence extending to the whole substantial composite, the human person.

One element of chemical dependency pathology, powerlessness, begins in a particular faculty — the appetitive faculty, or will — but eventually, deeply, and inevitably affects the whole person.

Other elements, such as chemical dependency mental obsession and emotional compulsion, are rooted in and properly assigned to particular mental faculties and particular emotional faculties respectively.

Exploring the Pattern of Pathology

The pathology of chemical dependency takes root in and grows out of a person's committed love relationship to drugs. As defined in Chapter Four, this pathology is the firmly set, complex configuration of the destructive effects caused directly and immediately in a person by that person's committed love relationship to mood-altering chemicals. Taken together, these effects constitute the specific form or structure of this illness, its typical intrinsic pattern. A study of the pathology of chemical dependency involves an exploration of this pattern. We must examine the following:

1. the principal elements that taken together make up the characteristic pattern of the illness;

2. the progression of each of these pathological elements through the four successive stages of chemical dependency (pleasure, relief, maintenance, and escape to oblivion);

3. the destructive effects that exist in the person due to the presence of each pathological element; and

4. the general and particular symptoms that appear in the person as a result of the pathological element.

Our procedure, therefore, will be to define each element in the pathology, trace its development through the four successive stages, identify some of the resulting conditions in the chemically dependent person, and then describe the symptoms of the pathological element.

In the next chapter, we examine the first pathological element, namely, psychological dependency or need.

The following chart summarizes our location of pathological elements in the person.

Location Sites of Pathology in Faculties of Soul and Body

Faculties	Pathology
Mental Powers Intellect Imagination Memory	Obsession Rational Defense System Delusion Low Self-Image
Volitional Power Will (Appetitive Faculty)	Powerlessness
Emotional Powers Pursuit Emotions Avoidance Emotions	Compulsion Rigid Negative Attitudes
Social Powers Communication Interpersonal Relations	Desocialization
Whole Person Psyche	Psychological Dependency
Whole Person Soma	Physical Dependency
Whole Person All Powers	Psychophysical Powerlessness

A Note on Essential Symptoms

At the end of each chapter on pathology, we will present an outline of the essential symptoms of the element of the pathology under discussion. In describing these symptoms, we distinguish between "general" and "particular" symptoms. Both are caused directly by the chemical dependency pathology, which means they are equally *essential* symptoms.

Following are definitions for each type of symptom:

- **General symptoms** are the broad signs or indications, caused by the essential elements of the pathology, which appear as *personal characteristics or general personal attitudes of dependents*. Thus, for example, rigid negative attitudes are manifested generally as personal negativism. A dependent is a rigidly negative person.

- **Particular symptoms**, by contrast, are the more limited signs or indications caused by the pathology that appear as concrete behaviors and behavior patterns or as any individual outward manifestation of a dependent's interior dispositions. They are the particularized ways by which general symptoms are expressed — the particular or *integral parts of general symptoms*. Thus, for example, a negative person shows his or her negativism by being touchy, hypersensitive, hypercritical, gloomy, pessimistic, depressed, etc. These are particular symptoms of chemically dependent rigid negative attitudes, just as personal negativism is the general symptom.

CHAPTER SIX

Chemically Dependent
Whole Person
Psychological Dependency

Dependency, or **dependence**, is a state or condition of being dependent or reliant upon another person or thing for essential being and existence, or for a particular mode or manner of existence, or for well-being, aid, support, or assistance of some kind.

Every person is by nature a dependent being. All people share the universal "creature condition" of essential and existential dependence upon other creatures in the universe and ultimately upon a Higher Power, God. In common with all creatures, no human being is self-creating or self-existing. All of us depend essentially, absolutely, and forever upon the self-existing Being for coming into and continuing in existence.

Every person, moreover, shares the human condition of dependence on other people for generation, survival, and personal and social development. Dependency, therefore, is an intrinsic condition, an experience common to all, and as such, it is neither good nor bad.

On the other hand, every person is also independent or autonomous in many ways, though on a limited scale. We are by nature "dependent-independent" beings. Achieving a balance of dependence-independence is a lifelong process, and the goal of that process is what we call "maturity." Many people mistakenly believe this process to be a struggle peculiar to adolescents and to youth. In reality, it is a major life problem for everyone — and no one ever quite makes it. The main difference, it seems, between mature and immature persons is that mature persons recognize and accept their immaturity. They do not try (immaturely, we might note) to cover up their immaturity. And it should be added here that if immaturity were the cause of chemical dependency, as some claim it is, then every human being without exception would be chemically dependent.

Dependency Relationships

Dependency is essentially a relationship. One person *tends toward* or *is related* to another person or thing in order to receive aid, assistance, or support of some kind. Dependency relationships may be healthy and normal, or they may be unhealthy and abnormal. We are all acquainted with sick relationships between one person and another. Everyone, it seems, experiences them at times, and we probably all know some people who tend to lean too hard on almost everyone all the time.

A person with an abnormal need for acceptance and approval, for example, is pathologically dependent on others. Such a person lacks self-acceptance and self-approval. He or she becomes sick in futile efforts to control others (and self, too) in order to manipulate acceptance and approval from them. At the same time, such a person becomes an easy subject for control and manipulation *by* others. This is because he or she compulsively tries to comply with all of their expectations.

Any abnormally dependent person has a sick need for the reward he or she expects to get from the object of a sick relationship. In the same way, chemical dependents have a sick need for the rewarding experiences they expect to receive from drugs. As a direct result, they compulsively attempt to control their own lives and the lives of others in order to continue using drugs. So evident is this manipulative control that chemical dependents are notorious for their "conning" abilities.

Chemical dependency, therefore, is an illness that in many respects resembles any other sick dependency. The difference is that mood-altering chemicals, not other persons or things, are the special *object* of this dependency. In other words, the relationship to mood-altering chemicals *specifies* this illness and makes it this kind of a dependency and not some other kind. It is directly out of this relationship that the pathological elements of the illness flow.

Gradually, however, chemical dependents become subjected to the power the drugs have over them. Ultimately, the drugs in effect control and manipulate their behaviors, their other relationships, and their whole lives.

Casual Dependencies

Some dependencies on mood-altering chemicals, as already noted, may be casual and only occasional. In these cases, the user depends on the drugs for the rewarding experience, but only at the time of actual use. This attitude is truly "take it or leave it"; it is a casual relationship. Such a casual dependency may be regular and even frequent. On each individual occasion of ingestion, the user depends on the drugs both physically and psychologically for the effects produced. But the quantities ingested, the manner of ingestion, and the truly social circumstances surrounding it may be such that pathological abuse and dependency do not develop. Something more than this is required for chemical dependency, namely, an abnormal psychic need for mood-altering drugs. This is what we mean by "psychological dependency" or "psychological need."

It should be clearly understood (though sometimes it is not) that physical "addiction" is not required for chemical dependency. A temporary, occasional physical dependency, as just noted, is present with *any* use of drugs. This occurs

59

simply because the user must physically ingest the drugs to achieve any expected reward. But this kind of physical dependency is not addiction any more than the physical ingestion of food is addiction to food. When physical addiction is present, it usually develops some time after psychological dependency has taken root. With some drugs, no apparent physical addiction occurs even with long-continued use or abuse.

Definition of Psychological Dependency

With this background, we define **psychological dependency** as an irrational need, caused by a person's committed love relationship to drugs, to rely on the ingestion of mood-altering chemicals in expectation of achieving rewarding psychophysical experiences — or more concretely, in order to achieve welcome changes of feelings, moods, and mind.

Psychological dependency affects all the psychic or life powers (including the physical powers). Consequently, all vital or life activity is impaired. Because all the human powers are affected, "psychological dependency" really means "whole-person" dependency. The following powers are all directly affected:

1. the *spiritual* powers, including personal values and personal behavior in relation to values;

2. the *mental* powers, including the functions of intellect, imagination, and memory;

3. the *volitional* powers, including freedom of choice and responsible control of appetites and behaviors;

4. the *emotional* powers, including the various pursuit and avoidance responses that arise from psychosensory and suprasensory affect;

5. the *social* powers, or the powers for person-to-person, group, and community relations and communication; and

6. the physical powers, which are necessarily affected in our total personality when we are psychologically affected in any way.

The *physical* powers are necessarily affected, too, because a human being is a psychophysical composite. The *whole person* is affected because this composite is ultimately integrated and unified existentially in and by the substantive human personality. In other words, because our individual "personhood" makes us whole, unified human beings, it is as persons that we are "put together." And it is by personal activity, through our psychological or personal life powers, that we "get it all together" in our lives.

It becomes increasingly evident, as we explore the dimensions and elements of chemical dependency, that we are confronted with an illness that involves the whole person and all interpersonal relations. It also becomes increasingly clear that this illness cannot be understood by engaging in drug research or by delivering drug education that focuses exclusively or predominantly on the drugs themselves or on social environments. Finally, it becomes evident that, both in principle and in application, treatment for chemical dependency must keep the primary focus of therapy on the psychological dependency. Direct constant attention must be given to the dependency's essential cause — the patient's committed pathological love relationship to mood-altering chemicals. At the same time, treatment must also take into account the whole person and all of his or her interpersonal or social relationships.

THE PROCESS OF DEVELOPMENT

A drug user takes the first step toward psychological dependency when he or she has a significantly rewarding, welcome experience. Users find this experience rewarding enough that it creates a subjective, individualistic motivation to commit themselves to repeat the use of drugs to achieve again that rewarding experience. What marks the transition from predependency to pathological dependency is this *personal commitment to getting high on drugs.*

At this point, reasonable use passes over into individualized or singular abuse. This is the "solitary use" that is often referred to in chemical dependency literature. At this point, the person is no longer using drugs casually, but very purposefully, in a calculated way, in expectation of achieving for *himself or herself alone* a personal, subjective "high" or euphoria. This high is sought regardless of social circumstances and without reference to socio-cultural or ethico-religious norms. By this commitment, the person has set up a permanent relationship between himself or herself and mood-altering chemicals. A lasting bond has now been established that seals and cements the person-to-drug relationship. This is universally the point of entry into pathological drug dependency. It is a first common denominator of all particular, individual dependencies on mood-altering chemicals, and it places the dependent in the first stage of the illness, the pleasure stage.

THE PLEASURE STAGE — A Drug-Oriented Life Style

In the initial or pleasure stage of pathological dependency, drug abuse increasingly becomes a primary focus of the drug user's attention and interest. With increasing frequency, the user relies on drugs to alter feelings and moods. The dependency may grow unrecognized at first and for some time if the occasions of abuse afford sufficient "protective cover." For example, if the occasion is a joyful one, such as a wedding or dinner party, drugs are commonly used in our culture to heighten the joy. If the occasion is one of sadness, such as a funeral, chemical comfort is quite acceptable. In these social scenarios, the dependent appears to use drugs "just like everybody else." But the motivation has changed significantly: ingestion is now egocentric, not sociocentric.

As pleasure stage dependency advances, the dependent relies on regular drug use, as a matter of course, to alter feelings and moods. Having discovered the *mood-swing*, the dependent now deliberately seeks it out. In doing so, he or she unwittingly builds a chemically dependent way of life, a *drug-oriented life style*.

THE RELIEF STAGE — A Drug-Centered Life Style

In the pleasure stage, dependents discover the welcome effects produced by drug ingestion. They then go on to experiment with drugs as a remedy for various discomforts: for pain and suffering, for depressions, anxieties, and tensions, for social and psychological conflicts, and for family, financial, or employment problems. As dependents find "instant comfort" through drugs, another highly subjective, egocentric motive becomes prominent, namely, *relief*. In pleasure stage dependency, dependents rely on drugs predominantly for pleasurable alterations of feelings and moods. But as the next stage approaches, they increasingly abuse drugs for relief.

Throughout the pleasure stage, the drug relationship becomes increasingly important as other relationships grow less important. In the relief stage, drugs and their use become the primary center of dependents' attention. Their life style is no longer simply drug-oriented; it is now *drug-centered*.

The personality structure of dependents changes under the influence of the drug relationship, too. Subconsciously, they reorient and restructure their *internal* environment to accommodate their need for drugs. They develop hatred, aversion, rejection and other negative attitudes, especially against family members but also against any persons or situations that threaten interference. They direct chronic hostility against anything and anyone that does not or will not conform to this drug-centered way of life. They pursue occasions, companions, associates, jobs, and recreations that will support the dependency by reinforcing the rationalizations, projections, alibis, excuses, and other defenses used by dependents to justify and maintain their drug relationship. If, at any stage in this process, concerned persons succeed in intervening to bring dependents into treatment for their illness, the dependents will invariably arrange to get into the care of therapists who will support the dependency and thus enable them to continue their accustomed abuse of drugs.

Levels of Experimentation

Drug abusers commonly depend on drugs for relief or comfort. This fact leads some to believe that chemical dependency must be a sign or a symptom of some other illness or problem that is causing the discomfort and creating a need for relief. What is not recognized is that until drug users first *learn* that drugs "do something" for them, they will not go on to further experiment with drugs as possible remedies for their ills and problems. A more precise look at experimentation will perhaps make this clearer.

Experimentation with drugs takes place on several levels. Dependents direct their first experiments toward discovering if drugs will bring them any rewards and, more particularly, whether or not they will produce pleasurable mood-swings. On this level, the goal sought is pleasure, and the motive is an expectation of pleasure.

Dependents direct second-level experiments toward discovering whether or not drugs will produce relief if they are applied to the discomforts arising out of life's difficulties and problems. On this second level, the goal sought is relief, and the motive is an expectation of relief. This prepares the way for relief stage dependency. Increased ingestion for relief marks the transition from the initial pleasure stage to this second stage.

With the advent of the new stage, dependents rely on drugs predominately for relief. They still expect and experience pleasure, of course, but this need diminishes with the growing need to ease the tensions, anxieties, and discomforts caused by self-prescribed and self-administered drugs. In a sense, it now becomes a "double dependency," that is, a sick dependency for relief and a sick dependency for pleasure.

During this stage, dependents begin to rigidly structure their personal and social lives around drugs. Impelled by compulsion, they manipulate their personal lives, the people around them, and the events in their lives to assure the continuation of the drug relationship and of drug abuse. They arrange business appointments, work assignments, social engagements, marriage and family relations, leisure, and recreation with a view to supporting and protecting the drug involvement. They evaluate and judge everyone and everything in relation to this sick need for drugs. People, things, and situations are all cultivated or avoided, accepted or rejected, included or excluded insofar as they enable dependents to continue with their now chronic drug abuse and their rigidly drug-centered life style.

THE MAINTENANCE STAGE — A Drug-Dominated Life Style

In the third or maintenance stage, abuse of drugs for pleasure and for relief diminishes, and abuse for survival becomes predominant. In this stage, dependents manifest a *drug-dominated life style*. They can barely function even at minimal levels without drugs, and they will suffer psychologically and may also have physical reactions if they are suddenly deprived of drugs. Their predominant goal and motive is now *maintenance*, that is, to preserve life itself.

Maintenance stage dependency frequently, though not always, involves physical addiction. Acute withdrawal symptoms may result if drug ingestion is abruptly terminated without appropriate supervision. This, of course, inspires fear in dependents. However, it is primarily psychological dependency and not physical dependency that impels continued maintenance drug abuse. Fear of withdrawal is often expressed by dependents as a "reason" for continued ingestion, but on examination it usually turns out to be a defensive cover-up to protect their psychological need for drugs. This is clearly evident, for example, among dependents who are being maintained in their dependency by methadone. It can also be seen among the numerous dependents for whom placebos appear to be just as effective in reducing anxieties and alleviating withdrawal symptoms as are their drugs of preference.

THE ESCAPE STAGE — A Drug-Terminated Life Style

In the fourth or escape stage, the purpose and motivation for continued drug abuse shifts again. The dependent seeks *oblivion*, through intoxication and ultimately through death, as the rewarding experience. The psychological miseries of loneliness, anxiety, depression, hatred and resentment, guilt, and remorse drive dependents into despair. Physical miseries and social complications may also multiply beyond endurance. In this condition, the dependent relies on drugs as an escape to blot out the various miseries of life and finally to blot out a misery-laden life itself. The drug-dominated life style now becomes a drug-*terminated* life style. The frequent complete intoxication that marks this stage is a living death for dependents, and it is the prelude to total and final self-destruction.

RESULTING CONDITIONS

Depersonalization and Desocialization

As psychological dependency develops in a user, the need to continue the drug relationship becomes the most pressing of all needs. As a result, dependents lose their integrity or "put-togetherness." All life powers are disordered, disoriented, and impaired in their functioning. The dependent loses self-awareness, self-respect, self-esteem, and finally self-identity. This state of personal disintegration is what we mean by *depersonalization* and what is popularly expressed as "coming apart at the seams," "falling apart," or "breaking down."

Another condition resulting from psychological dependency is *desocialization*. With their person-to-drug relationships occupying top place, dependents' person-to-person or social relationships are totally disoriented, disordered, and disintegrated. Meaningful relationships with "significant others" are so chaotic and painful that they are, in many cases, terminated by dependents, if not by concerned persons who can no longer bear the strain.

Irresponsibility

As the illness progresses, its victims grow pathologically dependent not only on drugs but on other persons and things. Dependents become irresponsible, unable to manage even the ordinary affairs of personal, family, or work life. Consequently, they shift responsibilities to others, who are thereby forced into painful dilemmas. Either others take up the responsibilities dependents cannot assume — and thus cover up the illness and enable continued drug abuse — or they refuse to take over dependents' responsibilities and leave many urgent matters unattended.

Irresponsibility is so typical of chemical dependents that some mistake it as a special kind of personality or character defect that *causes* the illness. In reality, it is an *effect* of the illness. Clinically, we find that dependents are at least as sensitive to responsibility as anyone else. A major factor in their inner distress is their inability to live up to their personal standards of responsibility. Many, in fact, are persons noted for their responsibility but whose drug involvement deprives them of their ability to function responsibly.

In the case of chemically dependent youngsters and young adults the pathology of addiction blocks the normal process of maturation, leaving them, as one young man expressed it, "21 going on 10." It is not uncommon to hear young people in treatment saying things like "I just don't get what you mean about being responsible. I don't know what I'm supposed to do!" or "I don't know *how* to act!"

And, indeed, there are those who clearly do *not* have a well-developed sense of responsibility — and it's not because they've temporarily "lost" it through chemical dependency. The fact is they *never* had it. One thing is for sure: if addiction sets in, irresponsibility only worsens. As one treatment specialist noted, some persons must "habilitate" before rehabilitation is possible.

Conflicts and Consequences

Family members and other concerned persons experience a deep conflict or dilemma when faced with the irresponsibility and destructive behaviors of dependents. On the one hand, they feel love and concern for dependents, and they have a desire to help them by "easing their burdens." On the other hand, they feel deep hatred and resentment of the dependents' attitudes, defenses, and behaviors. They may even have a desire to get revenge by allowing dependents to suffer even more self-inflicted punishment.

What concerned persons usually fail to realize is that one of the most effective ways to assist dependents in becoming aware of their condition is to allow them to experience the consequences of their own irresponsibility and destructive behaviors. Concerned persons must do some considerable sifting and sorting before they come to see the great difference between their intensely negative attitudes toward dependents and the quite objective fact that, *for their own good, dependents must be allowed to experience the consequences of their own irresponsibility.*

As in any case of pathological dependency, the chemically dependent are ultimately not only influenced by but also controlled by and totally subordinated to their relationship to drugs. Under this debilitating influence, many grow so irresponsible that they become wards in institutions where all or the majority of their responsibilities, including even the care of their most elemental bodily needs, are assumed by others. Ultimately, psychological dependency results in a total disintegration of personality and of life — a life that will terminate in insanity or death, whichever comes first.

SYMPTOMS OF PSYCHOLOGICAL DEPENDENCY

Psychological dependency or need is the principal element in the pathology of chemical dependency. "Psychologically dependent" describes the condition of a *total person*, all of whose psychic powers are involved in a committed permanent relationship to mood-altering chemicals. As in the case of the other pathological elements, psychological dependency produces general and particular essential symptoms.

General Symptom: Drug-Involved Life Style

Every chemically dependent person manifests the general symptom of a *drug-oriented* and then a *drug-centered life style*. The personal drug involvement affects the whole personality, and this is shown by the way the person conducts or manages his or her life. It is a drug-involved manner of life, way of life, or life style. In initial stage dependency, the psychological need for drugs produces a reorientation of life revolving around and gradually focusing more completely on the drug or drugs of preference. It is a drug-oriented life style. In the chronic and later stages, this reorientation is completed, and the dependent settles into a rigidly drug-centered life style.

Particular Symptoms

Every chemically dependent person manifests many life-style symptoms. These particular symptoms show up in various ways in the different areas of the dependent's life. Each of these particular symptoms (and the general symptom, too) is caused directly by the underlying pathological element, psychological dependency. The presence of these symptoms, therefore, demonstrates the presence of chemical dependency within the person. The following are some particular symptoms of a drug-involved life style.

1. The *prominence of drugs* in the life of the dependent, as shown by the apparent *importance* placed on drug ingestion; by the *regularity* (whether frequent, continuous, or periodic) of actual drug ingestion; and by the repeated ingestion of drugs *for the purpose of getting high* and sometimes, though not always, to the point of intoxication.

2. The *singular* or *individualistic* ingestion of drugs, that is, the taking of drugs in order to achieve a personal subjective rewarding experience. Dependents ingest drugs in a "solitary" manner; they drink "alone" or smoke or take pills or shoot up "alone" in the sense that they are seeking their own individual high. On any particular occasion of ingestion, they may or may not be in the company of others who are using drugs, too. The significant fact for diagnosis is that they are seeking their *own subjective high*, whether other people are around or not.

   Dependents often use a screen to cover up individualistic drug abuse. They do this in two predominant ways. First, they will tend to seek consistently the companionship of people whose drug abuse is similar to their own and who can therefore be counted on to support the dependents' own drug abuse and enable them to continue it. This is drug-centered manipulation — the use of collective social defenses to protect one's own drug relationship and to conceal one's psychological need. Secondly, in truly social situations, while others focus their attention on sociability, with their drug use as a matter of relative indifference, dependents bring their own purposes to the occasion. For them, there is no such thing as indifference to drugs, nor is there any sociability that takes a higher priority than the individual high they are after.

   Another motive for seeking such social companionship or such social situations is to be assured of ready access to the drug or drugs of preference.

3. *Arranging occasions for ingestion* in order to assure availability of and access to one's drug or drugs of preference. This ranges all the way from rendezvous with connections, to regular shopping at liquor stores and pharmacies, to setting up parties under the pretext of being a good host, a pleasant companion, or a generous entertainer. It also appears in the form of arranging schedules and appointments, conducting business meetings, setting up conferences, luncheons, dinners, etc., to assure the availability of one's favorite drug or drugs.

4. *Seeking occasions for ingestion and making decisions and choices based on drug availability.* Drugs appear as a factor in the decisions and choices

a dependent makes about social relations, occasions, and events. A dependent will tend to avoid "dry," "straight," or moderate drug-use occasions in preference to those where drugs are abundant: cocktail parties, happy hours, pot parties, etc. Other symptoms appear in the form of seeking business luncheons and entertainments, professional appointments, recreational activities and vacations, etc., with an eye to the drug aspects of the situation. Another version of this symptom appears in the scheduling of appointments and time commitments around one's psychological dependency, that is, to accommodate one's need for drugs and to be sure other matters do not interfere with this need.

5. *Drug ingestion in solitude* is the ultimate form of solitary or singular ingestion. It is taking drugs "alone" in the narrowest and most obvious sense, but it is not by any means the most common form of individualistic ingestion. When "drinking alone" or "solitary" ingestion is known by dependents to be a conspicuous symptom of dependency, they will sometimes go to great lengths to make sure they never drink alone, or at least are never caught taking drugs in solitude.

6. *Self-administration of prescription drugs.* Prescription drugs are not taken by dependents according to prescription but are self-administered at their own discretion, according to their subjective psychological need for a pleasant high, for relief, for maintenance, or for escape. On their own initiative, they vary their dosages as to frequency and quantity and as to what "symptoms" or ailments the drugs are applied to. Eventually, almost anything becomes a symptom in need of medication: stresses and strains, insomnia, being up-tight or dragged out, the "blahs," a "problem," a tension-creating situation or responsibility, loneliness, depression, *ad infinitum*. Often this diagnostic symptom will be easily confirmed by checking out a dependent's prescription and supply sources, where it may be found that a physician has been persuaded to prescribe drug taking on an "as-needed" basis, with the patient deciding the need. It may be found, too, that several physicians and pharmacies are simultaneously supplying drugs to the same person.

7. *Medicinal ingestion of social drugs.* Once it has been discovered that certain "social" drugs, especially the various forms of alcoholic beverages and marijuana, produce pleasant mood-swings, experiments follow. These social drugs are tried out as remedies for various physical and psychological discomforts and problems, that is, as medications. If they are found to bring relief, they may be applied henceforth with relief as a motive. Social drinking gives way

to medicinal drinking; the beverage alcohol becomes a medicine. Social use of pot moves into remedial abuse; from a "social solvent," it becomes a pain-reliever and a problem-solver.

8. *Changes of personality.* "She's not the woman I married" and "He's not the same person he used to be" are typical expressions of this symptom as described by concerned persons. This "change of personality" is due to the reorientation of life style caused by the drug relationship. While it manifests itself more obviously as a rearrangement of external circumstances of life, it is further and more profoundly symptomatic of a reorientation of the internal environment of dependents. They are not the same persons they used to be because a comprehensive psychological reordering is in process, including changing personal values, changing mental and emotional attitudes, changing interests and motivations, and changing associations and occupations. The inner psychic powers are restyled as well as the outward style of life to meet dependents' drug needs.

9. *Manipulation of personal life* to accommodate the drug relationship and ingestion. With drugs as a central focus of life, dependents' own lives are compulsively (and therefore relentlessly) manipulated to fit the demands of their drug relationship.

10. *Manipulation of other people* to accommodate the drug relationship and ingestion. The same need impels manipulation of other people to compel them to rearrange their lives to accommodate the dependent's way of life. This manipulation is one of the most common characteristics of drug-dependent persons, one of the earliest to appear, and one of the clearest (and most abrasive) symptoms of psychological dependency.

These are some of the more conspicuous particular symptoms of psychological dependency. Many others become evident as one explores the numerous aspects of life included in a "life style" and observes dependents as they function in each of these areas of life.

Robert M. McAuliffe and Mary Boesen McAuliffe

WHOLE-PERSON PSYCHOLOGICAL DEPENDENCY
SUMMARY OF ESSENTIAL SYMPTOMS

General Symptom: Drug-Involved Life Style

Particular Symptoms:

1. Prominence of drugs in dependent's life.
2. Singular or individualistic ingestion.
3. Arranging occasions for ingestion.
4. Seeking occasions for ingestion.
5. Drug ingestion in solitude.
6. Self-administration of prescription drugs.
7. Medicinal ingestion of social drugs.
8. Changes of personality.
9. Manipulation of personal life to accommodate the drug relationship and ingestion.
10. Manipulation of other people to accommodate the drug relationship and ingestion.

CHAPTER SEVEN

Chemically Dependent
Whole Person
Powerlessness

Powerlessness, as an essential element of whole person chemical dependency pathology, has two aspects.

The first aspect of powerlessness is an impaired condition of the appetitive faculty of the human will, which is prevented from exercising its natural power to make deliberate free choices with regard to personal behaviors. The faculty of the will is so impaired that it cannot reasonably control the dependent's ingestion of mood-altering chemicals or his or her sick love relationship to these chemicals.

The second aspect of powerlessness is the impaired condition of all the faculties of the dependent, both cognitive and appetitive. As the disease progresses, the dependent's power to function through the exercise of any and all of his or her faculties gradually diminishes. Ultimately, it becomes impossible for the dependent to reasonably manage any area or aspect of life. This is "whole person powerlessness," as distinguished from the "simple faculty (will) powerlessness" described above.

The Heart of the Problem

When we take up the subject of power, we are at the heart of the problem of addiction. We are also at the heart of the solution to the problem.

The driving force of the disease is power — the power of a committed pathological love for mood-altering chemicals, a love that is greater than oneself. The driving force of recovery from the disease is also based in power — the power of a love from a Higher Power that is infinitely greater than oneself.

The healing of addictions then — perhaps of any and all addictions — is essentially a simple trade. An addict's personal pathological love relationship to mood-altering chemicals must be exchanged for a healthy personal love relationship with a Higher Power, or God.

So effective is this simple formula that its application has produced the greatest global revolution that the world has ever known in the healing of alcoholism and other addictions. Millions upon millions of addicts have been healed since

Alcoholics Anonymous formed in 1935. Despite some notable secular disdain for this simple AA formula by some workers in the addiction field, no other addiction therapy process has ever come anywhere near producing such an abundant harvest of recovering addicts.

Fundamental Aspects of Power

Before we continue our discussion of the nature of powerlessness in a chemically dependent person, let us take a look at the nature of power itself.

Power has two fundamental aspects. First, it is a capacity to accept, to receive, to allow something to be done. Second, it is a capacity to produce, to dominate, to move, to do something or to get something done.

Political power, military power, money power, word power, and personal power tend to associate, if not to equate, power with domination. All share the implication of a force or energy applied to produce effects by exerting a dominative control over something or someone. But this is only half of the power picture. Power in its other and more basic aspect is a capacity to accept or to receive. Physical power, for example, exhibits these two aspects clearly. Before a locomotive has the dominative power to move a train, it has the receptive power to take in the fuel that makes it run.

More directly to the point is the human intellect. The intellect has the power to receive or accept data, and it has the power to run this data through reasoning processes and arrive at conclusions, decisions, and judgments. Still more directly to the point, and of profoundest significance to chemical dependency, is the human will. The will has first the receptive power to accept impressions of desirable goods and attractive action alternatives. Secondly, it has the dominative power to make selections and to guide or control behavior in accordance with these personal choices.

Will Power as Acceptance

"Will power" essentially consists of free choice. It is in the first place a simple acceptance of one good in preference to others and an acceptance of one action alternative in preference to others. A person of "good will" is one who is open and ready — that is, *willing* — to accept alternative goods and actions. In this sense, "will power" is above all a preferential acceptance, not an act of domination. It follows that the first and greatest exercise of will power is *acceptance*, not domination. When a person freely chooses to accept a thing, a fact, or a reality as it is essentially and existentially, that person demonstrates far greater will power than when he or she seeks to gain control over that reality by imposing dominative power.

Note well that both acceptance and domination are *acts* — actions, activities, or functions — of will power. We emphasize this because "act" and "action," "activity" and "function" are so frequently equated with dominative control, whereas "acceptance" is commonly equated with "passivity," "inactivity," or "inertia." We tend to overvalue acts of domination and to undervalue acts of acceptance; yet both are essentially and equally acts. And far more strength of will is often required to "serenely accept the things I cannot change" than to "courageously change the things I can." It is much easier to comply with the admonition, "Don't just sit there, *do* something," than it is to respond to the invitation, "Don't just do something, *sit* there."

Powerlessness, like power, also has two aspects. It is in the first place a lack of capacity or an inability to accept or receive. It is in the second place an incapacity to produce, to control, to dominate.

Power and powerlessness are of many varieties: mechanical, atomic, electric; political, financial, military; spiritual, religious, moral; and so on. In all cases, power carries the same twofold basic meaning, namely, a capacity or capability to receive and to produce some action or activity. In all cases, powerlessness, too, means a contrary incapacity to receive and to produce some action or activity.

Human Power: Intellect and Will

A human being is endowed by nature with many kinds of power, including some that are also found in other creatures and some that are unique to man. Unique to our human nature is our *rationality*, a special kind of psychic power that enables us to receive and to produce mental and volitional activity directly, and by extension, other activity, too. It is a nonmaterial, transcendental power that surpasses and goes beyond the confines of space and time and place and that transcends the limitations of physical matter and quantity.

Our intellectual and volitional powers are the two transcendental powers that enable us to accept and to produce rational activity and to extend rational control to a great deal of our other activity. This rational activity covers a lot of territory, certainly, but in the ultimate analysis, it all originates in the action of these two psychic powers.

Our intellect and our will work together in producing rational activity: our intellect as our principal cognitive or knowing power and our chief data processor and our will as our principal appetitive or loving power and our chief motivator or activator. Our intellect receives data provided by our other cognitive powers and then goes to work processing it, sifting and sorting impressions and ideas in order to arrive at some truth about what is objectively real and what is not. On the practical level, our intellect receives and processes data in order to arrive at conclusions about how to act, that is, it makes decisions or judgments about the most prudent thing to do in each practical situation. Our intellect presents this to our will for action. Then our will, impressed with the goodness, correctness, or desirability of the action, is moved or motivated to actually carry out what our intellect proposes as the practical thing to do. The constant interaction of our

73

intellect and will is the core of all rational activity; out of it comes every *reasonable* thing we do.

The importance of this where chemical dependency is concerned can hardly be exaggerated. Recall, for example, that drug "use," drug "misuse," and drug "abuse" are defined in terms of their reasonableness or unreasonableness, and that the whole area of personal and social values, ideals, and behavior standards comes down to what is rational or irrational — that is, reasonable or unreasonable — for a human being.

Other Powers

Looking beyond this human power of rationality and the other particular psychic powers that belong to us as individual human beings, we find two other general power areas that are of special significance to everyone, as well as to the problem of chemical dependency. One is the vast area of "other-people power," and the other is the even vaster area of the Higher Power, God.

By "other-people power," we mean all of the capabilities of other people to help us, that is, to provide aid, support, or assistance to us in meeting the needs that we cannot handle alone. Such needs are many and so are the other people who are available to help us.

By the Higher Power, we mean the absolute power of the supreme self-existent being whose creative power has brought the universe into existence, whose continuing act of power conserves or sustains the universe in existence, and whose perfect knowledge and love combine to govern the universe with all things and persons in it according to a supremely intelligent and loving plan that we commonly call *divine providence*. Divine power, even more than other-people power, is always and everywhere available to help us in all our needs.

Powerlessness and Privation

In one sense, "powerless" means a simple absence or lack of power. A stone, for example, lacks power to think or breathe or walk around. But a stone is not intended by nature to do these things, so nothing has been lost. The stone's powerlessness in these respects is not a lack of anything due to it but only a simple absence of power. "Powerless" in another sense means a lack or a loss of some power that belongs to a thing by its nature. Thus, a dog has the power to breathe, to walk about, and to eat and digest food. If these are lacking, it is not just a simple absence of power; it is a lack or a loss of something due to a dog by its nature. The dog is deprived of power that belongs to it. Hence, this lack of power is called "privation."

In regard to human beings, as with stones and dogs, some powers are proper to our nature and some are not. We are not deprived of anything due to us because we cannot fly like birds or swim like fish or leap like kangaroos. Such powers do not belong to us; they are simply absent. But if we cannot think or choose, feel joy and sorrow, hope and love, or relate to other people comfortably, we are deprived; we lack things due to us by nature. For a human being, therefore, to be powerless means to be unable to do all or some of those things that our nature is intended to do. It does not necessarily mean that any basic powers are totally rooted out of us, but rather that we lack the capability of exercising them so as to achieve the purposes for which they are intended.

If I am drunk or stoned, for example, my intellectual power is not totally destroyed, but it is impaired. I am incapable of rational thought; I am powerless to think. If my mental powers are obsessed with drugs, they are not destroyed, but they are impaired; mental energy or power is not available to apply to other matters. Drugs impair my thinking powers and may greatly deprive me of my capacity to think. In this condition, I am partially, perhaps even totally, powerless to use my reason.

Definition

Powerlessness, in the chemical dependency context, means a lack or loss or privation of power that belongs to a human being by nature. The psychic or life powers outlined in Chapter Four are so damaged and weakened by the drug relationship and by actual drug abuse that they are partially or totally unable to carry on their proper functions; normal functioning becomes impossible and dysfunction occurs. We define **chemically dependent powerlessness** as essentially the state or condition of persons who, as a direct and immediate effect of their committed pathological love relationship to mood-altering chemicals, are without the ability in and of themselves to recognize or to remedy their condition or to appropriately manage their lives.

Five major points in this definition should be noted:

1. The state or condition that the person cannot recognize or remedy *is* his or her illness, chemical dependency. Dependents may or may not be able to recognize and to handle other problems, but they are powerless in regard to this one. They are intellectually incapable of receiving reality data about their condition, and they are mentally, emotionally, and rationally powerless to accept the reality of their condition.

2. This powerlessness, like the whole pathology of the illness, is *caused directly by the drug relationship*, not by some "other problem" and not even directly by actual drug abuse. Actual drug abuse contributes, of course, by preparing the way for a commitment to drugs, but repeated drug abuse itself is an effect of the obsessive-compulsive relationship to chemicals

75

rather than its cause. A person without this relationship does not abuse drugs repeatedly. If drugs are used at all, it is reasonably. Moreover, a dependent may terminate ingestion temporarily or even permanently, but the drug relationship may still remain and therefore so may the pathology.

3. This powerlessness has two basic aspects, one having to do with recognition or awareness of the illness (the power to accept or receive reality data about the condition) and the other having to do with remedying it (the power to dominate or control the condition). Dependents are helpless in both respects. They have within them no resources either to know that they are chemically dependent or to recover from the illness. And they are helpless to reasonably regulate their drug ingestion, to terminate it freely and comfortably, or even to predict where it will take them next.

4. An important qualification is included in this definition. The dependents *in and of themselves* are without the capacity to help themselves. This must be added because although chemical dependency seriously impairs the functioning of our psychic powers, it does not totally destroy any basic human powers until its final phases. At any point between its beginning and end, therefore, a crisis may occur or be created that helps dependents to focus attention on their real problem and shocks them into momentary awareness of their condition. With the intervention of outside help at such crisis points, they can recover the use of their psychic powers and restore their lives to order.

5. A final point, not explicit but implied in the definition, relates back to the several comments already made about chemical dependency being a committed pathological love relationship between a person and drugs. Love, as we have seen, is an attraction we feel toward some good that appears to us as beneficial or enjoyable and therefore as desirable. The good, in other words, exerts a power over us: the power to draw us, to stir desire, to motivate us to pursue it, and to reward us. Drugs exercise exactly this kind of power over us. Since they contain within them the power to give us very welcome rewards, the love affair develops quickly, grows deep, and is extremely hard to break off. When we make our commitment to drugs, we invite them, in effect, to come to us and to possess us, to exercise their power over us. Implicitly, we surrender ourselves to them; we give

ourselves over to their power. And they do indeed take over.

We do not do this consciously, of course, or by any formal contract, any more than an avaricious person makes a formal commitment to money or invites money to take over and to possess him. But we do it, nonetheless. And that's the point. Without realizing what we are doing, we set up as a committed love relationship what is in fact a contest of power: our power as rational persons versus the power of mood-altering chemicals. And again, without realizing it, once we make our commitment to drugs, we have already lost the contest. From then on, it is only a matter of time before drugs make their victory complete. Our beloved has betrayed us and has led us away captive. We are not only left powerless over drugs, but we are left powerless to manage satisfactorily any aspect of our lives. A higher power has taken over: it is the power of mood-altering chemicals.

Loss of Control

To be "out of control" or to "lose control" of one's drug ingestion is one aspect of chemically dependent powerlessness. Three points must be made at once to avoid adding to the confusion and controversies already revolving around "loss of control."

- First, this is a *symptom* of chemical dependency, not a distinct pathological element. It is an effect of the powerlessness that is itself rooted in the obsession/compulsion that is essential in the illness.

- Secondly, it is not the *only* symptom of powerlessness, although this impression is sometimes given. It is one of many such symptoms and is not necessarily the most prominent among them.

- Thirdly, the terms "out of control" and "loss of control" do not adequately identify the phenomenon under consideration. These terms ordinarily both imply and convey that a dependent is totally powerless to regulate his or her drug ingestion. This is seldom, if ever, the case. We have never observed such an absolute loss of control in any client, and neither have our colleagues. What we do observe consistently, however, is a *relative* or *partial* loss of control. In every case and without exception, dependents and concerned persons can cite particular instances, occasions, and situations where some control has been exercised, and

invariably this raises doubts (in their minds at least) about
the presence of chemical dependency.

One possible solution might be to drop the terms "loss of control" and "out of
control" and replace them with "lack of control." But lack of control could also be
taken in an absolute sense to mean *total* lack of control, and the confusion would
remain. A more promising approach, it seems to us, is to take a direct look at what
real or *true* control is and what happens to it when chemical dependency sets in.

Real or True Control

Real or true control is *rational* or *reasonable control*, that is, an ability to ingest
or to abstain from drugs deliberately, freely, and comfortably for a reasonable
purpose (a defined beneficial purpose that regulates ingestion — or abstention).

Real or true control requires *deliberate decision*, which is a product of
unimpaired intellectual perception, reasoning, and judgment. But under chemical
influence, mental powers are disabled and their functioning is impaired. Perception
is warped by the drug relationship as well as by actual drug abuse; reasoning is
typically rationalization; memory is grossly distorted by blackouts, euphoria,
and repression, and cluttered with drug-related recollections; and imagination is
preoccupied with drug-related fantasies. All mental powers are caught up in a
drug obsession that is concealed from one's awareness by delusion. In this state,
it is impossible for one to truly deliberate about or to arrive at rational decisions
to control drug ingestion within reasonable limits, that is, in a manner that is
beneficial and not harmful to oneself or to others.

Real or true control also requires *free choice*. But dependents are driven by
an emotional compulsion to ingest mood-altering chemicals that bypasses free
choice. Contrary to impressions often given by popular dramatizations of junkies
and alcoholics, however, this compulsion is not always or necessarily experienced in
the form of an overwhelming conscious craving for drugs, or a feeling of desperate
urgency to take them. At times it is, of course, but everyone who has been through
the personal experience of chemical dependency attests to the fact that at times
drugs were ingested unexpectedly, impulsively, without premeditation or planning,
and without any conscious craving or special feeling of urgency. This occurs
because compulsion characteristically operates beneath the surface of conscious
awareness. It is subconscious. It operates to compel an action or series of actions
without passing through the mental and volitional channels of conscious control.
And it typically operates in opposition to or at variance with conscious deliberate
decision and conscious free choice.

What is true of compulsion generally is true of chemically dependent
compulsion in particular. Despite occasional superficial appearances to the
contrary, and notwithstanding vehement protests of dependents or deluded beliefs

of concerned persons to the contrary, dependents are out of control and governed by a compulsion that they do not know exists.

Discomforts of Abstinence or Change

A third major factor in real or true control is the *comfort* or *ease* and the *genuine spontaneity* with which we decide and act. In direct opposition to this, dependents are uncomfortable, ill at ease, and engaged in a constant struggle when they abstain even temporarily from their drug of preference. They deny the discomfort, of course, because the defense system is busy protecting the drug relationship. But as a rule, the efforts at abstention are so uncomfortable that concerned persons suffer along with, and sometimes more than, the dependents. Typically, when pressures for abstention are relieved and drug ingestion is resumed, dependents revert to their usual patterns of compulsive abuse.

Dependents are not only uncomfortable when they totally abstain from drugs. They experience similar discomfort when they are under pressure to change the manner of their drug ingestion. When confronted by others about their excessive and destructive manner of abuse, they will bargain for continued but more moderate use, believing that they are really in control. They may or may not keep the bargain for a time. In any event, they are extremely uncomfortable all the while they are struggling to alter their accustomed manner of ingestion. Predictably, they will break the bargain sooner or later — first, perhaps, sneaking "extras" that "don't count" for some reason or other, and ultimately creating some excuse for dismissing the bargain altogether and resuming the usual manner of abuse. Predictably, too, the responsibility for breaking the bargain will be laid onto others. What we are looking at here is a "marginal control" that always accompanies chemical dependency.

Marginal Control

This marginal or peripheral control is opposed to real or true control, and some measure of it is possible for any dependent at any stage of the illness. The presence of marginal control throughout the illness precludes the possibility of taking "loss of control" in a total or absolute sense. And a close look at marginal control reveals that it lacks the essential qualities of real or true control. It is not deliberately decided. It is not freely chosen. It is not comfortable. It is not done deliberately, freely, and easily as a fully rational or reasonable undertaking. At best, it is subservient compliance; more often it is defiant compliance; and in no case is it spontaneous acceptance.

This condition is often manifested as the "dry drunk syndrome" or the "abstinence syndrome" that has long been known to students and practitioners of alcoholism. This is a state of deprivation anxiety, experienced by abusers of other drugs, as well as of alcohol, in which dependents terminate actual ingestion but retain all the pathology of chemical dependency within them and therefore continue to exhibit its symptoms. It is a painful condition both for dependents and for concerned persons. Unquestionably, it is "control" of a sort because the dependent is "dry" or "clean," but it is not the real or reasonable control we are talking about.

The abstinence or dry drunk syndrome is, in effect, a neatly packaged example of marginal control that comes to our attention, as a rule, only after dependents have achieved some awareness that drugs are a problem and when they are making an effort to solve the problem by total abstention. Marginal control more commonly occurs, however, while dependents are still actively maintaining their pathological drug relationship, continuing their actual drug ingestion, and at the same time trying to convince themselves and prove to others that they can use their will power to keep it within reasonable bounds. It is in this context that most "control" hassles develop and that most of the doubts and uncertainties about the presence or absence of chemical dependency arise.

It is a mistake, as we have noted, to look for total and absolute loss of control. This is a figment of fantasy, not a fact of reality. It is equally a mistake to confuse marginal control with real control. Marginal control is a *characteristic* of chemical dependency, an integral part of it, demonstrating the presence of the illness and more particularly of the *powerlessness* factor in the illness. In no way does marginal control give evidence that one's drug relationship and/or ingestion is truly under control.

Programs of Marginal Control

Another somewhat less common, but no less delusionary, form of marginal control is exercised by some dependents in the relief or maintenance stages. In order to maintain their drug relationship and continue their ingestion, these dependents try to achieve or to regain real control by taking courses or going through programs that promise to teach moderate, controlled, or "social" use of drugs.

Although there are reported claims of successes in this regard, such claims appear always to be based on crude indices of success, such as quantities consumed, frequency of ingestion, "dry" or "clean" periods, length of employment, etc., and not on indices of personal recovery from the pathology or the removal of essential symptoms of the illness itself. Granted, any reduction of adverse consequences, whether personal or social, is a desirable goal. And granted, even temporary and partial reduction of these consequences is in some sense success. Still, the fact remains that we are here looking at accidentals, at complications, not at essential pathology and symptoms.

Before we can take seriously the possibility of restoring later stage dependents to moderate or social or controlled ingestion, we must have evidence based on factors essential to chemical dependency. We also must have data demonstrating that the control referred to is real control and not merely a more consciously cultivated form of marginal control that has received the endorsement and support of more sophisticated enablers. In other words, we must be certain that the alleged control is reasonable control, that is, an ability to ingest or to abstain from drugs deliberately, freely, and comfortably according to a defined beneficial purpose.

We do well in this regard to respect the concern of knowledgeable groups such as NIAAA/DHHS as expressed in the Ninth Special Report to the U.S. Congress on Alcohol and Health: "The appropriateness of controlled drinking as a therapeutic goal for alcoholism treatment remains highly controversial in the United States. Various patient characteristics influence whether controlled drinking is appropriate, including severity of dependence, extent of drinking history, psychological dependence, prior treatment episodes and current liver damage." (p. xxxviii) We should heed their warnings of the risk of serious harm coming to victims of the illness from those who propose to teach or condition chronic dependents to ingest moderately or "with control." However well-intentioned, such programs invite dependents to postpone or to abandon their personal recoveries from chemical dependency in favor of further self-defeating attempts at marginal control.

Social Defenses

Marginal control, as practiced by dependents and supported by enablers, is one of the factors that makes it so difficult for the untrained observer to recognize the loss of true control that shows itself even in the earliest stages of dependency. Another factor is the social defensiveness that commonly surrounds loss of control. This defensiveness forestalls the raising of questions about control until dependents have reached the relief, maintenance, or escape stages of their illness. This collective defensiveness is so effective in preventing recognition of early symptoms, including loss of control, that almost without exception a person's ingestion is already far out of control by the time any question is raised about it.

The fact is that true control is lost the moment the drug commitment is made and the sick drug relationship is thereby established, and it is evident to the trained eye almost at once. Even with no training, an observer who knows the early symptoms can pick up sufficient data during an hour at a cocktail party, for example, to identify those whose ingestion is out of control.

Many factors undoubtedly contribute to hampering early identification and treatment of chemical dependency: attitudes marked by ignorance, ambivalence, and confusion; the social defensiveness just noted; lack of definitions of and lack of consensus on what constitutes responsible drug use, what constitutes drug misuse, drug abuse, chemical dependency, and so on. Perhaps the greatest single block to early recognition, however, and to late recognition, too, for that matter, is the lack of definition and the consequent confusion about what is meant by "loss of control." Without an objective definition — one that includes "rational" or "reasonable" as its measure and that also includes the qualities of deliberateness, ease, freedom, and comfort of control — the whole matter is left to subjective judgment and to the personal opinion of any and every individual. And no certainty, obviously, can be based on individual opinions and subjective judgments.

PROCESS OF DEVELOPMENT

In predependency, when the essential qualities of real control are present, the dependent handles ingestion by deliberate decision and free choice. A person is completely comfortable "taking it or leaving it," and drug use is confined within reasonable limits as to time, place, occasions, quantities, and frequency.

THE PLEASURE STAGE

Once the dependent has committed to the drug relationship, all of the pathological elements, including powerlessness, set in. Each element feeds into and in turn feeds upon the others so that all progress together. As the various psychic powers become more dominated by the drug relationship, they become less capable of carrying on their respective functions. In other words, the person becomes dysfunctional — increasingly powerless to function normally.

The dependent's drive for drug-induced pleasurable highs, which characterizes initial stage dependency, very quickly blocks out efforts at rational control. Preoccupation with drugs-for-pleasure distracts and muddles the mind, and compulsion overcomes the will; hence, truly deliberate decisions and free choices about drugs are prevented.

Furthermore, the increase of drug-disordered behavior reduces both the power to relate comfortably with others and to live comfortably with oneself. Growing guilt and other negative attitudes severely limit one's power to respond with appropriate emotion in feeling situations. All the while, the ever-present, ever-active delusionary defense system is busy putting one farther and farther out of touch with one's condition and at the same time rendering one ever less able to see it.

Awareness of Diminishing Control

As we watch dependents move through this initial stage, we find that they are seldom *totally* unaware of their growing powerlessness over their drug ingestion. Bad trips, crashes, and hangovers are not deliberately chosen: they happen in spite of and quite contrary to deliberate choices. Of this much, at least, dependents are aware. Why these events happen remains a mystery to them, but dependents know they are not intentionally seeking such painful experiences.

There is another aspect to this awareness of diminishing control. Not only do personal experiences of bad trips force upon dependents some awareness of diminishing control, but some of the destructive consequences to others usually get through to them. You hear it expressed sincerely: "I'm sorry, I'll never do that again," or "That will never happen again." They dislike the way they are drinking or doing drugs. They dislike and disapprove of the harmful consequences, and they detest the feelings of guilt and anxiety that follow. So they decide and choose and sometimes volunteer promises that their drug ingestion will be different from now on. But it isn't. However deliberate the decisions, however firm the choices, and no matter how sincere the promises, the pattern is repeated over and over again. Obviously, rational control — either of ingestion or of its consequences — is impossible.

THE RELIEF STAGE

Three things occur in the relief stage that warrant special comment. The first is the fact that along with the rest of the pathology, powerlessness revolves around relief-motivated drug abuse. Throughout this stage, dependents find themselves less and less capable of controlling their need or resisting their drive to seek relief from discomforts and miseries by means of chemicals.

A second occurrence in the relief stage is that the dependents' efforts at control grow more desperate, more futile, and more pitiful. As in the pleasure stage, awareness of unwelcome effects to the dependents personally and to others cannot be completely blocked out. Because they sincerely want to avoid such effects, they often solicit the help of concerned persons, hoping thereby to obtain outside leverage to force themselves to develop more rational control. So dependents strike bargains with concerned persons, who note their sincerity and are therefore willing to offer them another chance. While such bargains last, no one is at ease. When dependents break or end these bargains and go back to their stereotyped patterns of drug abuse and drug-related behavior, everyone shares in the disappointment and discouragement. The whole bargaining process puts an enormous strain on everyone's nerves and is a huge drain on everyone's energies. And the tragedy of the situation is deepened by the fact that all involved are sincere.

Bargaining as Manipulation

Another side of the "bargaining coin," of course, is the compulsive use of it by dependents as a manipulative device to ward off threats of interference as drug abuse gets increasingly out of hand. When employed defensively, bargaining usually takes the form of defiance coupled with grandiose assertions of being able to "take it or leave it" and to "quit any time I want to." Having thus come on strong, dependents may make further bargains to abstain for a while or to modify ingestion, "just to prove I'm in control." With great difficulty, dependents may keep such bargains. Then, having "proved it," dependents resume their usual pattern of drug abuse, perhaps adding an extra binge or trip to celebrate the victory.

In any event, the terms and conditions that get into such bargains are ultimately set (and unset) by dependents themselves, and all outcomes of such bargains are reserved to dependents for final judgment and interpretation. No dependent has ever lost, or lost control of, such a bargain. If this happened, the powerlessness to control chemicals would be exposed, and the drug relationship might then be seriously threatened.

Fear of Insanity

A third common occurrence in relief stage powerlessness is fear of insanity, both on the part of dependents and on the part of concerned persons. It is by no means caused exclusively by this pathological element. But the feeling of "everything getting out of hand" or of "the bottom dropping out of everything" is essentially fear inspired by a sense of powerlessness or loss of control. And since manipulative control is among the foremost characteristics of both dependents and concerned persons, this sense of losing control can run anxiety up to the panic point.

With the approach of the maintenance stage, the circle becomes more vicious. Dependents try more desperately to control their ingestion and to control concerned persons so that threats are aborted and enabling continues. As ingestion continues and worsens, concerned persons try more desperately to control dependents' ingestion and to control them personally, often with dire but empty threats.

No one succeeds, everyone loses, and no one knows why. An eerie feeling that "it's all a dream," that "this can't be real," is experienced by all involved. It is a stark intuition of helplessness. This terrifying sense of being out of control underlies the chronic attitudes of insecurity, inadequacy, isolation, loneliness, and depression that characterize late relief stage powerlessness both in the dependents and in concerned persons.

THE MAINTENANCE STAGE

Powerlessness, through all stages of the illness, is like a two-edged sword swinging relentlessly back and forth, cutting dependents doubly with its every stroke. In the pleasure stage, dependents are powerless to control their pleasure-motivated drug abuse and are equally powerless to consistently achieve the heights of pleasure they seek through drugs. In the relief stage, they are powerless to hold in check their relief-motivated drug abuse, and at the same time they are powerless to gain the full measure of the relief they seek. And when in the maintenance stage they settle for maintenance of drug-dependent normalcy as their reward, this, too, becomes a two-edged sword. They are unable to control their maintenance-motivated ingestion, and they are equally unable to achieve the maintenance they seek through drugs. They are thus doubly defeated by powerlessness with every advance of the illness.

By the end of the relief stage, powerlessness over the drug relationship and over actual drug abuse is an accomplished fact. The special manifestation of this element in the maintenance stage is increasing unmanageability of life. From the very beginning of the illness, of course, a dependent's life is unmanageable despite all defenses and delusions to the contrary. Progressive unmanageability of life is largely a matter of degree, like the powerlessness that is its cause, and a "marginal" or "peripheral" manageability of life remains throughout the illness, as does marginal control of ingestion.

An Unmanageable Life

Managing one's life is in any case a complicated and difficult task. Its principles or essential guidelines are simple enough: decide your life goals, select the most suitable means to achieve them, draw up a plan or process to follow, and then get going.

Reducing these principles to practice, however, is no easy matter. To do so even moderately well requires consistent attention and a steady application of all our psychic powers functioning at their normal best. Obviously, any great diversion of our attention or excessive drain on our energies reduces our power to manage our lives effectively. When all of our life powers are "bent out of shape" by a pathological orientation to drugs, the task becomes impossible. In relief stage dependency, the life powers are already fixed in a drug-centered life style, and actual drug abuse is steadily reducing their effectiveness. With progressive loss of psychic power, unmanageability of life accelerates.

In the maintenance stage, where drug-normal survival is the supreme goal, there is little attention or energy left with which to manage other affairs of life. Dependents in this stage can neither hold nor pull themselves together. They disintegrate, that is, lose their personal integrity and grow disorganized and fragmented, both within themselves and in all aspects of their lives. Deprived of their power to relate to other people, dependents find their social and community life deteriorating, too. Without the power to think clearly or to act prudently, they find that no aspect of their life remains intact.

THE ESCAPE STAGE

Powerlessness, in its final stage, naturally calls to mind the "skid row" image: winos and junkies, pimps and prostitutes, decaying inner cities. This is the image of degenerate subcultures, where everyone is doing his or her own thing with little or no interference, and where the one central thing for all is drug abuse in quest of oblivion. In some ways, the image is faithful to the reality, but in other ways it is not. The drive to escape that marks this final stage of dependency casts aside or disregards conventional ties, styles of life, normative standards, and, ultimately, respect for life itself. In the mad plunge toward final oblivion, nothing is sacred, little or nothing of value remains. Nothing matters any more.

Powerlessness leaves one helpless and terrified, on the edge of despair with only two practical alternatives: get help or "get out." Help, as a rule, is not available, so the latter alternative is usually followed. Most chemical dependents today die of their illness. The vast majority are never diagnosed, never treated, never receive any kind of specialized help, and never recover. Without the inner resources either to recognize or to remedy their condition and without outside help to intervene, they have no escape from the illness except death.

The Skid Row Image

The ultimate depersonalization and desocialization conjured up by the skid row image is a fairly accurate picture of escape stage dependents. But in many respects the skid row image fails. First, because escape stage dependency is by no means confined to skid row, and secondly, because this image produces many and serious errors.

Far more often than it is found in skid row, escape stage dependency is present in executive suites, suburban homes, blue collar and white collar families, hard-hat, soft-hat and no-hat jobs, government and company offices, staff and board meetings, farms, local clubs, bars, sports stadiums — and on highways and side roads, in parks and on lakes. Escape stage powerlessness, like the whole illness, is no respecter of persons, places, status, age, or talents. Anyone anywhere may be its victim. The president of a company, a nation, or a university is just as powerless under the influence of the drug relationship, just as helpless to control his drug abuse, just as incapable of managing his life or handling his responsibilities as the skid row wino or junkie. And, of course, such powerless persons in positions of power are far more dangerous in their potential for doing harm to others.

In at least six ways, the skid row image obscures or blocks understanding of chemically dependent powerlessness, as well as of the nature and incidence of the illness.

1. In the first place, this image gives rise to an assumption that the skid row extreme represents the *typical* case of powerlessness and unmanageability of life. This is untrue. Only a very small fraction of dependents — the nontypical ones — ever reach skid row, while powerlessness and unmanageability of life begin with the pleasure-stage drug commitment and continue progressively throughout the illness.

2. The skid row image gives rise to false assumptions about the other pathological elements and, indeed, about

chemical dependency as a whole. The impression is given that the maintenance and escape stages of the illness that are common on skid row are *representative* of the illness itself and are the norms for measuring its incidence. This, of course, leaves the pleasure and relief stages completely out of the picture and consequently overlooks most cases of chemical dependency.

3. The image makes skid row residents the *standard of comparison* for other individual drug relationships. Then, because "I am not like one of them," I conclude that I am not chemically dependent.

4. The image implies a geographical location, a special *place* where chemical dependency is typically found. That place, of course, is at a safe and comfortable distance from our community, our neighborhood, our home, our business. Chemical dependency is not a problem here; it's over there in skid row.

5. The image distracts attention from *our* drug problems and from *my* drug problem in another way. As individuals or as groups, we may feel genuine concern for skid row residents as part of our more general concern about poverty, underprivilege, and drug-related social conditions. Motivated by such concern, we may contribute time, energy, personal services, and perhaps money toward the betterment of these conditions and these victims. Our attention may be focused so intently on them and on their drug problems that we fail to look at our own. And because we are doing something constructive about their problems, we can come to feel a *false assurance* and develop a false sense of security about our personal drug involvement and about the personal drug problems of others in our family, neighborhood, community, business, school, etc.

6. Finally, the image of alcoholics and other drug dependents as "skid row dependents" carries with it a *moral and social stigma* that continues to be a major obstacle in the way of recognizing and admitting drug problems. While much has been accomplished toward lessening this stigma, it is far from removed. In virtually every case, dependents and their concerned persons resist diagnoses and intervention in part, at least, because they share the common assumption that acknowledging such problems is admitting

to what they regard as the shameful moral weakness of "skid row degenerates." This same unspoken (and often unrecognized) moralistic assumption deters many physicians and other professionals and most ordinary people from acknowledging or dealing with drug problems even when they are obviously present.

Skid Row Myths

Before leaving skid row dependents and the popular defensive applications of their image, we note in passing the existence of some myths that reappear from time to time, usually to fill up newspaper space but occasionally with more serious intent.

One such myth has it that the difference between an "alcoholic" and a skid row "drunk" is that an alcoholic is powerless to help himself whereas a drunk freely chooses his booze. As with the mythical distinction between "heavy drinkers" and "alcoholics," no evidence has ever been presented that proves this assertion. All available evidence points up the fact that "alcoholics" and "drunks" are essentially the same, whether they are on skid row, on "easy street," or somewhere in between.

Another myth quotes skid row drunks as saying, "We *prefer* to live like this." Without a glance at the awful reality of chemical dependency in its skid row victims (or in its other victims) and totally ignoring the delusionary defenses that accompany the illness, some take the statement for objective truth. In their eyes, skid row is no longer seen as "the street." Instead, it is made to appear as a kind of haven, an idyllic place of retreat, where certain romantic spirits seek their fulfillment in an unstructured, freed-up life style. The harsh realities of skid row are thus glossed over, and the gross destructiveness of chemical dependency among skid row residents goes unrecognized and unattended. A more cynical attitude toward helpless persons or a crueler judgment and rejection of suffering human beings is difficult to imagine. No one in his or her right mind could prefer to live like that, and no one in his or her right mind could believe that skid row myth.

RESULTING CONDITIONS

Two frightening alternatives present themselves to dependents as they struggle to maintain and to defend their conviction that they retain their power over their drug involvement. The two alternatives are, of course, either they are in fact in control, or they are not. If they are in control, then they are deliberately deciding and freely choosing to act as they do both in regard to their manner of abusing drugs and in regard to their drug-related destructive and sometimes criminal behaviors. On the other hand, if they are not in control, they must admit that they are sick with a sickness that is destroying them mentally, socially, emotionally, spiritually, and physically.

As long as their deluded belief in control prevails, the accumulated weight of their guilt becomes a crushing burden driving them deep into anxiety and depression and finally into despair and self-destruction. But on the other hand, if they admit they are sick, this implies surrendering to treatment and discarding their whole drug-centered way of life. It also implies admitting defeat; admitting failure to control significant areas of their lives; acknowledging to themselves and to others the fact and extent of their rationalizations, projections, and other defenses; and accepting and dealing with their irrational negativism, their wretchedly low self-image, and the other pathological elements of their illness, which will be discussed in detail in later chapters. Either way the prospects are grim, and either way the suffering is great.

Dependents are powerless to see clearly the implications of either alternative. The glimpses of awareness they do receive only serve to add more fears to the terror they feel already. This conflict, like so many others, remains unresolved throughout the illness. The result is an ongoing state of ambivalence, ambiguity, indecisiveness, and procrastination that both flows from and contributes to powerlessness and unmanageability of life.

The Struggle for Power

The bitter "struggle for power" to maintain or to regain control over one's drug ingestion is seen both by therapists and by recovering dependents as a central issue in the recovery process. Some of the most enlightened and enlightening literature in the chemical dependency field has been written around it. It is the starting point, the first step, in the Alcoholics Anonymous Twelve Step Program: "We admitted we were powerless ... "

This struggle for power is so deep-seated in the pathology of chemical dependency that even after treatment for their illness, dependents' deluded belief in their power to control their ingestion may continue or revive. If their admission of powerlessness is a token compliance and not a total acceptance, they do in fact continue to assume that they are in control. For reasons of convenience, they may find it expedient to comply by "going through the motions" of admitting that they are powerless. Invariably, however, this compliance is shown for what it is when the pressures for conformity are relaxed. Drug abuse is then resumed and continues out of control.

Furthermore, the struggle for power is so subtle that even when dependents have no conscious reservations about their admission of powerlessness, they may *subconsciously* reject the fact that they are out of control. They can be quite sincere in believing that they have totally accepted their sick condition, including their powerlessness. But their obsession with drugs is so deep and their compulsion to ingest them is so strong that they cannot resist "experimenting" again — and again, and again — in attempts to prove to themselves that they are not really powerless to control their use of drugs. Invariably, such deluded experiments result in disaster.

Enablers' Encouragement

Persons who are actively pursuing their drug relationship sometimes receive encouragement from enablers to try to develop more effective marginal control. Recovering dependents who have not fully accepted the reality of their powerlessness also may become prey to well-meaning but ignorant enablers. These are friends, associates, therapists, and others who encourage them to resume their drug ingestion on a moderate scale, or who insist on prescribing the use of mood-altering drugs as part of a therapeutic program.

Some dependents are misled by this encouragement. It always carries with it a false assurance that they can safely resume ingestion on a limited basis or that they can be conditioned to modify their behavior so effectively that they can reestablish rational control. The consequences are invariably disastrous to dependents and to concerned persons. Aside from the ethical and professional considerations implicit in placing dependents at such risk, one fact is clearly demonstrated, namely, that dependents who experiment still remain the victims of their chemically dependent delusion as well as of their powerlessness. They are not yet in touch with a very significant aspect of reality: their powerlessness over mood-altering chemicals.

An Admirable but Tragic Defense of Freedom

Underlying the delusionary insistence of dependents that they are in control is a tragic, but nonetheless heroic, defense of personal freedom. Obstinate refusal to admit powerlessness over drugs and the consequent unmanageability of life appears on the surface to be little more than stubborn defiance. But deeper understanding of this resistance reveals that what we witness is the tenacious struggle of human beings to preserve a most precious possession: their personal freedom.

The power to deliberately decide and to freely choose one's way of life and one's behaviors and to assume the personal responsibility and accountability that such freedom carries with it is among the highest of human values. The freedom to make my own decisions, to be free to do as I choose, to take responsibility, and to be held accountable for my own decisions and free choices is so precious to me that I will die defending it.

This, in effect, is what dependents do. Blinded by delusion, they believe with sincere conviction that they are *free*. To admit that they are obsessively-compulsively dependent on drugs would be to admit that they are not free. Their fight-to-the-death struggle against admitting their compulsive dependency and accepting their powerlessness, therefore, is a genuine (but nonetheless deluded and futile) attempt to assert and maintain a most precious human possession: their freedom as responsible persons. From this standpoint the struggle, for all of its pathos, is in some sense admirable. Certainly, it renders eloquent testimony of the value we place on our freedom. It is a tribute to the courage we can muster in its defense, and it illustrates dramatically the amount of suffering we will endure to preserve even its illusion.

The struggle is also ironic because, paradoxically, we win only when we lose it. When dependents finally accept their defeat by the power of mood-altering chemicals, their way to freedom is opened. Indeed, the only hope and possibility of success lies in total acceptance of failure. When personal powerlessness over drugs is finally accepted without reserve, we can come to grips with reality, and the way is paved to accept the indispensable help of others, including the help of the "Power greater than ourselves." With such helping power available to us through acceptance of our failure, the road to recovery is opened. Personal freedom, responsibility, and accountability become realistic, practical possibilities in a drug-free style of life.

SYMPTOMS OF POWERLESSNESS

Chemically dependent powerlessness is manifested principally by a dependent's inability to exercise deliberate decision and free choice regarding his or her drug relationship and by an inability to exercise control (will power) over drug ingestion and its effects and consequences. Secondarily, it is manifested by the inability to function normally (according to the dependent's own personal standards of "normality") in any area of life. This total or partial dysfunction is caused by drug-related impairment of all psychic or life powers.

General Symptom: Inability To Control Drug Ingestion

Dependents' inability to control their drug ingestion freely, comfortably, and within reasonable limits is a general symptom of their powerlessness over mood-altering chemicals.

Particular Symptoms of Inability To Control Drug Ingestion

1. *Repeated drug abuse*, demonstrating that the obsessive-compulsive drug relationship, not the dependent's will power, is in control.

2. *Repeated unplanned, unpremeditated incidents or episodes* of drug abuse that surprise dependents and sometimes cause them dismay.

91

3. *Repeated patterns* of unplanned ingestion. Getting high or getting drunk or stoned in regular or consistent patterns manifests the depth and rigidity of the compulsion that controls dependents.

4. Repeated episodes and/or patterns of drug abuse in spite of *expressed intentions, desires, efforts, and promises to control.*

5. *Denial of lack of control* in spite of data to the contrary. Minimizing, rationalizing, projecting, and justifying this lack of control are further symptoms of powerlessness, as they are of delusion.

General Symptom: Inability To Change Manner of Drug Ingestion

Dependents are unable to change or alter significantly and permanently their accustomed manner or mode of drug ingestion. This is a general symptom of their powerlessness. *Marginal* control, change, and alteration are almost always possible, of course, as we have developed elsewhere. Dependents can temporarily and in some marginal respects modify their ingestion. This is not true or real control, however.

Particular Symptoms of Inability To Change Manner of Drug Ingestion

1. *Expressions of regret*, embarrassment, shame, or remorse about *drug abuse episodes*, along with promises to change. "I won't do that again." "I promise, that won't happen again." "From now on, it will be different." "I'll take it easy next time." If a similar episode of drug abuse occurs after such expressions, it is a clear symptom of powerlessness to change the manner of ingestion.

2. *Expressions of regret about unwanted and unplanned drug-induced and drug-related behaviors*, which may disgust and even shock dependents, along with expressed intentions and promises to change. If such behaviors occur again, it is proof of inability to change.

3. *Persistence* in their manner of drug abuse in spite of the fact that they themselves do not like the way they are drinking or doing other drugs.

General Symptom: Inability To Terminate Drug Ingestion

A general symptom of chemically dependent powerlessness is dependents' inability to quit, that is, to end their drug ingestion and their drug relationship freely and comfortably and without the intervention of crises or help from outside of themselves.

Particular Symptoms of Inability To Terminate Drug Ingestion

1. Continuing or resuming ingestion after an expressed *intention*, desire, or promise to quit.

2. Continuing or resuming ingestion in spite of *efforts* to quit.

3. Continuing or resuming ingestion in spite of serious, even disastrous, *results* to themselves or to others.

General Symptom: Inability To Recognize Drug-Involved Condition

Chemically dependent powerlessness is evidenced by the general symptom of dependents' inability to recognize their drug-involved condition. Their delusionary defense system renders them helpless to perceive that the central cause of their personal and social dysfunction is their drug ingestion and their ongoing relationship to mood-altering chemicals.

Particular Symptoms of Inability To Recognize Drug-Involved Condition

1. *Sincere unawareness* of dependents of the sick drug relationship, of the extent and manner of actual drug abuse, of the various elements of the pathology, of the symptoms and of the consequences and complications resulting from their chemical dependency. This lack of awareness is but another way of saying that dependents are "powerless" to recognize their condition due to their drug-impaired mental state.

2. The various *symptoms of delusion* are also symptoms of mental powerlessness where drug matters are concerned, because the impairment of mental powers that produces delusion renders the mental powers totally or partially dysfunctional.

General Symptom: Dysfunction in Any and All Areas of Life
(Unmanageability of Life)

A general symptom of chemically dependent powerlessness is dependents' dysfunction in various areas of life or inability to manage the affairs of their lives according to their own standards or norms of appropriate life management, due to their drug involvement.

Particular Symptoms of Dysfunction (Unmanageability of Life)

1. *Spiritual deterioration:* inability to maintain their conduct in accord with their own value systems in spite of a desire and of efforts to do so.

2. *Social deterioration* (desocialization): inability to relate comfortably with other people in spite of a desire and of efforts to do so.

3. *Mental deterioration:* inability to function mentally according to their natural and acquired capacities in spite of a desire and of efforts to do so.

4. *Volitional deterioration:* inability to make free, spontaneous choices in ordinary matters or to manage everyday affairs with their former effectiveness.

5. *Emotional deterioration*: inability to respond appropriately on the feeling level to persons, events, and situations.

6. *Physical deterioration:* inability to maintain former standards of physical health and well-being or to maintain levels of energy sufficient to fulfill the responsibilities of their particular state of life; and in late stages, inability to moderate or to terminate ingestion, even when serious physical complications develop.

7. *Growing self-suspicions of insanity*, neuroses, psychoses or of diabolical possession as they feel themselves slipping, "losing their grip," "going down the drain," becoming more and more depersonalized and unable to "turn things around" or to "get it together."

8. *Growing desperation*, alarm, and panic, alternating with frantic but futile efforts to get their lives under control

and set their affairs in order. Job changes, geographical changes, spouse changes, and running away are frequently the demonstrations of this desperation.

9. *Despair,* in the terminal stage, when the feeling prevails that "all is lost" and dependents give themselves over to self-destructive drug abuse and suicidal violence.

10. *Suicide attempts.*

CHEMICALLY DEPENDENT POWERLESSNESS
SUMMARY OF ESSENTIAL SYMPTOMS

General Symptom: Inability To Control Drug Ingestion

Particular Symptoms:

1. Repeated drug abuse.
2. Repeated unplanned, unpremeditated incidents or episodes of drug abuse.
3. Repeated patterns of unplanned ingestion.
4. Repeated episodes or patterns of abuse in spite of expressed intentions, desires, efforts and/or promises to control.
5. Denial of lack of control in spite of data to the contrary.

General Symptom: Inability To Change Manner of Ingestion

Particular Symptoms:

1. Expressions of regret, embarrassment, shame, or remorse about drug abuse episodes, along with promises to change.
2. Similar expressions about unwanted and unplanned drug-induced and drug-related behaviors.
3. Persistence in the manner of drug abuse in spite of self-disapproval of it.

General Symptom: Inability To Terminate Drug Ingestion

Particular Symptoms:

Continuing or resuming ingestion

1. After an expressed intention, desire or promise to quit.
2. In spite of efforts to quit.
3. In spite of serious or disastrous results to self or others.

General Symptom: Inability To Recognize the Drug-Involved Condition

Particular Symptoms:

1. Sincere unawareness of the sick drug relationship, extent and manner of drug abuse, pathology, symptoms, and complications.
2. The symptoms of delusion, which also show mental powerlessness.

General Symptom: Dysfunction or Unmanageability of Life

Particular Symptoms:

1. Spiritual deterioration.
2. Social deterioration.
3. Mental deterioration.
4. Volitional deterioration.
5. Emotional deterioration.
6. Physical deterioration.
7. Growing self-suspicion of insanity.
8. Growing desperation, frantic efforts to get life under control.
9. Despair, feeling that all is lost.
10. Suicide attempts.

CHAPTER EIGHT

Chemically Dependent Mental Obsession

Obsession, in a general sense, means to be caught up with some mental activity so totally absorbing that one seems to be seized by a force outside oneself. Everyone occasionally experiences temporary obsessions. A tune, for example, keeps running through your mind. You do not consciously invite it or start it up. It just pops into your head. You try deliberately to put it out of your mind, but it comes right back again. You may silence it for a while, but it starts up again, and it keeps repeating over and over in spite of your efforts to banish it.

Another common experience is the obsession that gathers around resentments. You are treated unjustly, or you feel you are, and you resent it. You try to say to yourself, "Forget it — it's not all that important." But before you know it, there you are again, fuming inside. Your mental powers get caught up in all sorts of unwanted and maybe even violent thoughts and fantasies, and your emotions are in turmoil. You go round and round struggling to put it out of your mind. Perhaps you succeed for a while, but then back it pops again.

These are temporary and more or less conscious obsessions. They usually last for only a short time, and they are pretty much up in the forefront of our awareness. Other mental obsessions are more subtle and hidden.

In the field of abnormal psychology, "obsession" is usually taken to mean a mental preoccupation that is beneath the level of conscious awareness. It is rooted in the subconscious and, for the most part, remains out of sight because its object or content has been repressed. Once it is tucked away in the subconscious, we no longer have to deal with it directly. In fact, we *cannot* do so because it is not available for deliberate consideration. But it surfaces from time to time and often in strange ways. It triggers lines of thought and fantasy that do not seem to be at all related to the original obsessional content. We just "come off the wall," out of nowhere, in some of the things we think and say and do. We are illogical, irrational. We appear to be out of touch with reality. This is essentially what chemically dependent mental obsession is.

Definition

We define **chemically dependent mental obsession** as essentially an intense, uncontrollable, and largely subconscious mental preoccupation with mood-altering chemicals and their rewards, caused by a person's committed pathological love relationship to mood-altering chemicals.

To clarify this definition, several points are in order. First, this is a *special* or *specific* kind of obsession, having its own particular object, mood-altering chemicals, and its own unique content, a person's relationship to these chemicals and their direct effects. It is not a vague, generalized obsession with roots somewhere in the distant, unknown, and perhaps unknowable past. Nor is it rooted in any personality deficiency or character defect. Nor does it have its origin in some obscure trauma. The only "trauma" that gives rise to it is the significant rewarding experience: the "high" received when a person takes drugs. And the type of personality or character that is prone to get hooked into it is any normal human being.

Second, it is an *acquired* obsession that undergoes a definite progression and that is reversible with termination of drug ingestion and with an appropriate program of therapy.

Third, it is largely *subconscious* — that is, the chemically dependent person is not fully in touch with it, or is not in touch with it at all, because of defenses that prevent awareness. It is as though a curtain were dropped to hide what is going on.

Concurrent Awareness

We are naturally built to have concurrent knowledge of what we think even while we are in the process of thinking it. We become suddenly aware of this at times when we find ourselves "standing aside" and watching what we are thinking or saying or doing. It is almost as though we are spectators on the sidelines. We may be startled, even alarmed, and we may fear we are getting out of touch with reality or developing a split personality.

Actually, this experience is nothing more than a "snapshot" awareness of the concurrent thought process that goes on all the time. "Concurrent" means running along with, like two track athletes running side by side. It is this "two-track" mental power that enables us to know that we know something. This power also enables us to know that what we know is an accurate representation of objective reality. This is what it means to know the "truth," which is simply a *known* conformity of the intellect with existential reality.

When our defenses, and especially repression, go to work, this concurrent awareness is badly impaired and often blocked out altogether. Hence, we are no longer conscious of some of our mental processes as they are going on. Certain mental activities then become *sub*-conscious, that is, beneath the level of conscious awareness.

Note further that we say "intense and uncontrollable preoccupation." Our mind is not only *focused* on drugs and their rewards, it is *absorbed* by them, "lost in thought" about them, heavily occupied with them almost all of the time.

Preoccupation of All Mental Powers

On one mental "track," of course, our drug-related activity remains a subject of conscious awareness. We may give the appearance (at least to ourselves) of being quite reasonable about our drug involvement. But without the corrective input of the other "track," we cannot recognize distorted signals, so we do not get faithful mental messages. It is as if one line of thought were a direct-track input and the other an input monitor. Our defenses block our monitor so we cannot accurately read the direct-track signal. Thus, we have no way of knowing that our "reasonable" drug relationship is in fact quite *irrational*. What actually goes on is beyond our power to monitor and is therefore both unknown and uncontrollable.

Finally, note that all of our mental powers are involved in this preoccupation. They are basically three:

1. our *intellect*, or thinking power;

2. our *memory*, or power to receive, retain, and recall ideas, experiences, and images; and

3. our *imagination*, or fantasy power.

All three are directly taken over and carried away by obsession. And because a human being is one substantial composite, all of our other life powers and activities are affected indirectly. As with the other elements in this pathology, one psychic power or set of powers is directly impaired, but the whole person is thereby involved and damaged.

THE PROCESS OF DEVELOPMENT

What will eventually become mental obsession begins very subtly, so subtly that it passes unnoticed. We ingest a mood-altering chemical and experience some welcome effects. We do not give it a second thought at the time. Later on, perhaps during the following week, we recall that it was indeed a pleasant experience. We have a passing thought about it and make a mental note that it was good and that it would be nice to have again.

Now before going any further, stop and look at what has happened:

- Our *memory* received the impression of the welcome effect of drug ingestion. It retained this impression and recalled

99

it unsolicited. It volunteered it on its own, served it up although it wasn't ordered.

- Our *intellect* became engaged when we gave our drug experience a passing thought, a fleeting reflection, and when we made a decision to try it again.

- Our *imagination*, too, became involved. We vaguely fantasized a future ingestion from which we expected another pleasant reward.

The Seed of Preoccupation

Without our knowing it, and unknown to anyone else, a tiny seed that can grow into a monstrous weed has started to sprout. All of our mental powers have been brought into action, triggered by a rewarding experience with drugs. And just for that brief, passing instant we were taken out of the immediate reality right here and now in front of us and transported into preoccupation with drugs.

Even in thus analyzing and describing it, it becomes exaggerated, made to seem far more conscious than it really was when it occurred. But the fact remains that for a transient moment our attention was removed ever so slightly from the immediate situation, from the task at hand or the person present before us, and was shifted to mood-altering chemicals. We were out of the here and now and into a preoccupation with chemicals.

The pleasant mood-swing has now been learned and is stored in our mental data bank. Also in storage are the feeling responses that went along with the mood-swing and the scarcely noticeable emotional responses that came with its mental replay. We are programmed now for future replays of the pleasant mood-swing and for acting it out again in deed. We are all set up to seek it once more when the proper button is pressed.

What we here describe appears to be essentially the genesis of chemically dependent mental obsession. In some cases, of course, its beginnings are much more obvious and in certain cases almost spectacular. Many dependents, for example, can very clearly remember their first drug experience as something quite special. Their preoccupation began at once. But this is not always the case. In at least as many instances, the initial experience and the first preoccupation that follows it seem to pass unnoticed. Only later does any noticeable preoccupation occur.

THE PLEASURE STAGE

From Casual Affair to Commitment

Before a distinct, ongoing preoccupation sets in, drug ingestion may continue for some time as a casual affair. Occasions may or may not be sought out deliberately, but the power to make deliberate decisions remains. The mind still functions rationally. As drug use is repeated more often, however, drug-centered thoughts, memories, and fantasies become more frequent. At one critical point, a subtle decision is made to continue to take drugs in order to get high. This is the mental input into one's commitment to getting high on drugs that establishes a permanent pathological relationship to chemicals. From this point on, drug ingestion is habitual drug abuse, and mental activity concerning drugs is pathological preoccupation or obsession.

The central focus of this initial stage of obsession is the pleasure that drugs afford. The pleasant mood-swings that are sought and enjoyed leave deeper and deeper impressions in one's mind. Thoughts and reflections grow more continuous and intense, memories multiply, and fantasies become more frequent and more vivid. Drug obsession is taking over. A whole body of drug-centered mental material builds up, revolving around pleasure as the rewarding experience. Ingestion becomes progressively less deliberate and more blindly impulsive. Unplanned and unpremeditated ingestion becomes the rule as the mind becomes absorbed in an increasing store of drug-related data. Meanwhile, another factor is entering in to increase the content of obsession and complicate the mental muddle.

More Data for Preoccupation

In the ordinary course of the illness, drug abuse produces unwelcome and unexpected consequences. The dependent exhibits drug-induced and drug-related behaviors that do not conform to his or her personal value system. These add two significant areas of preoccupational data. One area is created by the behaviors themselves, with their destructive effects and consequences. The other area develops around the feelings of guilt, remorse, and anxiety that follow upon the behaviors.

Added to these is a third area of data for obsession. This area arises out of the dependent's memory impairment. Total and partial *blackouts*, together with compulsive *repression* of intolerable memory materials, leave the dependent in a scary mental limbo. Not knowing what went on during drug abuse episodes is a frightening experience. About all one can be sure of after such events is that he or she survived. There is no assurance that others did, and there is no way of knowing what harm one has done.

The unknown is always a source of fear and worry, and in this case it can be shattering. It is particularly worrisome when others feed back bits and pieces of information about what happened and expect a dependent to know what they are talking about. The distressing effort to fit all the pieces together demands enormous mental attention. This drains off huge amounts of mental energy, especially since so many of the pieces are missing beyond recall. Such memory impairment alone might well provide enough problems for full-time preoccupation. But there are still other areas.

When discussing psychological dependency, we saw that a drug-oriented life style is in the process of being structured during the initial stage of the illness, and that this generates resistance and protests from others. As a result, the whole area of person-to-persons relationships becomes a matter for added preoccupation. And on top of all this, and intertwined with it, are the many wearying internal tensions brought on by the struggle to maintain one's own conviction that "everything is going just fine" and to keep up this appearance with others.

THE RELIEF STAGE

With the multiplication of obsessive materials, the dependent experiences a steadily increasing need for relief from mental burdens and from the corresponding emotional discomforts that are suffered. Hence, a transition takes place that signals the passage from the initial to the next stage of obsession — that is, from obsession with pleasure to obsession with relief as the rewarding experience expected.

In the relief stage, any lingering doubt about the obsessional nature of the drug relationship is removed. The victim is powerless to shut off or to control drug-centered mental activity. Quite the contrary, it now dominates and controls the dependent.

Drug-centered mental activity extends to every area of life:

- to the drug relationship itself;

- to actual ongoing drug abuse and its effects within and around the dependent;

- to the consequences of drug-related behaviors to the dependent and others;

- to the mounting guilt, remorse, and moral anxiety;

- to the negative attitudes that weigh the dependent down and drive away other people; and

- to the sick need for constant defensive manipulation.

Obviously, relief from all this mental anguish and confusion is imperative. It is at this stage that chemically dependent persons are often heard to say, "If you had all my problems, you'd drink, too!"

THE MAINTENANCE STAGE

Focus on "Normalcy"

When obsession moves on into its third stage, it centers on maintenance of drug-dependent "normalcy," as do the drug abuse itself and the other pathological elements of the illness. Other obsessive materials continue to multiply and intensify, of course, but now sheer survival becomes the principal focus of mental activity. Such intense concentration is required to maintain even a minimal level of functioning that very little mental attention or energy remains available for other pursuits. Mental agitation concerning the drug involvement is in sharp contrast to the general mental apathy displayed in regard to everything else.

Paralogical Thinking

Paralogical thinking may become apparent in this stage. Dependents hop, skip, and jump about in conversations and discussions, giving the impression that they are either bouncing off the walls or lost in space. They can no longer track logically but are confused and inconsistent. They appear to be responding to some erratic inner prompter or pursuing disconnected lines of thought, only parts of which are spoken.

We are not here referring to the incoherent thought and speech of a person who is directly under the influence of drugs. We are describing a phenomenon that is produced by the *relationship* to drugs and that appears even apart from actual ingestion. Viewed in isolation or out of the total context of the drug relationship syndrome, this paralogical-thinking phenomenon may give rise to misdiagnoses, as may any other symptom of the illness.

Fear of Withdrawal

Another whole dimension of maintenance stage obsession revolves around *withdrawal* and the fear of it.

In one sense, "withdrawal" means to stop drug ingestion, to terminate the administration of drugs. In this sense, it is the act or process of withdrawing drugs from an organism. In another correlative sense, it means the physical reactions of the organism when drug ingestion is terminated — that is, the physiological readjustments that the organism undergoes when drugs are no longer administered. Withdrawal, in this sense, is accompanied by symptoms ranging in severity from mild to acute. The degree depends on many factors, but it principally relates to two things: (1) how great a tolerance for the drug has been built up by the organism, and (2) how rapidly the drug is withdrawn from it.

Withdrawal is a common experience among dependents. Hangovers, coming down, spacing out, crashing, and so on, are its more familiar milder forms. The shakes, delirium tremens, convulsions, and psychotic episodes are among its more severe manifestations.

Three Areas of Obsession

In the maintenance stage of dependency, when physical dependency or addiction has set in, severe withdrawal reactions occur when ingestion is abruptly terminated or the size of accustomed dosages is considerably reduced. The *fear* of withdrawal becomes an obsession with maintenance stage dependents, adding three areas of obsessional materials:

- *Prospective Suffering*—The first area of added preoccupation is the prospective suffering that goes with withdrawal reactions. This is a well-founded concern, based as it is on past personal experience and/or on the experiences and reports of others. However, this is seldom the deepest fear or the principal concern. Maintenance stage dependents have usually weathered withdrawal storms "cold turkey" or with chemical assistance. They know that the sufferings, while painful, are endurable. At least they have survived in the past.

- *Prospective Loss of "Normal" Life* — What frightens and worries them more than these possible sufferings is the prospect of losing the mainstay of their drug-dependent "normal" condition and way of life. This is a second and deeper area of added preoccupation. At this stage, drugs have become the prime and central necessity for survival, for life itself as dependents have come to know it. To be deprived of drugs is to lose the one thing that in their eyes can keep them going. Understandably, therefore, they will fight to hang onto what they need for their maintenance, and they will put much mental effort into the fight.

- *Prospective End of a Love Relationship* — The third area of added preoccupation is still more radical, going deeper to the committed drug relationship itself, which is the backbone and lifeblood of chemical dependency at every stage. Withdrawal implies breaking off this most meaningful love relationship in a dependent's life. Here, drug obsession reaches its deepest level. Threats of interference wake the strongest fears and are resisted with the greatest cunning and defensive manipulation. All mental powers, and indeed all psychic powers, are marshaled and become involved in a life-and-death struggle to preserve the drug relationship.

Withdrawal and Enabling

Withdrawal, therefore, constitutes a major area of obsession for maintenance stage dependents. When fear of withdrawal is alleged as the reason for continuing on drugs, it sounds plausible enough. It has in it that grain of truth that hooks the unwary into taking it at face value. Those unacquainted with chemical dependency fail to see the deeper implications of the allegation. They may be unaware that it is used as a ploy to protect continued drug abuse and to preserve the drug relationship. They are thus placed in the only role allowed to them by dependents — that of enablers who can be counted on to support the dependency, both by noninterference and by providing maintenance dosages of drugs.

Methadone maintenance programs, for example, provide classic examples of this kind of enabling. Continued drug abuse and acute stage chemical dependency are protected by law, sponsored by public agencies, and paid for out of public funds. In theory, this relieves dependents of their need to scrounge for their drug supplies and to commit crimes in doing so. Part of the theory is that dependents are also relieved of much of their drug preoccupation, thus leaving their minds free for other more constructive pursuits. In fact, however, it turns out otherwise. The drug obsession, instead of diminishing, simply focuses more intently on conforming to the established maintenance routines and often, too, on obtaining additional drug supplies to supplement and add variety to officially administered dosages.

Testing the alleged fear of withdrawal reactions in clinical encounters with methadone dependents invariably yields the same results. When dependents are presented with the suggestion that their alleged fear is a ploy to enable continued drug abuse and to maintain the drug relationship, their first reaction is to step up the fear to panic proportions and to mount a dramatic show of distress. When confrontation is pursued, other defensive reserves are called up: hostility, rejection, put-downs, and appeals to sympathy. If these are weathered and the confrontation is pressed, dependents admit that they are not all that afraid of withdrawal reactions but are primarily concerned with keeping the drug relationship intact. They want to keep using because they don't feel normal without drugs in their system.

THE ESCAPE STAGE

In the last or terminal stage of obsession, the focus shifts again, from survival to escape to oblivion. A preoccupation with one's utter worthlessness now appears with and dominates all other obsessional materials. The mind goes over this track endlessly, as the dependent hears himself repeating again and again: "I'm no damned good — I'd be better off dead! I'm of no use to anyone any more. All I've done is hurt my loved ones, fail in my responsibilities, and make a mess of my life. I'd be better off out of it once and for all!" Such thoughts of desperation are fed by numberless vivid memories of failures and defeats and disappointments, of forsaken ideals, and of goals unachieved. These real-life replays feed into fantasies of yet more discouraging failures, with no end of them in sight, and no hope for anything better.

The obsession with ending it all, in the normal course of the illness, drives the dependent to self-destruction by almost uninterrupted intoxication and finally by suicide.

RESULTING CONDITIONS

Primary Results

The most obvious resulting condition is the serious impairment of the mental powers and processes, as described in the following:

- *Impairment to Intellect* — The intellect's attention is withdrawn from the existential present and hence loses awareness of here-and-now realities. It is unable to perceive reality accurately. With impaired perception, the database for insight, understanding, and reasoning processes is distorted; therefore, the intellect is incapable of rational deliberation, judgments, and decisions. It is impossible for a dependent to recognize his own sick condition. Impulses, rather than deliberate decisions, govern not only his drug abuse but his entire life. The overpowering burden of obsessional material and activity creates the mental apathy, indecision, and procrastination for which dependents are renowned.

- *Impairment to Memory* — The memory power is also impaired, dominated, and absorbed by recollections of past drug experiences, both good and bad. These recollections are painful reminders of a grim track record of inappropriate, destructive, and immoral behaviors. Memory is further damaged by the blackouts and repression mentioned earlier, and obsession is fed by the nameless free-floating fears and moral anxiety that result. In all three of its basic functions of reception, retention, and recall, the memory is seriously impaired.

- *Impairment to Imagination* — The third mental power, imagination, is adversely affected, too. It is absorbed in obsessive fantasies about drugs and their rewards and in this absorption loses its dynamic creative power. Although dependents sometimes claim that under drug influence, especially under the influence of the so-called "mind-expanding" chemicals, they gain marvelous creative insights and inspirations, the alleged creativity seldom materializes in fact. Truly creative persons, upon recovery, are as one in admitting that their drug induced "creativity" was a product of euphoria and delusion, not of insight or of inspiration. They recognize that their creative powers were in fact severely hampered and that their ability to perform was greatly diminished by their drug abuse. They further testify that it took a considerable while to regain their creativity after recovery was underway.

In one area, however, dependents display extraordinary creative imagination, namely, in protecting and supporting their drug relationship. The imagination, along with the other psychic powers, is drawn into the service of the drug relationship. Its energies are spent in inventing ingenious ways to escape detection, to cover up shady behaviors and shoddy performances, to assure a continuing drug supply and to protect supplies on hand, to mislead and deceive would-be interferers, and at the same time to reassure them with a rare assortment of excuses, alibis, explanations, and lies.

If ever we witness mad genius at work, it is as we watch a dependent weave his manipulative web of defenses around his drug relationship. This "creative manipulation" or "conning" absorbs a major part of his creative energy, compulsively channeling it into efforts to ward off threats against that prized relationship. What imaginative power remains is largely drawn off into the grandiose, quixotic fantasies that are so characteristic of the chemically dependent.

Secondary Results

While obsession directly and immediately impairs the mental powers, secondarily it affects all the other life powers.

- *The power of the will* to choose freely and to responsibly guide personal conduct is blocked because obsession takes away the ability to deliberate, evaluate, judge, and decide, all of which are necessary preparations for free choice and responsible behavior.

- *The emotional powers*, too, are affected because they correspond on the feeling or "gut" level to what goes on in the mind, on the "head" level. As the mental powers are taken over by obsession, the emotional powers become locked into parallel compulsion.

- *The social powers* are also badly impaired by obsession. Communication is the principal means by which we establish, maintain, and cultivate person-to-person relationships. But persons whose minds are obsessed cannot communicate. They are not available mentally for expressing or receiving the idea content of communication, nor are they alert to pick up or to send the other messages communicated. They are too distracted by preoccupation with past, present, and future drug involvement to give attention to a here-and-now social situation.

Almost everyone has had the wearisome experience of being pinned down at a cocktail party or "happy hour" by intoxicated dependents who repeat themselves endlessly in conversational monologues, only interrupting themselves from time to time to replenish their drug supply or perhaps to complain that you are not listening attentively. Or you may have experienced the frustration of attempting genuine communication with a person on marijuana or other drugs.

Under direct chemical influence, a person is unavailable for true communication. But a dependent is often "out of it" even when not actually under the influence of drugs. Witness, for example, the executives who cannot concentrate on the business interaction at hand — the board meeting, the staff meeting, the planning session — because of their preoccupation with drugs. Witness, too, the professionals who damage client relations and sometimes clients themselves, and the employees who cannot handle their jobs or relate to the customer across the counter because their drug involvement claims so much of their mental attention and energy.

Diagnostic Difficulties

In the relief and later stages, the dependent's obsession includes so much and such varied material that an extremely difficult diagnostic problem is presented. The primary obsession centers on and around the drug relationship, as we have seen. But the abundance of secondary obsessional materials tends to obscure the primary — so much so that any one of the secondary manifestations may become the basis for a primary diagnosis.

For example, a clergyman, noting a dependent's obsession with guilt and with guilt-producing behaviors, may diagnose the values/conduct conflict as the primary pathological entity. He may direct attention to the client's morals without realizing that the dependent does not have control of his morals because he acts under drug compulsion. In such a case, a clergyman will only add to the client's distress by focusing on morality instead of on chemical dependency.

Or a medical doctor, noting a dependent's abundance of and preoccupation with somatic disorders, may diagnose these as primary problems without realizing that they are in fact only complications of chemical dependency.

Or again, a social worker or a family counselor, observing a client's preoccupation with family problems, may conclude that social maladjustment is the central problem.

In fact, obsessional symptoms are so numerous and so extensive that anyone, professional or nonprofessional, has such a confusing muddle of secondary symptoms to pick from that misdiagnosis is practically unavoidable without special skills in chemical dependency diagnosis.

SYMPTOMS OF MENTAL OBSESSION

Chemically dependent mental obsession is a pathological preoccupation with mood-altering chemicals that involves the three mental powers of intellect, imagination, and memory. Because preoccupational material is extensive, its content is abundant, and many symptoms are presented even in the earliest phases of the illness. Broadly, any observable signs or indications of *drug-centered or drug-related intellectual activities, fantasies, or memories* are symptoms of this obsession.

Symptoms of this pathological element tend to cluster around the following: (1) the drugs themselves, (2) the drug relationship, and (3) decreased mental activity about other matters.

General Symptom: Concern About Drugs Themselves

One general symptom of mental obsession is an evident mental concern about drugs themselves. This concern shows itself as preoccupation about *actual drug ingestion*, about the drug *supply*, and about the *rewards* of drug ingestion.

Particular Symptoms of Concern About Drugs Themselves

1. Any *looking forward* to the next occasion of *actual ingestion* with pleasant anticipation or mild eagerness manifests concern about drugs themselves. Dependents may look forward to the end of a day's work so that they can enjoy the rewards of a couple of drinks or joints or pills or a hit in order to relax. They may look forward to Friday night or to the weekend or to payday, when they will have some fun with drugs. Or it may be a party, luncheon, vacation, or recreational activity where they expect to enjoy themselves with the aid of drugs. They may think about drug ingestion

and its rewards when their minds should be wholly attentive to the matter at hand, and they may anticipate having their drugs at a particular time of day or night of the week. This concern about ingestion clearly demonstrates that these people are not indifferent to drugs; they are not free to "take them or leave them," even mentally. When they are not actually taking drugs, they do not really leave them; they take the drugs right along with them in thought, in fantasy, and in memory. They are looking forward to actual ingestion and to the rewards of ingestion.

2. Any *uneasiness*, worry, or anxiety *when the drug supply is threatened*, depleted, or unavailable is a sure indication that supply is a matter of concern, not of indifference.

3. Any *laying away or storing up of a drug supply* shows concern about having a supply always on hand and available to satisfy one's psychological need. Dependents may be so preoccupied that they remain almost constantly aware of how much is currently on hand, how much will probably be needed over any given period of time, and when and where supplies are available and can be replenished. In its more sophisticated versions, this will be passed off as "being prepared for guests," or some such rationalization. In its cruder versions, it will be a straight matter of knowing the locations and business hours of liquor stores, bars, pharmacies, and physicians or of making sure of one's connections.

4. Any *hiding of drug supplies*. Keeping special or extra supplies on hand by concealing them in secret or unlikely places is a common manifestation of concern about supply and also demonstrates a dependent's psychological need. Chemical supports are stashed away just in case the need should be felt when other regular supplies are not available or when tapping into them might raise suspicions or eyebrows. This symptom sometimes takes sophisticated forms, demanding highly creative, imaginative input by dependents, along with intellectual planning that approaches genius levels. Unfortunately, one of the other mental powers — memory — is not always able to keep pace with dependents' imagination and intellect, and they cannot always find the stash they so ingeniously hid away. Hiding a supply also demonstrates dependents' awareness that they cannot predict with certainty just when they may feel the need for

drugs — a certain proof that obsession and compulsion, rather than deliberate decision and free choice, are dominating and determining their drug ingestion.

5. Any *talking about drugs*, what they "do for me," what they "did for me," what I expect them to "do for me" is an outward expression of what is going on in my mind. I am thinking about drug rewards. I am recalling them to memory. I am fantasizing about them. "That was awesome!" "What a blast!" "Oh, wow, did we get stoned!" These and other such familiar exclamations all say one thing: "I am mentally preoccupied with the rewards of drug ingestion." Or, more briefly: "I am chemically dependent."

6. Any *deep fascination* with or *absorbing interest* in conversation, literature, music, art, people, places, and events that feature, defend, or promote drug ingestion and drug-centered life styles or drug "subcultures." An interest in these may be passing, of course — simply curious and casual, one phase among many others of testing alternative life styles and clarifying one's cultural values. But when such interest is deep and lasting, it speaks clearly of one's inner preoccupation with the rewards that drugs have or may have to offer. It is a particular symptom of mental obsession as centered on drugs themselves.

General Symptom: Concern To Preserve the Drug Relationship

Another general symptom of this pathological element shows itself as a preoccupation or concern with preserving the committed personal relationship to mood-altering chemicals and with continuing the drug abuse that goes along with this relationship.

Particular Symptoms of Concern About the Drug Relationship

1. Any *attempts to conceal drug ingestion* by misrepresenting the manner, amounts, frequency, occasions, places, or other circumstances of ingestion show a concern to hide what is really going on and thus to reduce the likelihood of any interference with the drug relationship and of any interruption or modification of drug abuse patterns. A person who is not dependent is open and honest in this matter. They truly have nothing to hide — an attitude that dependents cannot duplicate but often imitate. Dependents, however, give themselves

away by taking the initiative in presenting a case for their casual drug relationship and their "take it or leave it" manner of ingestion. A common symptom is "coming clean with the whole story" when the drug relationship is under suspicion or when drug abuse episodes call attention to it. Such a display of "total frankness" is calculated to reassure would-be interferers by leaving them under the impression that they now know the "whole truth." It is often quite effective in disarming suspicion and forestalling further inquiry and hence in protecting the drug relationship and abuse.

2. Any *attempts to sneak drugs*, to take them on the sly, surreptitiously or secretly. Sneaking drinks, pills, joints, etc., is another effort to hide one's sick relationship to drugs. Sneaking takes many forms and often, but not always, goes hand in hand with hiding a supply. It may be done by slipping "boosters" into prepared dosages, by simply nipping or popping on the side, by concealing drugs in ordinary food and beverages, or by using innocently labeled containers as conduits. The diagnostic clue is covertness or, more crudely, *sneakiness* about how one is taking drugs. Any such attempts at concealment both require and reveal deep mental preoccupation.

3. Any *protective maneuvers or strategies*. These appear in the form of mild avoidance and evasion moves such as "Let's forget it," or "Let's not talk about it now," or "I wish you'd stop worrying about it," or in somewhat more forceful form as "Get off my back!" or "Mind your own damn business!" or "Shut up!" These maneuvers or strategies also appear in the form of any one or any number of the countless defenses that make up the chemically dependent rigid defense system and its symptoms, which will be covered later.

General Symptom: Decreased Mental Activity About Other Matters

Mental obsession with chemicals decreases mental activity with regard to other matters because it diverts attention, weakens concentration, and drains mental power away from other pursuits. A lessening of mental attention to and concentration on other pursuits and responsibilities, therefore, is another general symptom of chemical dependency.

Particular Symptoms of Decreased Mental Activity

1. *Loss of interest* or diminishing interest in other pursuits and occupations: work, business, hobbies, recreations, reading, family and group involvements, etc. From active interest

in these or in some of them, a dependent moves toward indifference, unconcern, apathy. In time, resentment and hostility against these former pursuits may be displayed because they hamper or threaten to interfere with the pursuit of the drug involvement.

2. Diminished *effectiveness* in tasks requiring special mental effort, such as studying, teaching, writing, communication, planning, and organizing.

3. *Inconsistent, illogical, disconnected reasoning,* coming "off the walls" or "out of nowhere" in discussions and conversations. The intellect is so engrossed in and distracted by its ongoing drug-related thoughts that it cannot produce or follow an orderly line of reasoning.

4. *Indecision, ambivalence, and procrastination.* Decisions are avoided and postponed while dependents straddle the fence, immobilized because they cannot get their thoughts together. Practical decisions that they will be required to carry out are put off because they cannot be sure when their need for drugs may take them out of action for a while. They handle this by making fewer commitments and accepting fewer responsibilities.

5. *Faulty memory,* "poor" memory, and "failing" memory are symptoms both of preoccupation with drug-related memories, good and bad, and of the various direct memory impairments that accompany chemical dependency.

MENTAL OBSESSION
SUMMARY OF ESSENTIAL SYMPTOMS

General Symptom: Concern About Drugs Themselves

Particular Symptoms:

1. Looking forward to the next occasion of actual ingestion.
2. Uneasiness when the drug supply is threatened, depleted, or unavailable.
3. Laying away, storing up a drug supply.
4. Hiding drug supplies.
5. Talking about drugs and their rewards.

6. Fascination with, absorbing interest in conversations, literature, music, etc., that feature, defend, or promote drug ingestion and drug-oriented life styles.

General Symptom: Concern To Preserve the Drug Relationship

Particular Symptoms:

1. Attempts to conceal drug ingestion.
2. Attempts to sneak drugs.
3. Protective maneuvers and strategies to cover up and/or defend the drug relationship and ingestion.

General Symptom: Decreased Mental Activity About Other Matters

Particular Symptoms:

1. Loss of interest in other pursuits, occupations.
2. Diminished effectiveness in tasks requiring mental effort.
3. Inconsistent, illogical, disconnected reasoning.
4. Indecision, ambivalence, procrastination.
5. Faulty memory.

Major Dimensions of Chemically Dependent Mental Obsession

Chemically dependent obsession is a subconscious, intense, uncontrollable mental preoccupation absorbing intellect, imagination, and memory

With the pursuit of *good*, i.e., the *positive* aspects of drug involvement; to achieve them, to preserve them and to protect them:

- one's actual drug ingestion
- one's committed drug relationship
- one's drug-centered life style
- one's drug supply
- one's psychological and physical survival

- to enjoy its rewards
- to repeat it
- to assure occasions, opportunities

- pleasure
- relief
- maintenance
- escape to oblivion

With the avoidance of *evil*, i.e., the *negative* aspects, effects, consequences of drug involvement; to remove them, to conceal them, to escape them, to fight them, to endure them:

- self-disapproved personal behaviors
- self-disapproved social behaviors
- drug-induced and drug-related harm, destruction

- painful consequences and complications

- waning ego strength, low self-image, worthlessness
- threats of interference

- negative feelings

- fear of insanity, death
- worries about loss of control, helplessness

- to self
- to others

- withdrawal, hangovers, spacing out
- hurting, embarrassing, disappointing loved ones
- legal, financial, job problems
- physical complications

- guilt, shame, remorse, embarrassment, moral anxiety
- fear, hatred, resentment, suspicion, self-doubt, paranoia
- loneliness
- discouragement, despair
- sadness, self-pity

N.B.: This is only a general outline with some examples, not a complete listing of the areas and contents of obsession

CHAPTER NINE

Chemically Dependent
Emotional Compulsion

The highly sophisticated guidance systems that put men on the moon and robotic explorers on Mars are ultimately based on two simple principles: *pursuit* and *avoidance*. The power thrust of a rocket or missile is systematically guided in positive pursuit of an objective or target. A negative feedback system is built in, designed to enable the rocket or missile to avoid any obstacles that may be in the path of pursuit. These two basic principles, applied in technology with such dramatic results, are found operating everywhere in nature. And in man we find a special guidance system geared to pursuit and avoidance. It is called **emotion** because it "emotes" us — that is, "moves us out" in pursuit of what is (or appears to be) good and beneficial to us, and moves us out of the way of what is (or appears to be) bad or harmful to us.

"Emotion" and "feeling" are commonly used to mean the same thing. Although the latter may have a broader meaning than the former, we use them interchangeably in this context.

Emotions: Appetitive Responses

Emotions or feelings are our affective or appetitive responses to "good" and "evil." By *good* we mean things that are or appear to be good for us or beneficial to us and therefore desirable. By *evil* we mean things that are or appear to be bad or evil for us, that is, harmful and therefore undesirable or repulsive. We respond positively to good and pursue it. We respond negatively against evil and avoid it. And for both pursuit and avoidance, we have a number of different (but related) emotions.

For the pursuit of good, we feel love and desire, and when the good is possessed we feel pleasure or joy. For the avoidance of evil, we feel hate and aversion, and when evil is present we feel pain or sorrow.

Following is a more complete description, with proper definitions, of appetitive responses.

Affective or Appetitive Response to "Good" and "Evil"

Pursuit Emotions	Avoidance Emotions
When the good is not yet possessed:	When the evil is not yet present:
Love: the attraction of an appetite toward a compatible good.	**Hate:** the revulsion of an appetite against an incompatible evil. A feeling of revulsion against a disagreeable evil.
Desire: the movement of an appetite in pursuit of a compatible good. A strong inclination or feeling of urgency to pursue all agreeable good in expectation of enjoying it.	**Aversion:** the movement of an appetite away from an incompatible evil. An inclination or feeling of urgency to turn away from or to reject a disagreeable evil in expectation of avoiding it.
When the good is possessed:	When the evil is present:
Happiness Feelings:	**Suffering Feelings:**
Pleasure, joy: a feeling of delight or satisfaction in the possession of a compatible good. A comfortable feeling, a feeling of contentment or well-being accompanying one's union with an agreeable good.	**Pain, sorrow:** a feeling of sadness or dissatisfaction in the presence of an incompatible evil. An uncomfortable, depressed, discontented feeling when a disagreeable evil is present.

The above emotions have to do with *simple* goods and evils — that is, they move us when there is no particular difficulty involved in pursuing (and enjoying) goods or in avoiding (and suffering) evils.

When *difficulties* are involved, either in pursuing some good or in avoiding some evil, then our "emergency" emotions respond. They are hope and courage in pursuing difficult goods and despair and fear in avoiding difficult evils.

Pursuit Emotions	Avoidance Emotions
When the "difficult good" is not yet possessed:	When the "difficult evil" is not yet present:
Courage: a feeling of strength or power sufficient to overcome difficulties in the way of obtaining a compatible good. A feeling of adequacy to overcome obstacles in the way of attaining a desired good.	**Fear:** a feeling of disgust, uneasiness, or dread caused by a threatening evil. A feeling of apprehension when evil or harm is expected.
Hope: a feeling of confident expectation that a difficult good will be attained by whatever help may be necessary. A feeling of certainty that a good is possible to attain through help that is now available or that will be provided.	**Despair:** a feeling of expectation that a good is too difficult to attain or an evil is too difficult to avoid. A feeling of inadequacy, powerlessness, or helplessness to overcome by any means the difficulties in the way of attaining a desired good or avoiding a threatening evil.

If the good pursued is too difficult to obtain or the evil avoided is now upon us, **anger**, an "emergency" emotion, moves us to defend against, ward off, and overcome the evil.

Pursuit Emotions
When the "difficult good" is about to be lost or the "difficult evil" is now upon us:
Anger: a feeling of intense displeasure and craving for revenge against someone or something that has inflicted evil. A feeling of great antagonism aroused by the presence of an evil or the loss of a good, with a strong urge to get even with whoever or whatever caused it.

Feelings Are Facts

All of these emotions or feelings, along with all of their shades and mixtures considered in themselves, are simply facts of reality. They are part of our natural equipment for pursuing what is beneficial or helpful and avoiding what is harmful or hurtful.

And while there are moral aspects to feelings, the feelings themselves are neither morally good nor morally bad. They just *are*, like eyes, ears, noses, and feet. Unfortunately, however, because negative feelings are uncomfortable, we tend to regard them as bad. Hate, aversion, desperation, fear, and anger are then viewed as evil in a moral sense. And since the first elemental moral principle is to "do good and avoid evil," we try to do good by doggedly pursuing and pretending to have only "good" feelings, and we try to avoid evil by determinedly avoiding and pretending we do not have "bad" feelings.

In doing so, we get all mixed up both morally and emotionally. We become phonies, impulsively putting up false fronts that are in no way in accord with our true feelings. We may or may not succeed in deceiving others, but we are certain to deceive ourselves. And since negative feelings are as natural to us as breathing, sleeping, and eating, we experience them, willing or not. If in our judgment they are morally evil, we take on huge burdens of unreal guilt and may well go through life depressed.

Response vs. Reaction

Emotions are naturally flexible. They are sensitive to the goods that promise well-being and joy and to the evils that threaten harm and sorrow. The continual input of reality to emotions is quickly — almost instantly — "processed" by a healthy mind, and we choose responses both appropriate and spontaneous. We are not only flexible, spontaneous, and appropriate in our personal feeling life, we develop empathy with the feelings of others. Their emotions, in effect, become our own; we stand in their shoes and walk in their moccasins. This, of course, is an ideal condition and few attain it perfectly. But allowing for a reasonable margin of imperfection, many achieve great and accurate empathy.

With emotional health, we are comfortable, basically serene within ourselves and in tune with the feelings of others. Trouble begins when one or several of our emotions begin to get out of hand and in effect set up on their own. They resist the mental processing phase, bypass freedom of choice, and go off on a do-it-yourself binge. They take over and run away with us.

Love, for example, is triggered by a desirable good and is drawn to its pursuit. Money or sex or chemicals might be such a good. The attraction can be so great and the rewards expected so significant that other goods and other emotions are thrust aside or trampled in a mad scramble to go after and get the object of our pathological love.

Hate, too, can take over and often does. A person or thing or situation or event can be so threatening to us that our hatred of it gets out of hand. It can be magnified out of all proportion to the actual threat presented. This distorts our perception of other threats and immobilizes other emotions. We may become dominated by a pathological hate.

Similar things happen with other feelings. We can be overwhelmed by desires and pleasures, overcome by aversions and fears, anxieties and sorrows. In each case, the essential process is the same: the mental processing and free choice phases that produce spontaneous control are resisted and bypassed, and emotions go off on their own. As they do so, they build patterns of "deviant" emotional behavior. Inappropriate feeling reactions repeat themselves over and over until they harden like ruts or calluses. Such stereotyped patterned *reactions* deviate or depart from the appropriate flexible *responses* that characterize healthy emotions. This, in summary fashion, is the genesis of compulsion.

The following is a selected, but by no means exhaustive, list of feelings. Keep in mind that we all experience an extraordinary range of feelings, and that within those countless numbers are yet another myriad of subtle shades of feeling.

Feelings Identification List

Love	Hate	Desire	Aversion
attraction	revulsion	urgency	repugnant
affection	dislike	craving	turned off
expectant	hopeless	excited	deflated
warm	cold	happy	sad
kind	scornful	encouraged	discouraged
respectful	disdainful	alive	dead
Pleasure/Joy	**Pain/Sorrow**	**Courage**	**Fear**
delighted	disgusted	brave	cowardly
satisfied	dissatisfied	strong	weak
agreeable	disagreeable	bold	intimidated
fulfilled	empty	adequate	inadequate
peaceful	miserable	confident	panic
high	depressed	powerful	powerless
Hope	**Despair**	**Anger**	
expectant	downhearted	annoyed	bitter
trust	mistrust	irritable	rebellious
acceptance	rejection	frustrated	defiant
included	lonely	resentment	mad
supported	abandoned	vindictive	explosive
successful	failure	hostile	hateful

Compulsion

Although rational processing and free choice are bypassed by runaway emotions, they are not just left there standing by and looking on. Instead, they are drawn into the service of sick emotions to cover up their tracks.

The intellect, especially, gets into the act by inventing *rationalizations* to make deviant emotional reaction patterns appear to be quite normal and reasonable. Explanations are provided that do not explain but only cover up reality. If a glimpse of truth about what is going on should break through into consciousness, it is quickly turned aside as the intellect creates many "reasons" to justify the unhealthy emotions.

The mind in the service of sick feelings surrounds them with so many defenses that the sickness is effectively concealed from its victim. He or she is out of touch with it. It is not part of the reality that can be recognized and hence for the victim it does not exist. The sickness continues to operate, of course, but subconsciously, beyond the power of personal recognition or control. It is now operating as emotional compulsion, which is essentially an irresistible impulse to act (or to react) on the feeling level without regard to appropriateness or reasonableness and without volitional control. It is a state or condition in which one is impelled, forced, constrained to act by a subconscious inner impulse that operates apart from rational decision and free choice.

Definition

Chemically dependent emotional compulsion is essentially an intense, uncontrollable, and largely subconscious emotional impulse or urge, caused by a person's committed drug relationship, to ingest mood-altering chemicals abusively and to experience their rewards. It is caused directly by the dependent's personal love relationship to drugs and is initiated (along with the relationship itself) by his or her commitment to getting high on drugs. It is an integral element in the essential pathology of chemical dependency.

Following is a description of the major elements of chemically dependent emotional compulsion:

- It is largely *subconscious*. For the most part, its victim is not aware of it and has no way to become aware of it by any personal resources. If he or she is told about it, it will be sincerely denied. Dependents believe with unshakable faith that they know what is going on in their relationship to drugs.

- It is *uncontrollable*. The dependent is "out of control," both of the actual drug abuse and of the sick relationship to drugs, despite a deep subjective conviction to the contrary.

121

- It is an *intense* and compelling impulse. This urge arises from and is nurtured by the expectation of rewards that motivates all dependents. It is so intense that although the expected rewards are no longer in fact obtained, the drive to achieve them remains.

- It is so *deep* that it operates beneath the conscious psychological or physical craving that dependents, and other persons as well, sometimes experience. And it asserts itself out of nowhere without preplanning or forethought, with no conscious decision or choice. At one moment a dependent is not taking drugs and a moment later he is. The urge strikes and the action follows at once. If confronted about it, dependents will often admit that they had no intention of taking drugs — they just did it for no reason at all. Paradoxically, these same dependents will staunchly maintain that they can "take it or leave it," that they are handling their drugs with control.

Special Points About Compulsion

Two special points must be made about this compulsion before going on to trace its progression:

First, it is acquired and is therefore reversible. It can be "unacquired" when drug ingestion is terminated and the proper treatment is obtained to remove the mental obsession and the emotional disorder that accompanies it.

If there is such a thing as irreversible compulsion, this is not it, as the full recoveries of many dependents testify. It is rather one of the several elements in the pathology specific to chemical dependency. It develops along with the other elements and neither requires nor presupposes any preexisting pathology. And along with the other elements, it is gradually reduced and finally eliminated as recovery progresses.

Second, it directly and exactly parallels mental obsession with drugs and their rewards. The cognitive powers or faculties always provide the initial stimuli that trigger and draw into action the appetitive or affective powers. If a thing is not known in some way, it cannot be the object of emotion. We cannot love or hate or desire or reject what is utterly beyond our awareness.

Once set in motion, compulsion moves together with obsession much as one panel in a revolving door moves exactly in relation to the others. They originate simultaneously and develop together as the disease process advances, and they diminish and terminate together as recovery is achieved. Their intimate interaction arises from the substantial unity of spirit and matter, of mind and feeling in the human composite. Nothing affects us emotionally that does not also and at the same time affect us mentally, and nothing ever goes on in our mind that does not cause and carry with it some feeling responses.

Hence, when we get drug-induced good feelings in our guts, our head is busy making mental notes of it. When we recall and fantasize and think about those good experiences, we get corresponding feelings in our guts. Before dependency sets in, our fleeting mental reflections bring with them barely noticeable emotional inclinations. As these reflections grow in frequency and intensity, they elicit stronger inclinations. Then throughout all stages of dependency, the two accompany and reinforce each other. Increasing preoccupation triggers greater urgency, and stronger feelings of urgency stimulate more intense preoccupation. The revolving door becomes a merry-go-round, and eventually we reap a whirlwind of obsession/compulsion.

Appetite, Love, Desire

To get drug problems into proper perspective, to see them for what they are, we must realize that they are essentially love relationships. Love is the primordial emotion. It is the primary feeling response that stirs desire and moves us into action in pursuit of a good that we love. Drugs are good, so they are naturally attractive to us. The attraction we feel toward good is love. Good draws (*ad* + *trahere* = "to draw toward") us to itself. And built into us is *appetite* for good.

The word "appetite" is from the Latin *appetitus*, which means *to strive after, to desire eagerly*. Its root is *ad* + *petere*, which means *to seek after* or *to seek toward* some good. Appetite is a strong tendency, an inclination or urge to be united with, to partake of, to possess and thus to share in something good. Appetite is our natural, built-in desire for good. Sex appetite, for example, is our built-in urge to be united with and to share with another person the pleasures and joys of sexual union. It is a natural desire to seek after the rewards of sexual experience. Our appetite for food is our innate urge to seek after food, our natural desire to enjoy the rewards of eating.

These are only two of our many natural appetites. Actually, we have appetites for every good that is possible to us as human beings. And all of these appetites operate on the same principle, namely, *love*, which is essentially the attraction felt by an appetite toward a compatible good.

Love is positive. It is the dynamic power that moves us into action to possess the goods we love. It is the first initial impulse, the primary affective movement that prompts us to desire, to hope for, to expect, and to actively pursue the goods that appeal to us. Love of some kind, in fact, is at the root of all our actions.

And love is aggressive. We aggressively go after something or someone we love, and we aggressively repel or fight off anything or anyone that threatens to keep us from the things and persons we love. Love is a relationship to *good*, and we hate as *evil* whatever threatens to prevent us from possessing the goods we love or to separate us from or deprive us of the enjoyment of these goods. We also hate and reject, we fight off and destroy if necessary, anything or anyone that threatens harm to our beloved. We are jealous of our beloved. "Jealousy" means "zeal," and if we are not zealous to protect our beloved from harm or to preserve our love relationship, there is something missing, something lacking in our love.

Love and Hate

There are those who regard hate as the primordial emotion and who consider hate and anger as the root and source of aggression. They fail to see that hate is only possible as an offshoot and outgrowth of love. Unless I love what is good, I cannot hate an evil opposed to it. Unless I am positively aggressive in pursuing my beloved, I cannot be negatively aggressive in warding off threats to my love relationship.

Love, not hate, is our primary prompter. In putting hate ahead of love, the basic mistake lies in placing evil ahead of good. A person fascinated or overawed by evil may become preoccupied with it. He or she may come to view the universe upside-down or backside-to, as though evil and hatred were the primal all-pervasive forces instead of goodness and love, whereas evil cannot even be known except as a privation or absence of good. And hatred cannot be triggered at all except in reference to a more primary love.

Drug Problems Are Love Problems

It bears repeating that drug problems are love problems, and love centers on good, not on evil. Hence, drug relationships are built on love of drugs for the good experiences they can bring. This is the key to understanding such problems. They are, of course, **sick** love relationships. But they start out in the first place with the positive pursuit emotions, and only secondarily do negative avoidance emotions enter the picture. The rigid negative attitudes examined in Chapter Eleven include hardened and locked-in negative feelings. They are secondary to and arise out of the positive feelings and attitudes that generate drug compulsion.

Drug abusers and chemical dependents are sometimes hassled over why they take drugs. Their first answer is usually, "Because I like them. I like what they do for me. They make me feel good." Their answer is straight, honest, and right to the point. They love drugs; they love what drugs do for them; they love the way drugs make them feel. As far as they are concerned, there is no great mystery about the "why" of their drug involvement. It was caused in the first place by their love of drugs, and it continues on the strength of their commitment to their beloved drugs. Every love relationship, after all, involves a commitment if it is to last, and drug relationships are no exception.

The answer to the question, "Why do people get hooked?" is only complicated and obscured when other reasons and other problems are assumed to be the cause. The simple answer of real people with real drug problems — the straight-from-reality answer — is *love*.

If you think it is a strange notion that a flesh-and-blood, thinking, feeling person could fall in love with an inanimate object, a mere thing, then we ask you to consider for a moment the world of advertising. The psychology of advertising has long played on the knowledge that all forms of attraction are based in love and that the slightest promise of love will grab many a potential customer's attention. Ads push the notion that we can have exciting personal relationships with new cars, find passion and pleasure in a piece of chocolate or pastry, or experience romantic feelings with a fine cup of coffee or glass of wine. If you believe the world of advertising, a new tool or even a vacuum cleaner might be your next best friend, and the love of your life might come with leather seats and a sunroof. Our human appetites are ultimately based in love, and we are, by nature, made to love "the good." That includes those things that simply make us feel good, even on a very superficial level. Given all that, is it any wonder that people fall in love, really in love, with mood-altering chemicals?

THE PROCESS OF DEVELOPMENT

THE PLEASURE STAGE

The initial stage of dependency, the pleasure stage, begins with the commitment to a drug relationship for the sake of getting high. The budding love relationship is sealed and bonded — and sick. Love of drugs is now out of hand. One's commitment is, in effect, a pledge to bring all other psychic powers and all aspects of one's life into the service of this relationship. And what was (or may have been) at one time a free rapport with chemicals is now a pathological relationship. Freedom steadily yields ground to feelings of strong urgency to enjoy again and again the pleasurable rewards of ingestion.

As freedom diminishes, the dependent yields more readily and more frequently to this growing urgency. Impulsive episodes of drug abuse multiply and bring with them behaviors that are both personally unacceptable and socially disapproved. This causes embarrassment, shame, guilt, and remorse. It also brings on self-rejection and social rejection. As the now compulsive positive pursuit of drugs takes off on its own, negative avoidance feelings are building up, bit by bit, to the pathological negativism that is another element in this illness.

As compulsion gathers force, it relentlessly presses forward the reorientation of life style spoken of earlier. The drug relationship, like other sick love, is increasingly destructive both to self and to others. It sweeps aside, drives out of its way, any goods other than drugs. It impairs and then destroys one's sensitivity to other goods, and it steadily reduces one's capacity to love anything but drugs. It also runs roughshod over other emotions as they are forced into its service.

THE RELIEF STAGE

In the second stage, the most significant added aspect of compulsion is its drive for relief. Reliance on chemicals for pleasure and for changes of feeling stunts emotional life as it deadens feeling powers. The upward swing to euphoria is great while it lasts. But when it is over, a downward swing inevitably follows. Like a pendulum swinging in an ever-broadening arc, each higher up-swing is succeeded by an opposite back-swing into deeper pain and misery.

But unlike the arc of a pendulum, the mood-swings move steadily downward. The highs are not so high and the lows keep dropping lower, until a state of chronically depressed emotional life is reached where it is now "normal" to feel bad. The need for relief from this ongoing state of misery shifts the motive of drug abuse to a compulsive quest for relief.

Another factor operates to increase the need for relief. Rationalization, repression, and other defenses are busy putting dependents' negative feelings out of sight by keeping dependents out of touch with the awful reality of these feelings. But it is impossible for dependents to remain completely unaware that they are doing things they do not like: the destructive effects and consequences of their drug-related behaviors come crashing in on them at times. And there is only one solution, only one way to relieve their guilt: more drugs. Drugs are now compulsively abused to relieve the miserable effects of compulsive drug abuse.

Appearances of Control

By this time, dependents no longer have free choice. They are quite literally compelled by an inner force that is beyond their power to rationally control. Their wills are coerced, and they are controlled by a power greater than themselves, the power of mood-altering chemicals. And yet in some ways, they appear to be in control, and they sincerely believe and insist that they are. In support of this belief, and usually encouraged by external pressures, drug ingestion may be cut down for a time. Dependents may even agree to total abstention for a while, and they may in fact stick to their promises. If they do, then this is alleged (and often accepted by concerned persons) as proof that everything is under control and that there is no dependency problem.

It is often a convincing performance, but it is deceptive both to dependents and to others. It is convincing to dependents because they are thereby reinforced in their delusions that they are in control and all is well. They are more convinced than ever that they have no problem. The performance is convincing to others because they are thrown into self-doubt and confusion. They tend to reproach themselves for their meddling and misjudgments, and they are thereby reinforced in their enabler roles.

Compliant Control

We witness here a classic example of compliant control. Dependents, having compulsively covered up their compulsive drug relationship, are sincerely unaware of its existence. Hence, their genuine belief that all is well. So when the heat is on to change their drug-involved life style, they set the stage for what they regard as a just defense of their innocence. They place the conditions on their promises, and they set the terms for all agreements. When these are accepted by their prosecutors, they set their compliance meter to run for as long as the heat is on and to expire as soon as the pressure is off. During the trial, they bear down hard, exercising *marginal control* for as long as necessary to conform to their pre-set arrangements. When the trial is over and they are vindicated, compliant control is abandoned and compulsion takes over again.

As the relief stage advances, the compulsion driving every psychic power and dominating every aspect of life becomes more evident. Dependents become more rigid, pursue their drugs more fixedly, and resist more harshly any threats of interference. Relief is an increasing need in every area of life: relief from negative feelings of fear, guilt, remorse, and chronic depression; relief from the hurt of social rejection and from the much deeper hurt of self-rejection; relief from the memories and half-memories of the destruction and social consequences resulting from antisocial behaviors; relief from loneliness, discouragement, suspicions, and self-doubts; and relief, as already noted, from the miseries caused by relief-seeking drug abuse.

THE MAINTENANCE STAGE

The third stage of dependency brings a shift in basic motivation from relief to maintenance. The compulsive drive to abuse drugs now centers largely on survival. The dependent, however, views this drive and its various behaviors as "normal":

- It is now "normal" to have drugs in one's system, either constantly or frequently. Hence, continuing or frequent intoxication is the normal condition.

- It is also now "normal" to carry around in one's guts a heavy burden of negative feelings, the weight of a chronically depressed emotional life. Hence, it is normal to take drugs to keep this mass of miserable feelings medicated so their full weight will not overwhelm and crush one completely.

- It is now "normal" to pursue with narrow singleness of purpose the drug-centered way of life to which one has long since become accustomed. For a dependent at this stage, no other life style is conceivable. There are no realistic

127

alternative life styles available to him or her for decision and choice. Hence, it is normal to sustain this mode of existence by means of the same kind of drug abuse that produced it.

- It is now "normal" to apply as the remedy for withdrawal distresses the drugs that caused them in the first place, just as it is now normal to maintain one's drug-dependent normalcy by rigidly maintaining the sick relationship to drugs that brought it on. And although thus describing it gives it the appearance of a more or less deliberate process, it is not a matter of one's decision or choice. One cannot do otherwise because one is not free. One is driven by blind compulsion.

THE ESCAPE STAGE

The main characteristic of escape stage compulsion is its rigid fix on drug abuse for self-destruction. It is here that the devastating power of chemically dependent compulsion is seen for what it is — a relentless drive to self-extermination. Its fatal direction and force could be glimpsed in earlier stages; now its ultimate issue and full force become clearly apparent.

Earlier, we used a "funnel diagram" to illustrate the progress of the illness. Another look at it may be helpful at this point. Down through the middle of the funnel runs a straight and narrow path indicating the committed drug relationship. This never changes. It is fixed from the very beginning. It is a direct descent downward to death. The circle of other relationships steadily narrows as they are gradually damaged and then destroyed. The life style moves (and narrows) from drug-oriented through drug-centered and drug-dominated and ultimately to drug-terminated. But the central feature of the illness never changes: the committed pathological love relationship with drugs is set from the very start. It is the one, unique "stabilizing" feature of the dependent's whole personality and entire life. And it remains in its full vigor when everything else is lost.

Often we hear reference to the "vicious circles" dependents are locked into: Drug abuse → harmful effects → drug abuse to remedy harmful effects of drug abuse → more drug abuse to remedy harmful effects of more drug abuse to remedy harmful effects of more drug abuse → etc. Actually these are not just circles, they are aspects of a deadly, ever-diminishing downward spiral.

We might liken a dependent's tie to drugs to an animal tethered to a stake. Envision the beast going round and round in one direction with the stake-end of its tether fixed firmly in place. As the animal goes around, the circle decreases until finally the animal is choked to death against the stake. The image is grim, but no image however grim or gruesome can depict the depth and all-pervasive destructive power of this compulsion.

RESULTING CONDITIONS

Dependents are variously referred to as "not themselves any more," as "out of their minds," as "beside themselves," as "mad" or "insane," as "possessed." All of these references imply some power at work in them that is inconsistent with and in opposition to their true characters and personalities. It is the power of drug compulsion. With drugs as its center, compulsion moves out to encompass all activity. It becomes the dependent's typical mode of operation, the characteristic manner of acting; out of it come the rigid stereotyped behavior patterns of a thoroughly compulsive person.

If this compulsion can be broken — and *only* when it is broken — is there any hope for recovery. In the majority of cases today, the illness is allowed to run its full course, ending in compulsive drug-related self-destruction. Dependents suffer an overwhelming sense of worthlessness (see Chapter Ten) and an unbearable accumulation of negative feelings (see Chapter Eleven). When they realize that drugs themselves are no longer of any value for survival, they fall into a state of utter despair. They seek to escape this state in the oblivion of intoxication and then beyond it to the terminal oblivion of death.

Loss of Control

Probably the most obvious result of chemically dependent compulsion is the loss of control by dependents over their actual drug ingestion. They can neither freely choose nor reasonably regulate the quantities consumed, the frequency of occasions, or the circumstances of their ingestion. Their drug ingestion is therefore out of control. But it would be a mistake to understand "loss of control" as referring only to drug abuse *episodes*. Underlying such particular instances of actual drug abuse is the ongoing, ever present, and subconsciously ever-active committed love relationship with drugs, which is out of control at a much deeper level than episodic drug abuse. It is in the very nature of this drug relationship that compulsion is in control.

Chemically dependent mental obsession is like a guidance system keeping the drug relationship right on course and warning of threatened interference. But compulsion is in the driver's seat, and more — it is the very driving force, the fuel and power thrust of this relationship.

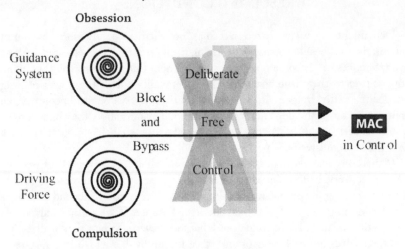

Dynamics of Loss of Control

Sooner or later compulsion lays waste to everything in the path of its forward pursuit. As it progresses, it draws into its wake all other emotions and psychic powers, all personal qualities, and all other relationships of the dependent. The dependent's life and actions in every respect bear the mark of compulsion. In view of this, it would be naive to regard lack of control or loss of control as narrowly limited to particular episodes of compulsive drug abuse.

Compulsive Negativism

Another result of drug compulsion is the negativism of dependents, which is also compulsive and which we deal with in Chapter Eleven. Chemical dependency, like any illness, is in itself negative, since it is a privation or negation of normal good health in the organism that is sick. But the *cause* of an illness is often another organism — a virus, a malignant invader that is positively pursuing its own development at the expense of the organism that is its host.

Drug compulsion is like a malignant cancer eating its way into the very fabric of the dependent's personality and chewing his life to bits. It is not a virus or cancer, of course, since this is not an organic disease. But the point of the comparison is sound: drug compulsion is essentially a positive thrust *for* something, an overpowering tendency *toward* something. It is not essentially a negative avoidance mechanism or merely a way of escape or a cop-out device as is often alleged. The extreme negativism of dependents is an *effect*, not the cause, of their drug involvement. Their drug relationship, as we have seen, is essentially a commitment of love. Their negativism is in direct reaction against any threats to their love relationship, and since the threats are many, their negativism is great.

This has profound implications both for understanding and for dealing with drug problems. To assume that drug abuse and the drug relationship are *negative* in their origin, nature, and progression is to miss the whole point both of love itself and of this runaway love, drug compulsion. It is a misconstruction of reality, like assuming the scenery is moving backwards and the hurtling train you are riding in is standing still. Or it is like viewing the erosion of a delta river bank as the source of the river rather than as an effect of its flow.

In either example (and in the above assumption), the view is 100% erroneous and 180 degrees in the wrong direction. We would search the scenery in vain for the cause of its backward movement, and we could dig forever into the eroded bank without ever finding the source of the river. With equal futility, but with far more frustration, we can search the scenery of a dependent's environment or dig into the negativism of his eroded life and never come close to the essential cause of his illness.

Suicidal Compulsion

Another result of drug compulsion is self-destructiveness, that is, suicidal tendencies. Two mistakes may be made in considering this drive toward death, and both can be fatal. One is to assume that a person is *first* suicidal and *then* chemically dependent. This is to wrongly believe that a person already has self-destructive inclinations and therefore gets into drugs to carry out those inclinations. The other mistake is to *underestimate* — or worse, to disregard — the suicidal nature of chemical dependency.

The first error becomes fatal when it leads to focusing attention on trying to discover what "other problem" is causing the suicidal tendencies and thus diverting attention away from chemical dependency itself. As the search for other problems proceeds, the illness continues to run its self-destructive course. And the search will still be going on as the dependent self-destructs.

Granted, there are persons already bent on suicide who take drugs to do the job, and granted, there may be some who are suicidal before becoming chemically dependent. Still, there is no clinical evidence and no hard research data to support the theory that chemical dependents are suicide-prone *before* they get into drugs. What we see clinically is that the average chemically dependent person becomes suicidal *after* and *directly because* of their drug involvements.

The second mistake, underestimating the suicidal nature of chemical dependency, is fatal when self-destructive tendencies are regarded as incidental or accidental to chemical dependency instead of essential to it. Then drug-induced self-destructiveness is minimized and the deadliness of the illness *from its inception* is in effect denied. Actually, the seeds of self-destruction are planted right along with the commitment to drugs that initiates chemical dependency. They take root at once and are nurtured and develop in one continuous, uninterrupted process of growth until they bear their deadly fruit.

Suicide, in other words, runs as a constant thread in a direct line from the initial drug commitment to death. Again and again we see family members and other concerned persons, including helping professionals, back away from the dependent's central problem and slip into enablers' roles because the deadliness of the illness is underestimated. Unless the dependency is seen as literally a matter of life or death, the "tough love" necessary to intervene and interrupt it cannot be generated. The dependent is deprived of the outside help without which his or her compulsive deathward descent cannot be halted.

SYMPTOMS OF EMOTIONAL COMPULSION

Emotional compulsion is a pathological urgency to ingest drugs and to experience their rewards. It involves principally our *pursuit* emotions, those by means of which we "go after" something (or someone) that we love, desire, want, or need. In this urgent pursuit, we are so dominated and driven by compulsion that both deliberate decision and free choice are blocked and bypassed. In a secondary way, our avoidance emotions are also involved because we compulsively hate and thrust aside anything and anyone appearing as an obstacle blocking or threatening gratification of our urgent need.

Three general symptoms appear as indicators of chemically dependent compulsion: (1) an urgency to ingest drugs; (2) unplanned, unpremeditated, or impulsive ingestion; and (3) continued ingestion in a manner displeasing to oneself. Each of these general symptoms is in turn manifested by corresponding particular symptoms.

General Symptom: An Urgency To Ingest Drugs

This urgency demonstrates an underlying drive to pursue drugs in order to experience the highs that are the rewards expected from ingestion. Beginning with relatively mild inclinations in early stage dependency, this compulsion goes on to become an irresistible, uncontrollable drive in the relief and later stages of the illness.

Particular Symptoms of Urgency To Ingest Drugs

1. *Restlessness, uneasiness, and anxiety at delays* that hinder, postpone, or interfere with anticipated ingestion. If the "ingestion meter" is set for five o'clock, for example, uneasiness will increase as the time approaches, and the dependent may explode if the meter runs out and the drugs aren't in. This "anticipation anxiety" may show itself in stronger forms, such as impatience, abruptness, sharpness,

or curtness — all indicating that a dependent is feeling a deep urgency to get on with the anticipated ingestion.

2. *Anger, hostility, resentment* at any real or imagined direct threat of intervention or of deprivation of drugs. The urgency of need triggers the defense system to protect the drug relationship by repudiating any such "attacks."

3. *Rapid or hurried ingestion* of drugs, especially at the beginning of a particular occasion of ingestion, clearly manifests dependents' urgency to satisfy their singular, subjective need for the rewards or the high they are seeking through drugs. Hence, "gulping drinks," "popping pills," etc., reveal not only the compulsion, but the commitment to getting high on drugs and the psychological need for them.

4. *Taking fortified dosages* is closely related to hurried or rapid ingestion and is in fact one form of it. But it is also an observable, particular symptom in itself. Alcohol dependents, for example, take concentrated drinks — mixtures of two or more kinds of liquors — or they take "doubles" to get a quick start toward their desired high. Marijuana dependents step up their ingestion by chain-smoking, or by oral ingestion along with inhalation, or by mixing pot and alcohol and/or other drugs. Pill dependents ingest several dosages at once or in quick succession to accelerate the effect and often supplement their pills with alcohol, pot, and other drugs.

5. *Taking "extras,"* that is, having a drink or a pill or a joint or a hit as a "preparation" for an occasion where social drugs will be served. This symptom is varied and is often tied in with sneaking drugs and hiding supplies, as for example, the "cloakroom extra"; the coat pocket, purse, or handbag extras; the glove compartment, car trunk, garage, and other "be-back-in-a-minute" supplements.

General Symptom: Unplanned, Unpremeditated, Impulsive Ingestion

This general symptom manifests the underlying driving compulsion that prevents a dependent from ingesting according to a plan. The forethought given to "doing drugs differently" and the sincere good intentions to ingest reasonably are swept aside when the compulsion hits.

Particular Symptoms of Unplanned, Unpremeditated, Impulsive Ingestion

1.   Impulsive *initiation* of ingestion, that is, starting to ingest for no special reason or for no reason at all. On the spur of the moment, with no forethought, no preplanning, and no immediate reflection, a dependent will take a drink, pop a pill, light up a joint, have a hit. The subconscious compulsion shows itself by thus impelling ingestion without conscious forethought or choice. "I don't know why, I just did it" would be a typical and accurate explanation.

2.   Impulsive *continuation* of ingestion beyond what was intended when the occasion began. Dependents will at times start out on an occasion intending to limit the quantity, time, or other circumstances of their ingestion according to a reasonable plan or pattern. But then, after ingestion has begun, they continue without regard to their premeditated plan. This is sometimes, but not always, rationalized as an abrupt, but necessary, "change of plans"; or it is excused because it "wasn't a good plan in the first place"; or it is projected: "You made me change my plans." The fact is that compulsion changed the plan without consulting the dependent about it beforehand.

3.   *Abrupt changes of plans or interruption of other plans* in order to initiate or to continue drug ingestion. When compulsion strikes, other matters take second place or no place at all. Previous engagements, appointments, schedules, and timetables are disregarded. One of the most common areas of changed plans is in home and family matters. Meals, recreations, promised projects, vacations, chores, etc., are forgotten or neglected in impulsive drug pursuits. Unexpected, unexplained, and inappropriate sudden departures, absences, and arrivals by dependent family members (or by friends and associates) are symptoms of the drug drive at work in these persons.

General Symptom: Continued Drug Ingestion in a Self-Displeasing Manner

One of the most obvious general symptoms of drug compulsion at work is the continuation of a manner of ingestion that is displeasing to the person who is ingesting. When people have only a casual relationship to drugs, their manner of ingestion is under real or reasonable control. If their ingestion gets out of hand on some occasion, corrections are made to assure that this will not be repeated. But a dependent does not have true control. It is marginal, and therefore, in reality, it is lack of control. When ingestion is out of control, it occurs *repeatedly* in a self-displeasing manner in *spite of* and *contrary* to the plans, intentions, precautions, and desires of the dependent. This demonstrates the presence of the underlying chemically dependent emotional compulsion.

Particular Symptoms of Continued Drug Ingestion in a Self-Displeasing Manner

1. Any *repeated incidents or episodes* of drug ingestion in a personally disapproved, unwanted manner. If, after a bad trip or an unwelcome drug experience, a person again abuses drugs in the same manner and with the same or similar results, it indicates that he or she may be "out of control" and governed by compulsion. If, after several such bad experiences, a person repeats the same manner of ingestion, it demonstrates the presence of compulsion.

2. Any *regular pattern* of self-disapproved ingestion. Before such a symptomatic pattern develops, at least several repeated incidents of such drug abuse will have taken place. Hence, a diagnosis of compulsion is certain if such a pattern is present.

3. Any *unkept or broken promises to alter or to modify the manner of ingestion*. A promise is a definite statement of a plan and implies an explicit commitment to a plan. Whether the promise is made to oneself or to others is immaterial. The promises are based on the fact that people do not like the way they are taking drugs and intend to change it. They disapprove of their own actions and wish and intend not to repeat them. If, despite sincere wishes, intentions, and promises, they do repeat them, it is clearly because they have no real choice in the matter. They cannot follow their own plans, fulfill their own wishes, or realize their own intentions because they are not in control — compulsion is. A chemical dependency diagnosis is certain in such a case.

4. Any *unkept or broken promises to quit or to totally abstain from drugs*. The same conditions apply to this as to the above, and a chemical dependency diagnosis is certain if such unkept or broken promises occur.

EMOTIONAL COMPULSION
SUMMARY OF ESSENTIAL SYMPTOMS

General Symptom: An Urgency To Ingest Drugs

Particular Symptoms:

1. Restlessness, uneasiness, and anxiety at delays that hinder, postpone, or interfere with anticipated ingestion.
2. Anger, hostility, resentment at real or imagined threats of intervention or of deprivation of drugs.
3. Rapid or hurried ingestion to get high quickly.
4. Taking fortified/multiple dosages.
5. Taking "extras," supplemental dosages.

General Symptom: Unplanned, Unpremeditated, Impulsive Ingestion

Particular Symptoms:

1. Impulsive initiation of ingestion.
2. Impulsive continuation of ingestion.
3. Abrupt changes of plans or interruption of other plans in order to initiate or continue ingestion.

General Symptom: Continued Drug Ingestion in a Self-Displeasing Manner

Particular Symptoms:

1. Repeated incidents/episodes of ingestion in a self-disapproved, self-displeasing manner.
2. Regular pattern of self-disapproved ingestion.
3. Unkept or broken promises to alter or modify the manner of ingestion.
4. Unkept promises to quit or to totally abstain from drugs.

Major Dimensions of Chemically Dependent Emotional Compulsion

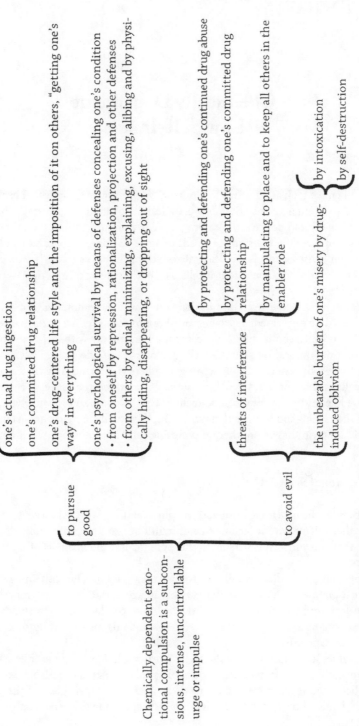

Chemically dependent emotional compulsion is a subconscious, intense, uncontrollable urge or impulse

to pursue good
- one's actual drug ingestion
- one's committed drug relationship
- one's drug-centered life style and the imposition of it on others, "getting one's way" in everything
- one's psychological survival by means of defenses concealing one's condition
  - from oneself by repression, rationalization, projection and other defenses
  - from others by denial, minimizing, explaining, excusing, alibing and by physically hiding, disappearing, or dropping out of sight

to avoid evil
- threats of interference
  - by protecting and defending one's continued drug abuse
  - by protecting and defending one's committed drug relationship
  - by manipulating to place and to keep all others in the enabler role
- the unbearable burden of one's misery by drug-induced oblivion
  - by intoxication
  - by self-destruction

N.B.: This is only a general outline, not a complete listing of the areas and objects of compulsion.

137

CHAPTER TEN

Chemically Dependent
Low Self-Image

When we look at ourselves in a mirror, we see our image reflected back to us. If we take the time to study that image, we learn a lot about ourselves. We note our size and shape and posture, the color and quality of our hair and eyes, the texture and tone of our skin, the signs of youth or age that appear in our face and hands and in our muscles and veins. This mirrored image speaks to us. It tells us what we look like, and to some extent it tells us what we are at this particular moment in time.

As we look at our reflection in the mirror, we have emotional responses. We feel pleased or displeased, approving or disapproving. We like or dislike what we see. When we leave the mirror, we carry the image away with us in our thoughts and imagination, and we take the feelings along in our affections.

How we behave toward ourselves and others is influenced by that image and the feelings that surround it. We preserve and develop the aspects of the image that we like, and we foster the good feelings that go with it. We try to change or be rid of the aspects and feelings that we dislike. We usually present our best image to others and try to hide from them those things about us of which we disapprove.

The Mirror of Personal Values

Besides the physical mirror and the physical image that it reflects to us, there is another mirror with a far more meaningful image that profoundly affects our lives. That "mirror" is our personal value system, and the image is of ourselves as *persons*.

Self-image is directly related to personal values. Our **self-image** is the habitual picture we have of ourselves. This image is the result of comparing our actual here-and-now behaviors and our habitual conduct with the standards we have adopted for self-measurement — our standards for evaluating ourselves, or our *value* standards.

"Values" are what we consider to be worthwhile to us. I value friendship, for example, and I value friends. I also value physical and mental health and emotional well-being, both for myself and for others. I value my own life and the lives of others. I value honesty and openness, clear-headed thinking, freedom of choice, justice, mercy, comfort, my home and car, sex, lakes, trees, stones, songs and sunsets, fresh air and blue sky.

My values are many: material things, persons, places, possessions, spiritual qualities, virtues, activities, feelings, experiences, and so on. And among my many values I have an order of preference, that is, some are more worthwhile to me than others. So I set up priorities among them. I form my priorities scale or hierarchy of values; I organize a personal *value system.*

The Supreme Value

But what is the basis for deciding what is worthwhile to me and what is not? The obvious answer is *happiness.* What will make me happy — what will bring happiness to me or bring me to happiness — is what is worthwhile to me. And contrariwise, what will not make me happy — what will bring unhappiness to me or bring me to unhappiness — is not of worth to me.

All of my decisions and choices of values, therefore, are based on what I think will make me happy and what I think will not. My supreme value as a human being is happiness, and everything else is or is not worthwhile in relation to this supreme value.

My values include both my goals and the means to achieve those goals, that is, both the ends and the things and actions and persons I need in order to reach those ends. Values clarification essentially consists in asking and answering two questions: "What do I value as my goals or ends?" and "What do I value as means to them?" Beyond this, values clarification is sorting out the priorities among my values and rearranging them, if necessary, in order to be as certain as possible that my supreme value, happiness, will be realized.

Standards of Measuring Values

All values presuppose a process of evaluation, that is, a matching up of what may or may not be worthwhile against some *standard* or *norm* or rule of comparison. For example, to evaluate the length of a piece of wood, I compare the wood with a ruler, a yardstick, or a measuring tape. My judgment or conclusion about the length of the piece of wood is based on how it conforms to the standard of measurement. Similarly, I use my value standards to measure the worth of my actions, of my possessions, and of myself as a person — the worth of what I do, what I have, and what I am.

In thus measuring worth or value, I employ several standards, such as economic, social, cultural, and family, and above all, *moral* standards. Moral value standards, like all the others, are ultimately based on the supreme human value — happiness. What will make me perfectly happy as an intelligent, free, self-deciding and self-determining spiritual/material person is of worth or value in a moral sense. Other goods can make me partially happy: they are worthwhile in particular ways to bring me some limited aspects of happiness. But ultimately, only moral goodness can bring complete and perfect human happiness. Therefore, my moral standards are the final norms or yardsticks to measure, to evaluate, and to judge what is and what is not of worth or value to me.

Another way we often speak of values and of value standards is as our "ideals," our "principles," or our "life goals." We strive to live up to our ideals, to pattern our conduct according to our principles, and to act in ways that move us toward achievement of our goals. But however we phrase it and however deeply we go into the matter of values, it comes down to this: we measure worth (including self-worth) with reference to our personal value system, and the most significant values we have are our moral values.

Fundamental Facts of Moral Reality

It belongs to moral science (ethics) and religious science (theology) to explore, to demonstrate, to define, to defend, and to explain all the whys and wherefores of morality. In this present context and for our immediate purposes, it is sufficient to state five fundamental facts of moral reality.

1. Everyone (with the possible exception of psycho/sociopaths) has moral standards, moral values, and a personal value system.

2. As human beings, our moral values are the values most significant to us.

3. We apply our moral standards as the principal guides and evaluators of the worth of what we do, what we have, and what we are as human beings.

4. God is the ultimate source of moral standards and values. The more immediate sources are the instruction, example, and guidance we receive from other people and the processing we do of our own personal experience.

5. Finally, our self-image or sense of self-worth is above all a result of evaluating what we do, have, and are in the light of our moral standards.

High Self-Image

When we look into the mirror of our personal value system and find that we measure up to our standards, ideals, or principles and are progressing toward our goals, we are pleased. We feel good about ourselves, we are satisfied and happy, and we respect and esteem ourselves; our self-evaluation tells us that we are worthwhile persons. This is what it means to have a high self-image. With it comes a feeling of personal security or ego strength, a feeling of inner "togetherness," a sense of self-identity, and an awareness of wholeness or personal integrity.

Low Self-Image

Below the healthy high self-image, there are many degrees of "in-between." At the bottom is the pathologically low self-image. It develops when we fail notably to measure up to our personal value standards. This happens when our here-and-now condition is not in conformity with the norms we have adopted for self-measurement. Our self-evaluation reveals to us the great distance between what we actually do and have and are and the ideals we have set up for ourselves, the goals we aspire to achieve. Then we see ourselves as of little or no value, as worthless. We have little self-respect, little self-esteem, and little self-appreciation. We are displeased with ourselves, unhappy, and dissatisfied. We reject ourselves as bad and, ultimately, we come to regard ourselves as "no damn good."

Values/Behavior Related to Self-Image

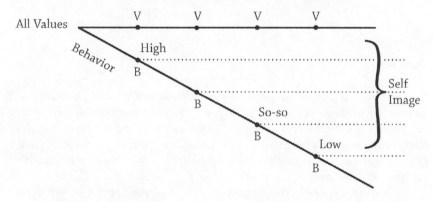

Moral values are of special significance to our self-image because our state of conscience revolves around them. "Conscience" comes from two Latin words, *con* (with) + *scientia* (knowledge). Conscience is the knowledge I have along with my actions or behavior that what I am doing is right or wrong. It is my conscious awareness — or the concurrent knowledge I have, as I am acting — that this action is or is not in accord with my personal moral values. This *knowledge* is the *cognitive* aspect of conscience; *innocence* or *guilt* is the *affective*, feeling, or emotional aspect of conscience.

141

When our conduct is in accord with our moral value standards, our conscience is at ease. We accept ourselves and we are comfortable within ourselves. We are serene, at peace. When, on the contrary, our conduct is not in accord with our moral value standards, our conscience bothers us. We feel guilty; we have a "guilty conscience." Then we disapprove of ourselves, we are unhappy, displeased with ourselves, and uncomfortable within ourselves. We reject ourselves and regard ourselves as worthless. This is low self-image in its most distressing aspect; it is "no damn good" in the ultimate sense.

Values/Behavior Conflict and Low Self-Image

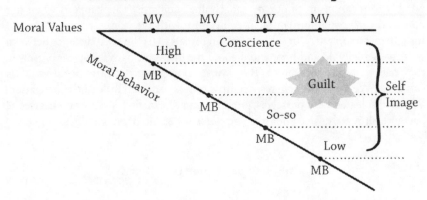

Definition

We define **chemically dependent low self-image** as the state or condition of habitually regarding oneself as of little value or personal worth and of having little self-respect or self-esteem as a direct result of one's relationship to mood-altering chemicals. It is a weak ego state, a condition of low ego strength resulting from a person's sick love relationship to drugs and from the values/behavior conflicts this relationship produces.

Whatever a person's self-image may be in predependency, it is certain that those who become pathologically related to mood-altering chemicals will behave in ways that are opposed to their value system. They will violate their moral value standards and incur guilt feelings. They will lose self-respect, self-esteem, and ego strength and will develop a pathologically low self-image.

Like the other pathological elements in this illness, chemically dependent low self-image can be traced through four successive stages. And like the other elements, it is reversible when ingestion of mood-altering chemicals is terminated and proper therapy is obtained.

PROCESS OF DEVELOPMENT

THE PLEASURE STAGE

People who abuse mood-altering chemicals will on some occasions behave unexpectedly in a manner that they themselves dislike. Others may or may not disapprove, but dependents disapprove of themselves. Their conduct in these instances is not entirely in accord with their personal value systems. They may feel embarrassed or ashamed when this happens, and they will probably resolve that it will not happen again. And it may not. They may succeed thereafter in controlling their drug ingestion in a way that is no longer abusive and that assures no repetition of unwanted behaviors.

But if they continue to consume drugs regularly and continue to ingest them somewhat excessively, thus moving toward chemical dependency, they will go on to behave on some occasions in a manner that is seriously discordant with their value systems. As a result, they experience guilt, lose some measure of self-respect, diminish in their own esteem, and have a somewhat lower image of themselves.

They may firmly resolve to control their drug ingestion and their conduct in the future so as to assure no repetitions. But when the strong inclination to take drugs impels them to abuse them again and to repeat their disapproved behaviors, their self-image continues to descend. This is characteristic of pleasure stage dependency. The quest of pleasurable rewards repeatedly produces drug-induced conduct opposed to personal values. And just as drug abuse continues throughout pleasure stage dependency, so also do unwelcome behavioral consequences.

As we have seen, drug-centered mental preoccupation and emotional urgency have already set in. Now more and more of the preoccupation is concerned with the unwelcome consequences of drug abuse and the resulting feelings of guilt. More and more of the urgency, too, is a drive for relief of guilt. As dependency moves toward chronicity, much of the urgency to abuse drugs grows out of a need for relief from guilt feelings, remorse, shame, and discouragement over one's "moral weakness."

THE RELIEF STAGE

In the relief stage, the dependent's life style becomes more rigidly drug-centered and obsession and compulsion take over, resulting in greater irresponsibility and destructive behavior. Despite good intentions and resolutions, more people are hurt and more damage is done. Chronic guilt feelings accumulate, along with the uneasy fears that accompany them. This graduates into diffused anxiety and then into massive, chronic, free-floating anxiety and a chronic state of depression. Added to the dependent's known behaviors are others they cannot recall because of blackouts and other memory distortions. These create additional moral anxieties. Many shameful memory materials are repressed, stuffed down into the

143

subconscious, where they add to the dependent's free-floating fears and eventually surface in the form of depression and additional compulsive behavior.

When dependents sees themselves misbehaving repeatedly against their own wishes, contrary to their own intentions, and in spite of their own sincere resolutions, they cannot avoid the suspicion that there must be something wrong with them. But because they do not associate this destructive conduct and the consequent guilt feelings with their relationship to drugs or with their drug abuse, they have no clue as to what is really wrong. Nevertheless, they are acutely conscious that they do not like themselves for what they are doing. Their self-respect and self-esteem move steadily downward. Their ego strength wanes. They regard themselves as bad people. They begin to hate and despise themselves, to accuse and condemn themselves, and to reproach themselves unmercifully. Pressure for relief from chronic guilt, anxiety, and depression, and from their self-inflicted reproaches feeds their obsession and compulsion. More and more, they are driven to abuse drugs to relieve this moral misery.

THE MAINTENANCE STAGE

In the maintenance stage of dependency, the self-image deteriorates to a level where dependents habitually regard themselves as worthless, in their own being and in relation to others. In this stage, however, a seeming improvement sometimes occurs, and very occasionally a "spontaneous" recovery is initiated. This is because serious secondary complications of chemical dependency frequently appear in the maintenance stage. Physical damage, financial and employment problems, the obvious deterioration of marriage and family relations, and perhaps involvement with the law present crises that may be sufficient to get the attention of dependents. These crises enable them to become at least partially and momentarily aware that they are in trouble. They may even be shocked into recognition of what their problem actually is. This may, in exceptional cases, generate the motivation necessary to terminate ingestion and enter a recovery program.

As a rule, however, the improvement is only temporary and more apparent than real. Under the influence of delusion, dependents continue to make sporadic, desperate efforts to "get it together" and to "shape up" by sheer exercises of "will power." But invariably they discover that they must continue or quickly resume their drug abuse in order to maintain the "normalcy" of their acutely dependent state. With the failure of these efforts, their self-esteem drops lower. With sheer survival as their motive now, and with all efforts directed to this, they lose both the motivation and the energy to try to repair their shattered self-images. From this condition, they pass on into escape stage dependency.

THE ESCAPE STAGE

In the light of our understanding of chemically dependent low self-image, it becomes easier to see why escape to oblivion leading to self-destruction can be viewed as a "rewarding experience." Moral values, as we have seen, are our most significant values because they are most properly human and personal. Hence, our deepest sense and conviction of personal worth depend directly on achievement of these values.

When we fail to live up to our moral values, we lose personal integrity — we even lose our grip on our personal identity. We do not know who we are, "where we're at," or "where we're coming from." We are nothing, nobody, so our life no longer has meaning or value. It is a sad, pathetic, tragic state. And the tragedy is made sadder and more pathetic because it is an innocent victim who suffers and dies. Dependents are largely unaware of the dominative, driving force of obsession and compulsion, and so they assume moral responsibility for all the destructive behavior coming out of their drug relationships. In doing so, they take on an enormous burden of guilt, a burden impossible to describe and beyond their endurance to bear. Their self-destructive rush to death is in major part a desperate drive to escape this crushing burden of guilt.

RESULTING CONDITIONS

While chemical dependency is not essentially a moral problem, the fact that it involves the whole person means that morality is necessarily an important aspect of it. Moral values, as we noted at the outset of this chapter, are the values most proper to us as free, intelligent human beings. Hence, the conflict between personal moral values and personal conduct is central in the pathology of this illness and is therefore a principal key to its recognition, understanding, and treatment. It gives rise to bitter internal warfare that shows itself in several ways.

On one battlefront, dependents find themselves facing two alternatives, each of which seems to threaten devastation: either they are *in control* and are acting deliberately and freely, or they are *not in control* and are acting compulsively.

If they are in control, as they believe they are, they are responsible and accountable. They must therefore judge themselves immoral in much of their behavior and criminal in some of it. Driving while intoxicated, for example, then becomes murderous, like spraying bullets into a crowd. In thus assuming they are in control, they take on the full burden of guilt for their deliberate misbehavior. At the same time, they leave unexplained the perplexing problem of how it is they keep on "freely" doing things they disapprove of, desire not to do, and deliberately *choose* not to do.

The other alternative has its own forbidding implications. If they are not in control, but are acting compulsively, they must admit that they are chemically dependent. They must accept their powerlessness over chemicals and the resulting unmanageability of large areas of their lives. Worst of all, they must face up to the necessity of terminating drug ingestion and breaking off their committed pathological love relationship to chemicals. They find this prospect more frightening and depressing, as a rule, than suffering guilt and moral anxiety and paying the penalties for destructive, antisocial, and illegal behaviors.

From time to time, dependents do, in fact, get glimpses of awareness that the real cause of their condition is their drug relationship. But the awareness is so threatening that their defense system automatically goes to work to put it out of sight at once, and dependents are left in their confusion and frustration, torn by inner strife.

Schizoid Symptoms

Another product of this conflict is the self-alienation that characterizes every chemical dependent and presents what appears to mimic schizophrenia. One "part" of me is divided against another "part" of me. On the one side is my personal value system, which I identify with myself. On the other side is my personal behavior, which I also identify with myself. When my values and behavior are in conflict, therefore, it is as if one self is at war against another self. It is the deepest and most damaging personality split that is possible to man. It is man against himself in the deadliest of duels. I am lined up against myself, I disapprove of myself, I condemn myself, I reject myself. And as my self-disapproved behavior multiplies, my self-rejection intensifies.

It is never easy to distinguish one's person from one's behaviors. Hence, when one's conduct is condemned and rejected, either by oneself or others, it is often taken personally, that is, it is interpreted and felt as personal condemnation and rejection. Instead of saying to myself, "*That's* bad," in reference to a bit of my bad *behavior*, I tell myself that "*I'm* bad," and take it in reference to my *person*. Often, too, when others mean to correct me for some particular bad conduct, they say, "*You're* a bad mother or father or daughter or son" instead of saying, "*That's* bad behavior." Understandably, I get the message both from myself and from others that I am no good, that I am a bad person.

My inability to distinguish my personhood and my personal values from my behaviors leads me to a wholesale condemnation of myself. In effect, I write myself off; I wipe myself out. In summary, the conflict and its outcome read like this:

> *I* (my personal conduct) am alienated from *myself* (my personal value system).

This self-alienation is a main contributor to the Jekyll-and-Hyde syndrome that chemical dependents invariably exhibit. It also causes many of the apparently schizoid symptoms that may lead to a misdiagnosis of schizophrenia instead of chemical dependency.

Sociopathic Symptoms

A further result of the dependent's inner warfare is the appearance of sociopathic symptoms. Inner moral conflicts and self-alienation, arising out of a discordance of values and conduct and producing guilt as their symptom, are a universal human experience. They are, in fact, so much a part of our human condition that one who does not have them is considered abnormal because he or she is *amoral*, without morality. For such persons, there is no moral good or bad, right or wrong, because they have no moral values, no norms by which to measure their behavior. The labels put on such persons are "psychopath" and/or "sociopath."

If one's first contact with dependents is when they are already in the mid- to later stages of the illness, a suspicion will very likely arise that they have no moral values. They will seem to be unaware of the devastation they are creating in their own lives and in the lives of others. Their only reply to feedback on the matter may be a wide-eyed, "What's wrong? Where's the problem?" They seem to have no principles, no sense of right and wrong, no capacity to judge between good and bad, appropriate and inappropriate, harmful and helpful conduct, no feelings of remorse. In other words, they *appear* to be psychopaths or sociopaths. But they are not, and the proof of it is their *misery* — the massive moral anxiety and feelings of worthlessness they suffer because their conduct is not in conformity with their personal value systems.

A sociopath has no moral principles and therefore feels no guilt. But dependents *do* feel guilt. They repress it, of course, but this only succeeds in diffusing it. It remains in their subconscious as moral anxiety and surfaces in one form as a general sense of worthlessness: "I'm no damn good." That desperate utterance is a confession of failure to live up to moral values. It is an expression of discouragement over efforts to do so, and a desperate cry for help in discovering why. What they cannot see, because delusion hides it from them, is that an obsessive/compulsive drive toward chemicals has taken over. Therefore, in spite of all their good intentions, sincere desires, and firm resolutions, they are powerless to bring their conduct into conformity with their values.

Memory Impairment

Dependents have trouble both with seeing and with doing something about their drug-related and drug-induced behaviors. Adding to their difficulty is the threefold memory impairment they suffer:

1. *Repression* — The first memory impairment is a result of *repression*. Some of the things dependents do and say, and even think or fantasize, are too horrible, morally speaking, for them to remember and still live with themselves. They would "break up" psychologically if these things were

retained in their conscious mind or recalled to memory. So they *repress* them; they violently thrust them down into the subconscious where they are out of sight. And repression works — almost. It works insofar as it succeeds in putting shameful, unwanted memory materials out of conscious awareness. But in two respects it works against the dependents. First, it puts them out of touch with part of reality, the reality of some of their worst behavior. It is as though such behavior never took place; for them it never existed. And second, as noted above, the repressed materials are diffused in the subconscious, where they create free-floating moral anxiety and are manifested by depression and feelings of worthlessness.

2. *Blackouts* — The second memory impairment is a result of *blackouts* experienced during drug abuse episodes. Here the dependents' memory reception is completely blocked so that what they say and do are not available for future recall. There is no way they can be in touch with their own behavior during a blackout, so there is no way to directly identify that behavior as their own. They must rely on what others say about it later. And, of course, they usually prefer their own opinion to that of others.

3. *Euphoric Memory* — The third memory impairment is *euphoric memory*. This partial blackout that occurs during drug abuse episodes leaves dependents aware of the glowing feelings that were experienced, the "high" or euphoria. But they are not aware of particular details, such as slurred and incoherent speech, staggering, belligerence and buffoonery, loud coarse laughter, and worse. As in the case of other memory impairment, this leaves the dependents unable to recognize the behavior as their own. And so, as in the other cases, they sincerely deny it both to themselves and to others.

With repression, blackout, and euphoric memory at work, it is no wonder that dependents appear at times to be totally lacking in moral awareness and insight. Reality data are unavailable to them. They are simply not aware of some of their worst behavior. They therefore present symptoms that appear to indicate psychopathy or sociopathy, and their illness may be misdiagnosed as such instead of as chemical dependency.

The Moral Degenerate Image

The typical self-image held by dependents and the image commonly projected upon them by others is that of moral degenerates. The basis in reality for this stereotype, of course, is the moral deterioration that accompanies their illness. Both in the minds of dependents and in the minds of others, the moral stigma persists.

Chemical dependency continues to be popularly regarded as a product of moral weakness rather than a result of an obsessive/compulsive drug relationship that is beyond the control of its victims. Several adverse consequences follow from this view:

- First, dependents themselves are deterred from seeking or accepting help. They believe that they *should* be in control and that by trying harder to think straight and use their willpower they can establish control. They postpone seeking help and thereby prolong their agony. In their eyes, to admit helplessness is an admission of moral weakness and to seek help is to expose oneself to the stigma.

- Second, dependents who are in the process of recovery often try to hide the fact from others because they may suffer censure, impaired social status, reduced job opportunities, and other disabilities. This concealment of recovery tends to reinforce the moral degenerate image. It also helps to maintain a low level of public awareness and thus reduces the chances of other dependents for finding the help they need.

- Third, family members and other concerned persons cover up the problem to protect both themselves and dependents from the stigma. In doing so, they become more rigidly locked into their enabler roles, and their self-image, like that of the dependents, continues to sink lower. It is ironic indeed that in protecting themselves from the blow to their self-image that might come from admitting the problem, they maintain themselves in the very situation that will most certainly destroy their self-image.

Damaging Moralistic Attitudes

The moral degenerate image is manifested in less direct ways, too. Harsh judgments, condemnations, and exhortations reveal moralistic attitudes that imply, if they do not openly express, the belief that dependents are degenerates.

149

One condemns only when moral responsibility is present. One exhorts only when freedom to respond is presupposed. The implication, therefore, is that the moral deterioration of dependents is a sign and product of their weakness or deliberate malice and not a result of compulsion, and that what is needed for recovery is clearer thinking about right and wrong and stronger willpower to do what is right.

Moralistic attitudes are sometimes expressed more subtly in advice and exhortations. These attitudes even appear in programs aimed at getting dependents to seek alternative highs, to clarify their values, to think positively, and to raise their self-image by concentrating on their good qualities and looking away from their negative aspects. Implied in these and similar approaches is the naive assumption that dependents are not impaired by their drug relationship, and that they are *capable* of reasonable decisions and free choices, of values clarification, and of thinking positively.

Also implied in these approaches are a number of moral judgments. For example, other alternatives are good and right; the drug alternative is bad and wrong. Positive thinking and positive qualities are good and right; negative thinking and negative attitudes are bad and wrong. And dependents get the moral message loud and clear: chemical dependency is morally evil and wrong — and therefore so are you. Whether they come from within dependents themselves or from others, and however subtly they may be disguised, moralistic attitudes toward chemical dependency always carry the implied judgment that chemical dependents are moral degenerates.

SYMPTOMS OF LOW SELF-IMAGE

The pathological drug relationship causes dependents to behave in ways they themselves disapprove of. They do and say things that do not meet their self-expectations, but instead are contrary to their own values, to their personal value systems, and especially to their moral principles or standards. As a direct result, dependents suffer guilt and moral anxiety, with a corresponding loss of self-esteem or self-respect, a lessening of personal integrity, and diminishing ego strength. The result is a chemically dependent low self-image or self-concept.

This pathologically low self-image is manifested by general symptoms of (1) lowered moral standards and conduct; (2) defense of irresponsible and/or immoral behavior; (3) feelings of guilt and moral anxiety; and (4) loss of self-esteem and/or self-respect.

General Symptom: Lowered Moral Standards and Actual Immoral Conduct

Dependents exhibit an apparent loss of moral values by the way they come to think about morality, by their attitudes toward moral behavior, and by their actual immoral behavior. Note that this is an *apparent* loss of moral values. In one sense, it is "apparent" because the evidence or data for it appears in the lives of dependents. But in another and deeper sense, it is "apparent" because it is not really, but only seems to be, a loss of values. Dependents do not actually lose their values, but under the influence of their drug relationship they can no longer *live up* to their values. The proof of this is the guilt and remorse they feel as they suffer chemically dependent moral deterioration.

Particular Symptoms of Lowered Moral Standards and Actual Immoral Conduct

1. *Dishonesty:* lies, alibis, excuses, sneaking drugs, stealing, etc.

2. *Destructive, antisocial behavior:* hurting, punishing, disappointing, and disregarding the feelings of others; creating disturbances; getting drunk or stoned; quarrelling and fighting; inflicting mental, emotional, physical, sexual violence on others.

3. *Serious injustices:* driving while intoxicated; neglecting and/ or abandoning family and other responsibilities; drinking or taking other drugs on the job; marital infidelity; violating personal and property rights.

General Symptom: Defense of Irresponsible Behavior

Dependents not only suffer evident deterioration of their values and conduct, they defend their irresponsible, unjust, and immoral behavior. This defensiveness is itself both a symptom and an integral direct general part of the pathology of chemically dependent low self-image.

Particular Symptoms of Defense of Irresponsible Behavior

Particular symptoms of this defensiveness appear in the form of the particular defenses used. The following are some of the more obvious:

1. *Denial* of such behavior or of the immorality of it.

2. *Repressing* it.

3. *Minimizing* it.

4.   *Rationalizing* it.

5.   *Projecting the blame* for it (blaming it on others).

6.   *Excusing* it.

General Symptom: Guilt and Moral Anxiety

Dependents feel guilty when their drug-induced and/or drug-related behaviors are in conflict with their values. Their guilt, when repressed or otherwise defended, is not absolved but is driven into their subconscious, where it becomes diffused as generalized, nonspecific moral anxiety. Both the guilt and the anxiety give rise to particular symptoms that reveal low ego strength and a negative, depressed self-image.

Particular Symptoms of Guilt and Moral Anxiety

1.   *Expressions of sorrow*, regret, remorse, contrition, sometimes even to tears, over drug-induced and drug-related behavior.

2.   *Expressions of shame* and embarrassment over drug-induced and drug-related behavior.

3.   *Apologies and sincere promises of amendment*: promises not to do it again, to make up for it, to handle it better in the future, to change for the better, to make amends.

4.   *Manipulation for forgiveness* by presenting "reasons" for mis-behaviors and pleading with and pressuring loved ones and associates for understanding, sympathy, and tenderness and by reminding them that they are not perfect, that "no one is perfect," etc.

5.   *Overcompensation to relieve guilt feelings*: splurges, trying harder to be perfect, being overly affectionate and overly indulgent, playing the "good guy" and the "good gal."

6.   *Free floating, wispy fears growing to massive moral anxiety.*

7.   *Depression* and expressions of discouragement, failure feelings, and despair.

8. *Suicidal tendencies*: direct expressions of suicidal thoughts and feelings, and actions that involve high risk of fatality, such as driving recklessly, engaging in physical violence, defiantly taking chances with one's life.

General Symptom: Low Self-Esteem or Self-Respect

A chemically dependent low self-image is revealed by the attitude of disesteem and disrespect dependents show for themselves. This general symptom is often observed and referred to as a feeling or a sense of low self-worth.

Particular Symptoms of Low Self-Esteem or Self-Respect

1. *Rejection of sincere compliments.* Dependents cannot comfortably accept praise, recognition, and acclaim because they do not believe they are worthy of it. It contradicts their own image of themselves.

2. *Servility or subservience*, a "doormat complex" that allows others to "walk all over" them because their self-regard is so low they feel that they deserve to be loathed, despised, and punished.

3. *Self-downgrading* or "putting oneself down." Self-reproaches, saying uncomplimentary things about oneself, pointing out and emphasizing one's defects all manifest one's low self-esteem.

4. *Feelings and convictions of inadequacy.* Low ego strength impels a dependent to experience deep self-doubt and self-mistrust and to feel incapable of taking on responsibilities or of fulfilling responsibilities already assumed.

5. *Grandiosity.* Putting up a "big ego" front as a cover-up and a form of overcompensation for low self-esteem; putting others down to build oneself up.

6. *Attempted suicide.* Attempts at self-destruction are the ultimate expressions of self-hatred, self-punishment, and self-rejection.

LOW SELF-IMAGE
SUMMARY OF ESSENTIAL SYMPTOMS

General Symptom: Lowered Moral Standards and Actual Immoral Conduct

Particular Symptoms:

1. Dishonesty: lies, alibis, excuses, sneaking drugs, stealing, etc.
2. Destructive, antisocial behavior: hurting others, punishing or disappointing them, getting drunk or stoned.
3. Serious injustices: driving while intoxicated, neglecting family, job and/or other responsibilities.

General Symptom: Defense of Irresponsible Behavior

Particular Symptoms:

1. Denial of it.
2. Repressing it.
3. Minimizing it.
4. Rationalizing it.
5. Projecting, shifting the blame for it.
6. Excusing it.
7. Any other defenses used to cover up irresponsible behavior and evade responsibility for it.

General Symptom: Guilt and Moral Anxiety

Particular Symptoms:

1. Expressions of sorrow, regret, remorse, contrition.
2. Expressions of shame and embarrassment.
3. Apologies and sincere promises of amendment.
4. Manipulation for forgiveness.
5. Overcompensation to relieve guilt feelings.
6. Free-floating fears, growing to massive moral anxiety.
7. Depression and expressions of discouragement, self-doubt, despair.
8. Suicidal tendencies and/or attempts.

General Symptom: Low Self-Esteem/Self-Respect

Particular Symptoms:

1. Rejection of sincere compliments.
2. Servility, subservience.
3. Self-downgrading.
4. Expressions of feelings and convictions of inadequacy.
5. Grandiosity.
6. Suicidal tendencies and/or attempts.

CHAPTER ELEVEN

Chemically Dependent
Rigid Negative Attitudes

To get a gut feeling for what negative attitudes are, take a look at your most meaningful person-to-person relationship: to your spouse, to a child, to a parent, brother or sister, to your boyfriend or girlfriend, to a companion or associate. Then do the same with your most treasured possession: your home, your job, your life savings, your favorite recreation, your TV, your car, your favorite pet.

Think about each of these along the following lines:

- In your person-to-person fantasy, imagine another person, a third party, threatening to interfere with and break up that relationship, to take your beloved away from you, to prevent you from ever seeing or even talking to your loved one again. What negative feelings do you get as you picture this intruder depriving you of your loved one forever? Perhaps you have actually lived through such an experience. If so, do a mental replay and try to get in touch with your negative feelings as you do so.

- Next, picture one person, or two or three people (a conspiracy!), determined to take away the thing you treasure most. They may steal it by fraud or armed robbery. They may destroy it so you can never use it again. They may threaten you with violence to scare you into handing it over. In one way or another, they are out to get your most precious possession away from you. What negative feelings do you experience as you watch these conspirators at work? Perhaps you have lived through this experience, too. If so, replay it again mentally and try to get in touch with your negative feelings as you watch it happen again.

You will likely find that your reactions were complex, that is, made up of several aspects or elements. You not only had negative feelings against those who threatened you, but you also had negative thoughts, and you probably were strongly inclined toward negative actions. Not just one, but several of your psychic or life powers were involved. You therefore experienced negative attitudes.

Negative Attitudes

Attitudes are complex. They are composed of a *knowledge element* (ideas, judgments, opinions, mental states, memories, fantasies, etc.), a *feeling or emotional element* (love, hate, anger, sorrow, etc.), and a *behavioral element* (certain kinds of conduct toward people, groups, events, and issues).

Negative attitudes are complex avoidance reactions that are composed of the following elements:

- *Negative knowledge*: negative ideas, negative mental outlook, negative judgments, negative opinions and convictions, etc.

- *Negative feelings* or *emotional reactions*: hatred, aversion, resentment and hostility, fear, anxiety, depression, sadness, self-pity, etc.

- *Negative behavior*: belligerence, defiance, aggression, attack, violence, etc.

These attitudes are called "negative" because they tend to *negate*, that is, to deny, to nullify, to render ineffective, even to destroy or to wipe out whatever and whoever threatens harm to our love relationships or to our persons. But note well, "negative" does not mean "bad," and negative attitudes are not necessarily bad attitudes, despite the fact that we commonly put "negative" and "bad" together. We put them together because we do not understand that love always has an inseparable partner: hate.

Love and Hate

If a dog is busy chewing on the meat it loves, it hates interference, and it negates any attempt to separate it from its beloved piece of meat. That is perfectly natural. So it is really good, not bad. If a little girl is busy playing with a toy she loves, she puts up a squawk if you take it away. She hates the interference, so she cries out her negation. She says, "Don't!" And that is negation.

In your fantasies about your person-to-person and person-to-thing relationships, your negative attitudes against would-be intruders were no doubt the best and most appropriate attitudes you could have had. The intruders were your enemies in the proper sense of that term. They were opposed to your own just interests and sought to injure you by interfering with and destroying your most valued personal relationships. Your negative attitudes against those enemies, triggered by their unjust intrusion, prepared you to negate them — that is, to resist their assaults, to fight them off, to repel them, and thus to protect your rights in those relationships. In fact, anger, the "emergency" emotion, kicks in, providing a shot of adrenaline, moving you forward into the fray. And that is good, not bad.

Negative attitudes of this kind are perfectly natural to us; without them we could not survive. We would be like defenseless doormats at the mercy of all enemies and of every evil. Natural, normal negative attitudes are products of reasonable hate; and hate, as we have noted, is an inseparable partner of love.

Love is the attraction we feel toward some good, toward a person or thing that impresses us as good for us or beneficial to us in some way. Love stirs desire and kindles expectation, and it motivates us to pursue our beloved. I seek to possess the good I love so I can enjoy the rewards of union. The deeper my love, the more intense my desire and the more ardent my pursuit.

Hate is essentially my dislike of anyone or anything that is opposed to my love. Hate is a feeling of revulsion against such threatened harm. It stirs aversion and prepares me to flee or to fight and thus to avoid or to overcome what stands in the way of or threatens my love. The deeper my love, the stronger my hate, and the swifter my flight or the harder my fight. If I cannot avoid or overcome the obstacles — and consequently lose or cannot possess my beloved — I am disappointed, discouraged, depressed, despairing, and sad.

Natural Negative Feelings

Now to bring this point home, go back over that last paragraph and count the negative feelings mentioned. Add fear and anger and loneliness, and you have almost all of the basic normal, natural negative emotions. Add the thoughts and behaviors that go with these emotions, and you have the basic normal, natural negative attitudes. All of them are good, in and of themselves. They are necessary for our preservation, health, and well-being. But like any other good thing (including love), they can get out of hand and make us sick.

Negative attitudes toward racial or ethnic groups would be good examples. We refer to them as racial or ethnic "bias." They include ideas, opinions, and prejudices (pre-judgments) directed against such groups; feelings of hatred, fear, and resentment against them; and overt harmful actions leveled against them. Such attitudes are not reasonable; they are irrational. They are not empathetic or even sympathetic; they are impulsive, automatic reactions. They are unjust and inappropriate, cruel and destructive, and therefore pathological. And if they become fixed, rigid, inflexible postures or positions, we call them *rigid* negative attitudes.

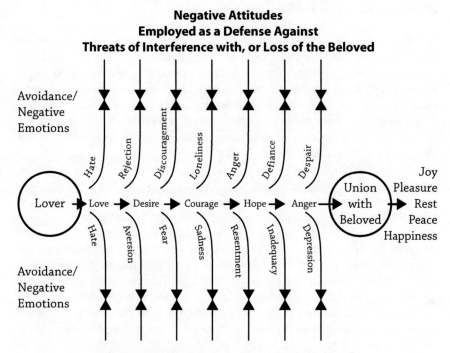

**Negative Attitudes
Employed as a Defense Against
Threats of Interference with, or Loss of the Beloved**

Threats of Interference of Loss of the Beloved

Rigid Negative Attitudes

Rigid negative attitudes are stances or attitudinal postures so deeply and firmly set that they affect the whole personality of the one who has them. They are so much a part of the person that they appear to be ingrained personal qualities or characteristics. Hence, we refer to someone as an "angry person" or a "sad person," for example, because the typical or characteristic attitudes displayed by the person are anger or sadness.

Some attitudes are superficial and temporary. They are formed rather quickly toward a person, a group, or perhaps a political or civic issue. They remain for a while but are soon discarded. Other attitudes, however, continue on, become habitual, and eventually become obsessional and compulsive. These are the ones of which we speak. People with such attitudes become inflexible, intolerant, closed-minded, and hardheaded. Their attitudes take on the appearance of character traits or personal qualities. Through "replays" of negative ideas and feelings and through frequently acting out negative behaviors, these rigid negative attitudes are built up so that eventually they become *rigidly negative persons*.

Attitudinal Reactions and Situational Responses

Rigid attitudinal posture reactions are quite different from appropriate situational responses. For example, if someone strikes me or insults me, I will respond with anger; I resent physical violence or insults to my person. An anger response is quite appropriate in this situation. However, I may be a person who carries anger deeply within me at all times, regardless of any particular situation. To be constantly angry inside is a rigid negative *attitudinal posture*; I constantly cultivate an "angry disposition." Anger, in this case, presents the appearance of a personal trait or characteristic.

An angry attitude is only one example. I may be attitudinally a guilty person, a fearful person, an insecure person, a self-pitying person, an inadequate person, a prejudiced, moralistic, arrogant, or manipulative person. Chemically dependent persons typically develop all these and other rigid negative attitudes.

Negative attitudinal postures, of course, are no monopoly of chemical dependents. Many persons who never use drugs are extremely and pathologically negative. But the negativism of which we speak is more than this, and it is specifically different. It is a particular element in the pathology of chemical dependency, and it grows directly out of the dependent's pathological relationship to drugs.

If negative attitudes already exist in a person, then chemically dependent negativism is added to and superimposed upon preexisting negative attitudes. If an individual is not already a negative person, then negativism is generated, *de novo*, out of the drug relationship. In either case, it is specific to this illness and is an integral element in its pathology.

A major destructive aspect of the illness is the parallel development of rigid negative attitudes in the family members and close associates of dependents.

Definition

With this as a background, we define **chemically dependent rigid negative attitudes** as firmly set negative positions or attitudinal postures caused by a person's relationship to mood-altering chemicals and directed against self, against other people, against God, and against anything that threatens the person's committed love relationship to mood-altering chemicals.

PROCESS OF DEVELOPMENT

THE PLEASURE STAGE

In the pleasure stage, dependents progressively reorient their lives around drugs and drug abuse in the process of developing a drug-centered life style. In doing so, they pressure and manipulate family members and associates, forcing them to alter their life styles to accommodate the dependent's. This generates negative reactions from others, who are disturbed, inconvenienced, and often seriously harmed in the process. (See the end of Chapter Nine for an extensive list of possible negative feelings. Any of these negative feelings may be or may become fixed, rigid, pathological attitudinal postures instead of situational responses.)

Dependents, in turn, react negatively because they dislike and resent such protests. They pass negative judgments upon the protesters and form negative opinions about them: they are not understanding, they are intolerant, they are not accepting of the dependents. So dependents behave arrogantly, aggressively, and selfishly toward others. They do this partly to feel justified within themselves and thus strengthen their drug relationship and partly to ward off possible interference with their drug involvement.

As dependency deepens and drug abuse patterns grow more rigid, dependents' demands on others to readjust become more and more unreasonable, and desocialized and antisocial behaviors multiply. The reactions of others become progressively more negative, and dependents react in kind and with increased aggression.

If you keep in mind the dynamics of the love-hate partnership, you will find the progression of chemically dependent rigid negative attitudes fairly easy to understand. A sick, compulsive love of drugs is what drives dependents on, and a sick, compulsive hatred negates all opposition to their sick drug relationship. But the negative attitudes developed as a result of desocialized and antisocial behaviors are only one of many elements in the negativism of dependents. The growing conflict between personal value systems and self-disapproved conduct produces in the dependents additional negative attitudes directed against themselves. As we noted previously, they dislike themselves, feel guilty and ashamed about their conduct, and reproach, pity, and reject themselves as bad. Progressively, they abuse drugs in quest of relief from the increasing misery of their negativism.

THE RELIEF STAGE

In this stage of dependency, negative attitudes are chronic; dependents are now rigidly negative persons. Because they are driven by compulsion, they are unable to abandon or to significantly alter their drug-dependent life styles despite painful remorse and sincere good intentions to do so. They are constantly disappointed with themselves and discouraged by their repeated failure to correct their behaviors or to alter the course of their lives. Their fear of themselves deepens, and they acquire a deep conviction that there is something very bad about them, that they are going crazy, and/or that they are totally and terribly evil.

Negative, destructive, antisocial behaviors multiply. Drug abuse in this stage intensifies in proportion to the dependents' need for relief from the morass of their negative life style. In this stage, too, drug abuse itself is often directed against those who attempt or threaten to interfere with the drug relationship. "If you don't stop hounding me, I'll get drunk," would aptly express the spirit of this defensively aggressive drug abuse. Predominantly, now, drugs are abused by dependents for relief from their own negative attitudes and from the negative reactions of others directed against them.

THE MAINTENANCE STAGE

In the maintenance stage, negativism is complete. Intensely negative feelings of self-hatred and self-rejection become even stronger, and the dependent projects these feelings onto others. "Desperation" drug use is now the center of life, and eventually drugs themselves come to be regarded negatively. They no longer bring pleasure or pleasant moods. They no longer bring much, if any, relief. And they are decreasingly effective in maintaining the dependent in a semblance of "normalcy." The dependent hates them for their failure to support him and for the power they hold over him. He hates them because they often inspire in him a terror of withdrawal. He fears the suffering that may follow if he ceases to use them, yet he continues to use them as if life depended on them — and at this point, in a tragic sense, it does.

THE ESCAPE STAGE

Escape stage dependency brings terminal negativism: a total, rigidly fixed, universal negativism toward self, toward other people, toward the universe, and toward God. At the heart of this is the self-alienation and self-rejection we spoke of in Chapter Ten. In despair, the dependent typically negates himself by removing himself from the scene through intoxication and through the ultimate self-negation, suicide.

RESULTING CONDITIONS

The ultimate result of chemically dependent rigid negative attitudes is an inflexibly negative person, one who literally lives in a lonely world of his own, full of misery and gloom. A dependent's whole personality and all interpersonal relationships are negative. Even when he migrates to lower levels of companionship or associates with others in a drug culture in order to find support for his life style, he is so completely locked into himself by his negativism that he is unable to relate to others. He finds, too, that fear, suspicion, mistrust, and violence are with him, inside and out, wherever he goes. He finds his drug culture companions in the same condition. "The street," in a drug subculture, is literally a hell of paranoia, of selfishness, and of negativism. And although not all dependents end up on the street literally, those who reach the escape stage of their illness are locked into the negativism of their own personal "street."

Desocialization

Negativism toward others, along with the breakdown in interpersonal relations that this entails, is an integral element in chemical dependency. Because the rewarding experience that is the desired goal of drug ingestion is highly *subjective*, by its very nature it is egocentric, self-centered. With repeated drug experiences, drug abusers become more *self*-centered, involuted, and desocialized, growing progressively more negative toward others. This is a principal reason why drug-centered communes fail. Community living requires of its members a relatively high aptitude for interrelating empathetically with other people. Regular drug abuse, with its desocializing subjectivism, makes it impossible for drug dependents to relate to one another and thus precludes the possibility of harmonious community life.

Depersonalization

Negativism not only desocializes dependents but also depersonalizes them. Their mental powers are filled with and dominated by obsessive negative ideas, opinions, judgments, fantasies, and memories about themselves and others. Their emotional powers are full of compulsive negative feelings toward themselves and others: hatred, guilt, remorse, anger, resentment, hostility, self-pity, despair, frustration, futility, and rejection. Their negative behaviors are seriously destructive of themselves and of others. The result is a disorganized personality and an ongoing mood of "smiling depression."

Blocks to Recognition

From this description of the negativism of dependents, it may be concluded that their rigid negative attitudes are so unbearable and so obvious that they are easily recognized by others. For a number of reasons, this is seldom the case. Frequently, for example, a dependent is "such a wonderful person, but . . . " Or, "She has such an attractive personality, except . . . " Or, "He's a great guy when he's not . . ."

The fact that there is often a beautiful side to a dependent's character keeps alive in concerned persons the hope that the unbeautiful side will somehow miraculously disappear. This locks concerned persons more firmly into their enabler role. The manipulative skill of dependents serves to keep this hope alive and thus to maintain protective cover for their drug relationship as well as for the negative attitudes it causes. Calm reassurances backed up by sincere displays of concern, affection, thoughtfulness, and generosity buy time for dependents to continue their sick drug relationship without serious or persevering interference.

As a rule, the complex pattern of chemical dependency — with its mood-swings, personality changes, Jekyll-and-Hyde syndrome, and drug-centered life style — develops very gradually. The pace is usually so slow that concerned persons recognize neither the presence nor the progress of the illness until it has advanced at least into the relief stage. The negative attitudes that are part of the pathology also develop slowly. At any given point throughout pleasure stage dependency, they are not so much different from "normal" negative attitudes. Hence, they are not seen as related to or caused by drug abuse or the drug relationship.

Also blocking recognition is the fact that dependents' defenses are constantly at work to conceal from themselves and others the negative side of their characters. It is the very nature of defenses to conceal the negative feelings, positions, behaviors, etc., that we don't like and are afraid to deal with. The defense system caused by chemical dependency is highly effective in concealing the negativism of dependents.

Concern vs. Concealment

When the pattern of chemical dependency is finally detected and a "no-nonsense" attitude is adopted by concerned persons, the manipulative skills of dependents are only challenged, not defeated. The "unbeautiful" negative side of their personalities emerges more prominently in the form of destructive, defensive aggression. Intimidation by means of threats, angry attacks, sullen moods, and withdrawal into silence are some of the more common defenses employed to drive away such threats of interference, but all of the defenses are employed. And if there is any timidity or hesitance shown by concerned persons in their "no-nonsense" position, they will be forced to back off and to continue to fulfill their enabler role.

Even at a firm "no-nonsense" point, however, the extent and intensity of the dependent's negative attitudes may still remain concealed. Often it is not until concerned persons attempt actual intervention to terminate the drug ingestion and to secure necessary treatment for dependents that the full destructive force of this negativism comes out. Faced with such immediate threats of interference, dependents discard all subtlety and all pretense at concealment. They vent the full force of their anger and hatred, striking out harshly and even brutally to repel what they consider to be the unjust and unprovoked attacks of invaders.

These negative attitudinal postures, which in and of themselves are so rigidly fixed, become even more securely locked into dependents by the rigid system of defenses surrounding their drug relationship and by the delusion from which they suffer.

SYMPTOMS OF RIGID NEGATIVE ATTITUDES

Their committed relationship to mood-altering chemicals causes dependents to become rigidly negative in their attitudes. They primarily direct this negativism against any threat of interference with their drug relationship or any interruption of their drug ingestion. This negativism is directed against themselves, against other people, against God, against life in general, and ultimately against life itself. These negative attitudes appear as *personal qualities*, rather than as occasional, passing situational occurrences. They are negative attitudinal postures or positions affecting the whole person. They are manifested by a negative mental outlook or mind-set, by a negative emotional state or mood-set, and by negative patterns of overt behavior.

General Symptom: Rigid Negative Mental Outlook

Personal negativism is manifested by the general symptom of a negative frame of mind or mind-set.

Particular Symptoms of a Rigid Negative Mental Outlook

1. *Verbal and/or behavioral expressions* of negative, pessimistic, gloomy thoughts; harsh, critical opinions; severe, unfounded, and unjust judgments, ("highly judgmental"); putting down or running down other people, verbally "laying 'em out"; downgrading good works; rejecting religion and dedicated religious persons as hypocrites; refusing to participate in community activities because they are foolish, ridiculous, or silly; reciting litanies of woe about "the establishment," the "old morality," the "new morality," the generation gap, the older generation, the younger generation, the sad, hopeless state of the world, of business, of politics, of family life, of anything and of everything. The failings criticized in others are for the most part projections onto others of dependents' own negative qualities.

2. A *suspicious attitude.* Dependents doubt and mistrust themselves and live in a constant state of suspicion as to what is really going on within them. They suspect there is something wrong with them; they sometimes think they have deep mental or emotional problems (which, of course, they have), but they cannot put their finger on them or identify their cause. Hence, suspicion is generalized, free-floating, nonspecific. Dependents thus appear to have a "suspicious nature." Motives and intentions — both their own and those of others — are suspected. The ultimate development of this is chemically dependent paranoia. It is not all unfounded suspicion, however. Hiding drug supplies, concealing ingestion, sneaking dosages, etc., all contribute

to creating a self-suspicious frame of mind. The suspicion that others disapprove and want to interfere is well founded. They certainly do, and often the only thing that prevents it is that they don't know how to intervene. Dependents read this as persecution: "Everybody is out to get me," and they become even more furtive in their chemical pursuits. Self-doubt and self-mistrust are well-founded, too, because there is no predicting when the next drug bout will be, how long the trip will last, or what its consequences will be.

3. *Intolerance towards others' opinions.* Those who venture to disagree with dependents' opinions, especially in regard to drug problems and chemical dependency, are severely censured. Any restrictions, public or private, that pose threats to dependents' access to their drug of preference or to the drug life style are rejected as destroying personal freedom and civil liberties.

4. *Stubbornness, hard-headedness, rigidity of mind.* The fixed mind-set presents the appearance of a character disorder, especially when taken together with the repeated self-destructive behaviors that seem to teach dependents no lessons, alter no opinions, and shake no convictions.

General Symptom: A Rigid Negative Emotional State

Negative attitudes are manifested by the way dependents feel about themselves, about other people, about God, and so on. They become rigidly fixed in negative feelings, postures, or positions and are thus locked into a depressed emotional life or mood-set that is a general symptom of chemically dependent rigid, negative attitudes.

Particular Symptoms of a Rigid Negative Emotional State

The following are among the more evident particular symptoms of rigid negative emotional attitudes:

1. The *hatred* posture (opposed to love). Our primary negative feeling or emotion is hatred, which is a feeling of revulsion against something perceived as evil or harmful to us. A dependent appears as a "hateful person" or a "hating person," one who is against many things and many people, postured or positioned in hatred. A "hateful person"

166

fairly breathes revulsion everywhere. The diagnostic clue is the concentrated hatred, especially against any "evil" influence that could harm or destroy the dependent's drug relationship. (To dislike, to loathe, to despise, and to detest are other terms for hatred.)

2.   The *aversion* or *rejection* posture (opposed to desire). Aversion comes after hatred in our negative feeling repertoire. It is a feeling of turning away from or withdrawing from a hated object and from the evil or harm we perceive in or expect from that object. We reject it and move to avoid it or put it away from us. We often refer to an aversion-filled person as a rejecting person or as a withdrawn, distant, aloof, evasive, or escapist person. Aversion, like hatred, is breathed everywhere by such a negative person. The diagnostic clue in this case is especially aversion against or rejection of any "evils" that might harm or destroy the drug relationship.

3.   The *loneliness* posture (opposed to sociability, companionship, friendship, and community involvement). Locked-in loneliness is one of the most painful experiences of dependents and is a direct result of rejection. When I reject things or people, I avoid them; I cut them off from me; I cut myself off from them, and I both invite and manipulate their rejection of me. Hence, I am left all alone, isolated, lonely, desolate.

4.   The *discouragement* posture (opposed to courage). This is a feeling of lack of confidence, weariness, and faint-heartedness in the face of difficulties that seem overwhelming. The problems that multiply in dependents' lives appear to be insurmountable. With neither solutions nor escape possible and with fear a constant companion, the dependents lose courage and with it the strength to pursue the struggle to overcome problems and reorient their lives.

5.   The *desperation* or *despair* posture (opposed to hope). This is a feeling of expectation that a desired good cannot be attained or that a hated evil cannot be avoided or prevented. A dependent is a person in despair, living a life of quiet (and sometimes not-so-quiet) desperation. "Something bad is about to happen" or "always expecting the worst" would describe the locked-in position. This is manifested in many ways: by feelings of failure and futility, hopelessness, dis-

couragement, disappointment, self-doubt and skepticism, cynicism, pessimism, powerlessness, helplessness, dejection, depression, despondency. All of these negative feeling positions are found in dependents, and all of them appear as personal characteristics. Thus, a dependent is a "desperate person," a "cynical person," a "discouraged person," a "pessimistic person," etc. "Smiling depression" is another apt description of the syndrome.

6. The *sadness* posture (opposed to joy). Pain and sorrow are depressed feelings caused by the loss of a good we love or the presence within or around us of an evil we hate and cannot be rid of. They range from mild dissatisfaction and discomfort to intense anguish and include hurt, sorrow, grief, misery, woe, desolation, melancholy, gloom, dejection, wretchedness and a host of others. Above all, a dependent is a *self-pitying person*: the "poor me" attitude is among his outstanding negative characteristics, and to feel sorry for himself is almost a second nature.

7. The *anger* posture. Anger is a feeling of extreme displeasure, antagonism, or hostility caused by the presence of some injury or hurt and inclining us to attack, drive off, and be rid of the evil and to punish the cause of it. Anger, too, has a wide range, from mild irritation to seething rage and fury. Exasperation, annoyance, wrath, ire, and indignation are all expressions of this negative emotion. Dependents are universally noted for their *resentment*, which is a special form of anger involving ill will (sometimes malevolence) and suppressed anger generated by a sense of grievance. It is "smoldering" rage, marking a dependent as a "hostile person." Diagnostic clues are primarily the deep resentments directed against anyone or anything perceived as attacking the drug relationship or interfering with continued ingestion. Like the other negative attitudes, resentment, too, is diffused and ultimately extends to all aspects of life, to all things, and to all persons, including dependents' resentment against themselves.

General Symptom: Rigid Negative Behavior

Dependents exhibit rigidly stereotyped patterns of negative behavior. Their deep-seated negative mental outlook and emotional state give rise to correspondingly negative overt *actions*. Individual actions develop into rigid, repeated *patterns* of inappropriate, destructive, and antisocial behavior that are a general symptom of chemically dependent negativism.

Particular Symptoms of Rigid Negative Behaviors

The following are among the more evident stereotyped behaviors that are particular symptoms of rigid negative behavioral attitudes:

1. The *"Big Ego"* posture (opposed to humility, which is essentially a just estimate of one's own worth). Egocentricity, self-centeredness, or selfishness is in essence a highly negative attitude in that it sets one's *self* up as the center of the universe. Grandiosity is another way of putting it. From this narrow, rigid center, dependents at least implicitly (and usually explicitly) negate the personal worth, the values, the behaviors, the ideas, opinions, and attitudes of others in preference to their own. They especially negate the legion of "enemies" who cannot appreciate the dependents' supreme worth and who question or "attack" their judgment regarding the quality of their personal drug relationship and who question their complete control of their ingestion. Egocentric or self-centered behavior is the diagnostic clue.

2. The *inadequacy* posture (opposed to self-confidence). This is a generalized negative personal state resulting from feelings of hopelessness and helplessness. "I can't . . ." or "Nothing works" or "It's too hard" would be typical expressions of an inadequate person. Such a person is in despair, a defeated, failure-oriented person. The behavior of such a person is dominated by the feeling of total inadequacy when faced with a personal need for positive action or when called upon to act. The response is inadequate behavior.

3. The *frustration* posture (opposed to accomplishment, achievement, success). Dependents have a very low tolerance for frustration, that is, for being "crossed" or for being denied what they want. This is variously referred to as "the little king," "the little queen," "his or her majesty," "the infant," "infantile impatience," etc. Most of dependents' frustrations are self-imposed, results of idealistic, unrealistic overexpectations laid on themselves and on others. They set themselves up for disappointments by these self-defeating demands and often come up with a self-diagnosis of "born

loser." Repeated self-defeating behavior is the chief diagnostic clue.

4. The *belligerent* posture (opposed to peace, harmony, concord). The anger, hostility, and resentment that dependents carry within them boil over frequently into actions without regard to the significance of a provocation or the appropriateness of a situation. Blustering, verbally attacking, threatening physical violence, etc., are expressions of this belligerent attitude. "Always looking for trouble," "trying to pick a fight," or "always storming around" would be typical descriptions of a belligerent person.

5. The *defiant* posture (opposed to acceptance, gentleness). Insecurity and fear prompt dependents to put up a front of angry defiance to challenge the "enemies" of their drug relationship and ingestion. They carry a chip on their shoulder and dare you to knock it off. Defiance is aimed at intimidating and scaring off adversaries by negating their power to interfere. The defiance of dependents, therefore, is both a defense and a symptom of negative behavioral attitudes.

RIGID NEGATIVE ATTITUDES
SUMMARY OF ESSENTIAL SYMPTOMS

General Symptom: Rigid Negative Mental Attitude

Particular Symptoms:

1. Expressions of a negative mind-set, outlook, frame of mind: pessimistic, gloomy thoughts; hypercritical words, actions; downgrading good works.
2. Expressions of a suspicious attitude, doubt and mistrust of self and others.
3. Intolerance towards others' opinions.
4. Stubbornness, hard-headedness, rigidity of mind.

General Symptom: Rigid Negative Emotional Attitude

Particular Symptoms:

1. Hatred posture.
2. Aversion or rejection posture.
3. Loneliness posture.
4. Discouragement posture.
5. Desperation, despair posture.
6. Sadness posture.
7. Anger, resentment, hostility posture.

General Symptom: Rigid, Stereotyped, Negative Behavior Patterns

Particular Symptoms:

1. Inadequacy posture.
2. Frustration posture.
3. "Big Ego" posture.
4. Belligerent posture.
5. Defiant posture.

CHAPTER TWELVE

Chemically Dependent
Rigid Defense System

The greatest of all blocks to recognizing, understanding, and dealing with chemical dependency is the defensiveness that goes along with it. The defenses that are present both in dependents and in their families are among the most prominent elements in the pathology of the illness. Defenses are also actively at work in other concerned and meaningful persons, such as relatives, friends, associates, employers — in fact, in almost everyone who is close to a dependent and who therefore might be helpful in dealing with the problem. Defenses also operate among professionals who are called upon for help or who set themselves up to deal with chemical dependency directly. The defensiveness surrounding drug problems is so common, in fact, that anyone who would hope to even see drug problems has to somehow break through the walls of defenses that surround them.

A Story of Defensiveness

The following actual story both illustrates and emphasizes the point that chemical dependency surrounds itself with defenses.

A 42-year-old man has recently had two heart attacks. After the first, his doctor told him to take life easier and especially to cut down on his drinking, which had been considerable for 25 years. The man did cut down for a couple of months but then went on much as before. He had a more severe heart attack several months after the first. Again his doctor cautioned him to ease up on his drinking. He did for a while but gradually went back at it again full-steam.

His doctor did not tell him to quit completely — that would have seemed too harsh. Instead, the doctor told him that he could only drink a little. Nor did the doctor tell him that he was alcoholic, because the doctor did not know it — the doctor's own defenses prevented him from recognizing it. And the patient could not recognize it either because his defenses were in the way.

An older brother was much concerned about this man. We spoke to him about his brother's drinking and pointed to it as a serious problem. Instant defenses went up: "I know he drinks a lot, but I don't think he is an alcoholic because he doesn't drink that much ... What else does he have to do? He isn't married, he works hard, and he has to have some recreation ... He has been that way all his life; that's just the way he is . . . Everybody he goes around with drinks a lot . . . There really isn't all that much to do in a small town, you know . . ."

Our suggestion that there was a drinking problem triggered a whole series of defenses. In less than five minutes, the alcoholic's concerned brother had denied the problem, minimized it, justified it, rationalized it, projected it, and excused it. The alcoholic, like so many others, will very likely die soon from another heart attack, and he will never have been diagnosed as chemically dependent. At his graveside his brother, and probably his doctor and others, will mourn. "It's a pity he died so young," they'll all agree, but the deadly disease won't be acknowledged as the cause.

Everyone Has Defenses

Everyone has defenses, of course, and a certain amount of defensiveness is natural, normal, and necessary for physical, psychological, and social survival. We naturally protect ourselves against bodily harm and getting physically injured, and we just as naturally protect our psyche from harm. We have a special, built-in warning signal — fear — that sounds an alarm and alerts our defenses whenever danger is near. Psychophysical responses ready us to run away or firm us up to fight. The emotion of courage buoys us for battle as we face the threat of danger. And if the going gets rough, we have a whole arsenal of anger at our disposal to help us with boosts of emergency power. All this is perfectly natural. We need it for survival. And we recognize such defenses as healthy and necessary to our well-being.

Take a common example from everyday experience. Feelings of insecurity and inadequacy give all of us a sense of vulnerability at times. Although there is no actual danger in sight, still we experience defensive responses. If at such times a stranger or a casual acquaintance would ask, "How do you feel?" our answer would probably be, "OK." We would not be open. We would not be straight. We would cover up. We might be more open with a close friend, but with a stranger, no. We protect ourselves by defensively hiding feelings of insecurity, inadequacy, and vulnerability.

We also act defensively to protect others, especially those close to us. If I am hurting inside, for example, I may cover it up so I will not upset or sadden others. If I have a miserable headache, I may say, "It's not so bad." I minimize my misery so as not to burden others.

We also cover up *for* others by protecting them with defenses. If someone wants to know how my delinquent son or daughter (or father or mother) is getting along, I will probably say, "All right," even though it is not so.

Above all, we are protective of our personal relationships because at root they are love relationships with persons and with things. Love, as we have seen, draws us into relationship with our beloved, stirs desire, and moves us to pursuit. Possession of some kind is our goal so that we can enjoy the rewards of union. If anything or anyone threatens such relationships, our hatred is aroused and so is our fear of separation or of loss. All of our defenses are alerted in such cases, and we are readied to avoid or to drive away the threat. We also surround our beloved with defenses so that no harm can come to the object of our affections. Our beloved is in a way another self, so we defend our beloved as we defend ourselves.

Psychological Defenses

Defenses are essentially protective cover-ups. They hide or conceal something by putting it out of sight. Among these are what have come to be called *psychological defenses*. We employ these particular defenses to protect ourselves from shame, guilt, anxiety, and loss of self-esteem. They have to do directly with safeguarding our ego strength by warding off threats of injury to our self-image or self-concept. Obviously, since they center on self-image, they center also on the values/conduct conflict that we explored in Chapter Eleven. Their purpose, however, is not to resolve that conflict but instead to remove it from conscious awareness so it will not trouble us.

As an example, let us assume you value justice, yet on some occasion you steal money. You have violated your values, so your conscience bothers you. You feel guilty — a very uncomfortable feeling. You may, of course, relieve your guilt by admitting your misdeed, returning the money, and thus restoring the balance of justice. Then your conscience will be at ease again.

But you may call up your defense system instead:

- You may *rationalize* your theft: "It wasn't stealing because the money was just sitting there with nobody guarding it."

- You may *minimize* it: "They have plenty of money so they won't miss a little of it."

- You may *justify* it: "They are greedy money-grubbers; they stole it in the first place."

- Or, you may *project* the responsibility and the blame elsewhere: "Society made me do it."

You may, in fact, use all of these defenses and many more to take away the sting of conscience and relieve the discomfort of your guilt. Then, once you have gone down that track, it is easier to go that way again — and again and again, until ultimately you are completely out of touch with the injustice of your stealing. Stealing in effect no longer exists for you; you have wiped out your conscious awareness that what you are doing is stealing. In other words, you have built a wall of defenses that hides from you the reality of your stealing.

You have temporarily eased your conscience and rid yourself of guilt. You have apparently salvaged your self-image and saved your self-esteem. You have preserved, for the moment, your ego strength — but at a price. It has cost you some part of your sanity. Your defenses have put you out of touch with a portion of reality.

Fear of Disapproval

Consider another example that perhaps hits closer to home. We all like to receive approval from others; we want to feel accepted. Hence, we fear the hurt of disapproval and rejection as we fear no other hurts. But all of us have things about us and within us — shameful thoughts and deeds and secret wishes — that would bring us disapproval and rejection if they were known to others. So we hide them; we protect ourselves by our defenses. To avoid the risk of rejection, we conceal our "true selves" and put up phony fronts. Eventually, we ourselves may come to believe our phony fronts. Our self-protective defenses have put us out of touch with some part of self-reality.

Once into this, we may go further. Our fear of disapproval can grow very sick; our craving for acceptance can become pathological. We take up self-protective roles and play sick defensive games to manipulate approval from others. We try to comply with all their wishes and live up to all their expectations. We adopt their values and so get out of touch with our own. We become compulsive people-pleasers and lose our own identity. We become "non-persons," nonentities capable only of reacting with defensive compliance whenever anyone pushes our "rejection button." We are then under the control of others and can be manipulated by them almost entirely at their will.

Definition

We define the **chemically dependent rigid defense system** as a complex pattern of psychological defenses that are compulsively and subconsciously used to conceal from oneself (and from others) one's pathological love relationship to mood-altering chemicals and the destructive effects to oneself and to others caused by that relationship. As with all psychological defenses, these center on the values/conduct conflict, but they also extend to include and to conceal much or all of the destructive behavior that is involved in the person-to-drug relationship.

Note that in the definition we take account of several factors that are essential in this pathological element of the illness. They are as follows:

1. These defenses are *specific* to chemical dependency. They are not merely the natural defenses of normal persons, and they are different from the defenses that may develop around some other problem, such as a sick relationship to money or to food or to another person. They are proper to chemical dependency because the drug relationship, not

175

some other problem, is their cause. Hence, whatever other defenses a person may have before making a commitment to drugs, these defenses build up only after, or along with, the committed drug relationship.

2. These defenses are basically *compulsive*, not freely chosen, and they are for the most part subconscious, not deliberate. This explains why dependents can appear to be so absolutely sincere as they put forth their often outlandish cover-ups, explanations, alibis, even lies. They really believe what their defenses are telling them. They are not aware that they are not seeing or stating the truth. They are sincerely deluded.

3. These defenses form a *system* or a pattern of defenses. Dependents employ a great variety of defenses as they react protectively in different situations, and they go through whole series of defensive reactions as occasions shift and change. By repeatedly going through the same routines, they become "programmed": their defenses are structured to operate automatically in a regular, methodic sequence. Just push the right threat button or pull the proper danger switch and the system goes into operation instantly.

4. This is a *rigid* defense system. It is firmly fixed, inflexible, and compulsive. Dependents cannot be reasoned with about their drug relationship because their compulsive defenses both block and bypass reason. They cannot be persuaded to change because they are not in free control; they are locked into a defensive rut from which they cannot escape by choice. Their lines of defense shore up the rut and shut them in. Their defenses are like walls of steel, baffling barriers protecting against any threat, real or imagined, to the drug relationship and its effects.

5. Finally, our definition identifies the key *focus* of these defenses, namely, the drug relationship and its destructive effects to self and to others. These include all the negative, harmful, inappropriate, shameful, embarrassing, guilt-producing behaviors that are not in accord with one's personal value system or even with basic human values. In other words, these defenses cover up the "negative side" or the negative effects of the drug relationship. And that is a principal reason why dependents always go back to their drug abuse in spite of the misery it causes.

People are often puzzled about why dependents will go on repeatedly hitting themselves over the head with a hammer, so to speak, when it causes so much pain to themselves, to say nothing of the suffering caused to loved ones. It is simply because they are no longer aware of the anguish after the event. The defenses hide from sight the negative miseries, while the positive "good times" are remembered.

Frequently, too, people are amazed at how dependents insist, against overwhelming evidence to the contrary, that they are only using, not abusing, drugs and that their relationship to drugs is quite reasonable and under their complete control. This, too, is a product of defenses. Dependents are aware, of course, that they have a drug relationship, but their defenses hide from them the sickness of it. As they sincerely see it, they use drugs normally, "just like anyone else."

Dynamics of Love

We have frequently referred to the drug relationship as a love relationship. Nowhere, perhaps, is this more clearly seen than in the operation of the chemically dependent defense system. Dependents are the lovers; the drugs are the beloved, the object of their affections. They cherish their beloved chemicals more than anything else they value. They frequently seek union with their beloved to enjoy the rewards of that union.

Their attachment is deep. They have sealed the relationship with their commitment; it is a permanent bond of companionship in oneness of mind, of heart, and of life. And as in any deep love relationship, the possibility of loss or of separation from the beloved brings sadness, and actual loss or separation brings profound grief. So, too, any threats of interference by third parties, any hints of interruption of the drug relationship, any prospects of being deprived of the beloved drugs arouse anger and hostility. Jealousy impels the lover to resist, fight off, and punish anyone who dares to interfere or tamper with this relationship. And no mother bear whose cub is threatened feels the fury or shows the fierceness of chemical dependents threatened with separation from their drugs. They will tolerate no break-up of this love relationship. They will defend it to the death — which in most cases they do.

PROCESS OF DEVELOPMENT

THE PLEASURE STAGE

The very fact that one makes a commitment implies and carries with it a readiness and responsibility to keep it. In order to keep it, one must be prepared to defend it. Hence dependents, from the first moment of their illness, are set up to build a defense system, a system that defends their committed relationship to drugs on two fronts: against themselves and against other people. Against themselves because there will be many times in the course of the illness that they cannot survive psychologically if they allow themselves to become aware of what is going on. Against others because as dependents restructure their lives to accommodate their drug relationship, the lives of others will be invaded and disrupted and those others will react by threatening the drug relationship.

In a drug-oriented society or cultural group, initial defenses are readily collected from the environment: "All my friends do it." "My job requires it." "My doctor prescribes it." "It's a social must for me." "I have to be a good host or hostess or a good entertainer." Thus, one lays down the outer parameters of the defense system by placing the responsibility for drug abuse on society, on friends and companions, on business associates, on professionals, on social custom and good manners. And thus one absolves oneself from personal responsibility.

Lines of Defense

It would not occur to dependents that their drug abuse is a product of their own sick relationship to chemicals or that they are already suffering from an illness that will carry them inexorably to insanity and death. Placing on others the responsibility for one's own actions is the defense of **projection** -— "throwing it out" anywhere, onto anyone, to avoid accepting the action as one's own. Although at first projection may take a half-kidding, half-serious form, it will become a deadly serious conviction, even to a state of paranoia, as the illness progresses.

A second line of defenses laid early in the illness is **rationalization**. This involves assigning "reasons" for doing things that are not the real reasons but give the appearance of justifying and explaining what one is already doing or intends to do. Reduced to its simplest form as employed by dependents, it reads: "I drink because ..." "I take pills because ..." "I smoke pot because ..." etc. The real reason is *"because I am chemically dependent."* Any other "reason" is defensive rationalization to cover up the real "because." But note that this is subconscious. Dependents are sincerely unaware of what the real reason is. They are unconsciously deceiving themselves and quietly plunging away from reality into delusion.

With the advent of unwelcome harmful effects of drug abuse in the form of self-disapproved behaviors, another line of defenses is built up around guilt. The groundwork of this part of the defense system is **repression**, which is essentially a violent intellectual denial of some aspect of reality. This denial is so forceful that it wipes out the reality from consciousness and leaves a person convinced that there is not and never was such an aspect of reality. The power of the human intellect is nowhere, perhaps, more dramatically shown in its negative aspects than in its ability to repress the valid data provided by other psychic powers. The intellect can repress conscious awareness of external events, of real, even vivid physical sensations, of actual personal experiences, of internal feelings or emotions, of memories and fantasies, of judgments and decisions, and of moral or conscience data.

The Intellect and Denial

In chemical dependents, this enormous intellectual power is completely in the service of defending the sick drug relationship, and of protecting them from awareness of it by denying its existence and the reality of its disastrous effects. The origin of repression, as noted above, is guilt, but it is also triggered by shame, embarrassment, and fear. And it can extend its negating power to any and all aspects of reality, even to denial of the natural universe and of God, the supreme reality.

Chemical dependency is sometimes called a "merry-go-round of denial" because repressive denial is so prominent a part of the pathology. But it is a merry-go-round of denial for another reason, namely, because every defense is in some way a denial. All these defenses, including those that develop early in the illness and carry all the way through it, involve at least partial denial. To *minimize*, for example, is to whittle down reality, to make an action or an event or a problem seem smaller and less significant than it really is — in other words, to deny its magnitude. To *justify* is to deny the real injustice of an action. To *rationalize* is to deny the real reason for an action, a thing, or an event. And to *project* is to deny real personal responsibility by laying it onto someone or something else.

Throughout the pleasure stage, a dependent's life style is progressively narrowing from drug-oriented to drug-centered. The pressures thereby placed on family members and others mount steadily. Their negative reactions against the dependent mount, too, so additional defenses are set up by the dependent to counter these reactions. Blackouts may occur, and these and other mental distortions bring added fears, worries, and anxieties. These, too, are covered by defenses.

THE RELIEF STAGE

By the time the relief stage is reached, the defense system is rigidly set. The negative attitudes that are also rigidly set are now locked in securely behind these walls of defense. The dependent is now inflexible as rock, unbending as cast iron, immovably fixed in the drug relationship.

Imagine a tunnel set in granite. Inside are reinforced concrete walls ten feet thick. Inside the concrete is a steel casing another five feet thick, leaving a two-foot opening through which to move. The tunnel is two thousand miles long and at the end of it is death, and you are in it moving through. See yourself inside that tunnel. Feel yourself inside it. Try to breathe or turn around.

This is the rigid tunnel in which chronic dependents live and move and have their being. It is a claustrophobic place, a stifling, suffocating situation to be in. This tunnel is formed by the dependents' defenses surrounding their relationship to drugs.

The Trip through the Tunnel

When they entered the tunnel, the dependents' fascination with drugs and with the rewarding pleasures to be gained prevented them from seeing where they were. They moved along within the narrow space unaware that they were so confined. It felt warm and snug at first, secure and comforting. It did not occur to them — or if it did, it mattered little — that they were getting far away from sunshine and green grass and fresh air and other people. They never tried to turn around or move aside or change their course.

And now they're caught. When they want to turn around or vary their position, they cannot. They are walled in, surrounded by barriers that do not bend. Their defenses, built up to protect their drug relationship so they might have life and have it more abundantly with drugs, now leave them no escape. There is no exit but by death. The defensive cover has become a tomb.

Actual drug abuse, of course, continues throughout the illness. In the relief stage, however, it takes an added twist. Drug abuse itself becomes defensive. The motive of ingestion is more and more to bring protection, to provide defensive relief from the effects and consequences of drug abuse. The merry-go-round of denial has now become a whirlwind, and the dependent is caught in its vortex.

THE MAINTENANCE STAGE

In the maintenance stage, the defense system, *as a system*, begins to break down. This happens because dependents can no longer hold up under the strain of trying to defend themselves in every direction at once. With their primary attention now concentrated on drug abuse for survival and their depersonalization and desocialization almost complete, systematic defenses disintegrate. Their main defenses become brazen, boldfaced lies and alibis uttered alternately with defiance, belligerence, and hostility and with incredible sincerity. Unusual and highly improbable excuses and explanations are offered in defense of drug abuse and drug-induced behaviors, with no apparent awareness of inconsistencies, contradictions, or of evident realities to the contrary.

THE ESCAPE STAGE

Little in the way of particular defenses can be added in escape stage dependency. Drug abuse as a means of escaping to oblivion becomes the general, all-protecting defense. While drug abuse itself is a defense in the relief stage, in this stage it is the principal defense. With complete escape as its goal and motive, oblivion is the only remaining defense capable of protecting dependents against the unbearable misery of the terminal stage of their illness and the final days of their lives.

RESULTING CONDITIONS

Defenses, like negative attitudes and other elements of this pathology, begin subtly and grow gradually. Neither dependents nor persons close to them become aware of the defenses until they have been in operation for some time and are already far advanced. By this time, dependents are so self-deceived that they cannot believe reality data when it is read back to them. They rely totally and completely on what their defenses tell them. They are invincibly surrounded by the bulwarks their drug compulsion has built. By relying totally and completely on their defenses, they have succeeded both in walling others out and in cementing themselves in. For them, there is no escape without assistance.

By this time, too, concerned persons, whether in work settings, church groups, clubs, or other social groupings, are almost hopelessly entangled in dependents' defenses, as well as in their own. In almost all defenses, there is some grain of truth, some toehold in reality that is the "hooker." For example, when a dependent pounces on a spouse, coworker, friend, or neighbor with *"You're* not perfect, either," or with "I drink just like my friends do," or with "I'm just a party person," all three statements do (or may) contain some element of truth. Certainly, few concerned persons would claim to be perfect, and usually a dependent's friends do drink very much like he or she does. By taking the hook, concerned persons become entangled, and the harder they try to escape this web of half-truths, the more hopelessly they become enmeshed in it.

So crisis after crisis comes and goes. Concerned persons remain locked into their enabler roles. Their own defenses prevent them from undertaking the intervention that might terminate the drug abuse and get recovery started. When they grow aware of the dependents' defenses and confront them, they are further confused and frustrated because the dependents seem so genuinely unconcerned, they act defensively and maintain staunchly that they have nothing to be defensive about. Concerned persons do not realize that dependents are sincerely deluded and actually unaware of their condition or of the destruction that they are causing. Dependents themselves are unaware of the huge wall of rigid defenses and negative attitudes they have constructed to protect their pathological love relationship with mood-altering chemicals. The nature, complexity, and "thickness" of this defensive wall are suggested in the following diagram.

The Baffling Barrier of Rigid Defense System and Rigid Negative Attitudes

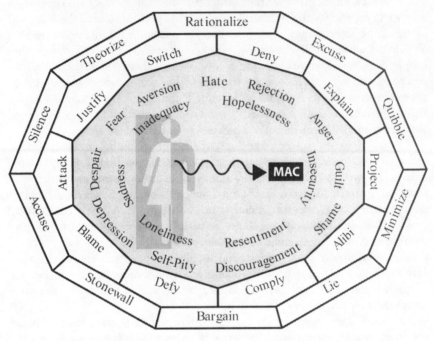

A Family Illness

Chemical dependency is a family illness. When any family member becomes dependent, the whole family becomes involved in the dependent's sickness and a parallel pathology develops in all family members. Among all of the pathological elements, this involvement is nowhere more evident than in the rigid defense systems that dependents and family members share. Each feeds upon and feeds into the other. All involved become deluded. Manipulation and countermanipulation become the central and sick dynamic of family life.

In two major respects, a dependent's defenses are directly destructive of family members and of family relations. A main line of defense, as noted earlier, is projection. Dependents project both responsibility for their drug abuse and blame for its harmful effects onto family members. If family members accept such projection, they also accept the guilt feelings that go with it. Then, when they are laden down with their feelings of guilt, the dependents "forgive them everything." Thus, they manipulate their feelings of guilt and remorse to defend themselves against their possible interference with their continued drug abuse.

A second defensive maneuver that destroys family relations is the remorse that dependents sometimes feel and lavishly display. In spite of their defenses,

182

they cannot completely and at all times conceal from themselves the fact that they sometimes behave destructively. Hence, they feel and display deep remorse at times and are obviously and sincerely sorry for their antisocial behavior and for harm they have done to the family. They openly reproach themselves and confide to the family their sorrow for what they have done (and the pity they feel for themselves). This both touches the sympathy of family members and stirs their guilt so that they relax their pressures for reform.

This open gate is too much for dependents' compulsive defenses to resist. So they manipulate the family's feelings of sympathy and guilt and take advantage of their lowered defenses to pursue unhindered for awhile their chemically dependent way of life. Unwittingly, the family members fall into the manipulations and continue in their enabler roles.

SYMPTOMS OF RIGID DEFENSE SYSTEM

In some respects, defensiveness is a symptom of pathologically rigid negative attitudes. This is because its object is to *negate* threats, to ward off or to avoid what one perceives as evil or harmful or dangerous. But defensiveness is a distinct form of negativism, and it is broader in extent than the negativism outlined in the previous chapter. While dependents' negative attitudinal postures form part of the territory defended, the defense system is in effect the armed forces defending and protecting not only this negative attitude part of the territory but many other areas as well. A dependent is not only a negative person, but is also an obsessive/compulsive person, a low self-image person, a drug-related, drug-oriented, drug-centered person, a deluded and powerless person. Dependents' defensive forces are marshaled and deployed to cover up their chemical dependency both from themselves and from others, and thus to protect *all* of these areas.

The total territory defended is everything having to do with drug involvement. Since this includes the whole person and all activities in all areas of life, the defense system literally covers everything. Particularly, the chemically dependent defense system covers (1) the personal committed drug relationship; (2) actual drug abuse; (3) drug-induced and drug-related attitudes and behaviors; (4) the entire pathology of the illness; (5) all of the symptoms of the illness; and (6) the complications and consequences of the illness.

In other words, the defense system of dependents distorts and conceals from them every aspect of their illness. They can perceive no part of their drug problem accurately. Therefore, the *self-reporting* of symptoms, which is to a great extent valid in identifying other illnesses, is of little or no validity in diagnosing chemical dependency. Dependents do not intentionally deceive the diagnostician. They simply *cannot* report their condition with accuracy because their perception of it is badly distorted by their self-deceiving defenses.

General Symptom: Defensiveness About Personal Drug Involvement

A rigid defense system is manifested by the general symptom of a dependent's defensiveness (defensive attitude) about the drug relationship, about drug ingestion, and about the consequences of these.

Particular Symptoms of Defensiveness About Personal Drug Involvement

The following are some of the more prominent particular symptoms of a chemically dependent rigid defense system:

1. *Defensiveness* about the six areas noted above. (The personal committed drug relationship, etc.)

2. *Denial* is the first line of defense. If denial succeeds, no further defenses are needed. In one sense, every defense is a denial because every defense distorts reality and therefore at least partially denies it. Hence, in some literature, the defense system is simply called a "denial system," as indeed it is.

   By *chemically dependent denial* as a particular defense, however, we mean any direct or explicit negation or rejection of the truth of a statement or the reality of a situation where one's drug involvement is concerned. For example, a dependent may be confronted with the truth, "You are defensive about your drug relationship." He or she may reply, "No, that's not true." In doing so, the dependent unwittingly confirms the defensiveness by the very statement of denial. If further confronted with the reality of regularly repeated drug abuse, the reply may be, "No, that's not the real situation." The denial may be a simple, direct negative reply that rejects and repudiates truth and reality. Or it may (and usually does) go further to contradict the original truthful statement, to declare such a statement to be untrue and unreal, and to assert that the contrary is true and real. Whether it is a simple negation or a contradiction matters little. The fact is that the dependent's response denies truth and reality and affirms untruth and unreality — and with complete and sincere conviction.

   Diagnostic clues are so abundant that it is difficult to single out any in particular. The main clue is the defensiveness about anything and everything having to do with drug involvement and its consequences.

3. *Minimizing* is the second line of defense. If denial does not succeed in wiping out reality, then the significance of the reality can be

made to seem unimportant or of little consequence. To minimize is to reduce to the smallest possible amount, extent, size, or degree. In their defensive minimizing, dependents represent what is said about their drug involvement as having the least degree of importance or value. In their own minds and in expressions to others, they depreciate or cut down the extent and frequency of their drug abuse, the depth of their drug relationship, the quantities of drugs consumed, the effects on themselves and others, the consequences, etc.

As is the case with denial, diagnostic clues are abundant. The following statements would be typical. "Sure, I use a little now and then." "Oh, I take a couple once in a while." "You exaggerate; it's not all that bad." "I only had two." Any apparent admission is immediately retracted by minimizing, which distorts the reality and so, in effect, denies it.

4.   *Rationalizing* is another prominent particular defense. To rationalize is to devise self-satisfying but incorrect "reasons" for one's attitudes and behavior. In the operation of this particular defense, the intellect especially is totally at the service of chemical dependency. Hence, the number and variety of possible rationalizations is unlimited. "I did it because . . ." "It happened because . . ." "I got drunk because . . . " "I got angry because . . ." Sometimes rationalizations give a false appearance that dependents are in control of their attitudes and behaviors, and that they really intended to do what they did or say what they said. At other times, rationalizations are calculated to make it appear that they knew what was going on and why something happened, even if they weren't on top of the situation. In other words, the dependent may say something like, "Although I didn't plan it to happen that way, at least I can explain why it did." *Explaining* is a variation of the rationalization theme. Making *excuses* and giving *alibis* are other somewhat more limited forms of rationalization, although in some literature the whole chemically dependent rationalization process and the defense system itself are referred to simply as the "alibi system."

A cautionary note for diagnosis: any "why" questions put to a dependent invite rationalizations and explanations. In fact, "why" questions are triggers for any and all defenses, and asking such questions is probably the surest way of getting sucked into and tangled up in a dependent's defense system. Asking *any* questions in expectation of accurate answers is a symptom of naiveté on the part of a diagnostician, and when dependents face such a question-asker, they know almost instinctively that they have won this round.

So valued is this questioning approach that dependents manipulate intensely to bring it about. They will invite it, even insist upon it: "Go ahead, ask me anything you want to know!"

5. *Intellectualizing* is closely akin to rationalizing and explaining, but it goes farther by taking attention away from facts and focusing it on analysis. To intellectualize is to avoid insight into a problem, especially an emotional problem, by performing an intellectual analysis. This puts things on the "head level" and gets them off the "gut level." On a broader scale, it gets away from specific concrete data and gets into analyses of why things happen or how things happen, rather than coming to grips with what happened and its immediate effects. A dependent, for example, when confronted with concrete data about his drug abuse, might try to create a discussion about what exactly is drug abuse, what are its degrees, what are the chemical constituents or psychopharmacological effects of certain drugs of abuse, etc. Or again, faced with data on his low self-image, he might attempt to initiate an intellectual consideration of various ethico-religious value systems. *Analyzing* is one form of intellectualizing. Another form is *theorizing* or *speculating*. To theorize or speculate is to formulate or propose hypotheses or suppositions as to why something occurs as it does. As a defense, it is a device that gets attention centered on abstract mental exercises, rather than on concrete, here-and-now existential data.

6. *Projection* is another effective weapon in the dependent's arsenal of defenses. To "project," literally, means to "throw out" or to "thrust outward." Dependents thrust outward onto persons, things, and situations their own feelings, attitudes, desires, and behaviors. By thus compulsively externalizing them and attributing them to others, dependents relieve themselves of responsibility, blame, and guilt. Projection, like other defenses, is not malicious or even conscious; it is one of many automatic, subconscious reactions of the rigid defense system.

Diagnostic clues will be found especially in the projection of guilt-producing negative attitudes and inappropriate, destructive behaviors that are drug-induced or drug-related. "Others" are fearful, suspicious, guilty, and so "they make me feel uneasy." *Blaming* is a mode of projection. "Yes, I did it, but it's all your fault. You made me do it." *Accusing* is a further form: "You are the one who did it!"

7. *Justifying* is another particular defense with many complex implications and variations. "To justify" means "to make just." Dependents, laden as they are with guilt, feel an acute need for justification,

a craving to "make things right," to "straighten things out," to make amends and ease their troubled consciences. To satisfy this need, their defense system provides many devices. Nowhere, perhaps, is the complexity and interweave of the defense system more clearly exhibited than in the operation of this particular defense. Dependents will use the following and more:

Project:	"Don't blame me because it's not my fault."
Blame:	"Yes, I did it, but it's all your fault!"
Accuse:	"You did it."
Minimize:	"It really wasn't all that bad."
Excuse:	"I couldn't help it."
Generalize:	"Lots of people do, don't they?"
Universalize:	"Everybody does it, right?"
Switch:	"You're not perfect, are you?"
Defy:	"I'm not going to get all uptight about your damned moral codes!"

So distressing is the guilt of dependents that they pour out a veritable avalanche of such diagnostic clues in their desperate efforts to relieve their massive moral anxiety.

8. *Complying* is a further particular defense. Compliance is yielding to, acquiescing to, "going along with" the demands, wishes, or expectations of others, usually under pressure from which there is no apparent or immediate escape. Dependents are experts at compliance in its many forms. One principal form of it is *defiant* compliance: "OK, I'll do it, dammit, if you insist, but just you wait!" or "Just you try to get me well; go ahead and try!" Another of its principal forms is *submissive* or *subservient* compliance: "Sure, you're right. If you want me to, I'll do it" or "Yes, I can see that it's the best thing to do, so I'll do it." *Agreeing* is a common form of compliance. By agreeing, one gives an impression or appearance of assent but in fact withholds any genuine acceptance or consent. When the pressure is off, compliance ends, whatever form it takes.

9. *Repression* is essentially a compulsive exclusion of painful or uncomfortable impulses, desires, fears, and memory materials from the conscious mind. In effect, it is a radical form of denial, but it is manifested less by explicit statements of negation than by a simple innocence and sincere unawareness that the repressed material ever really existed at all. This unawareness in the presence of hard data otherwise available to the diagnostician is evidence of repression.

General Symptom: Negative Attitudes Employed as Defenses

The particular defenses noted above form only part of the whole defense system. Another formidable array of defenses is found in dependents' employment of their rigid negative attitudes as defenses. Negative attitudes used as defenses present a general symptom of the chemically dependent rigid defense system.

Particular Symptoms of Negative Attitudes Employed as Defenses

1. *Hatred* and *aversion* are employed defensively in the form of expressing revulsion against others and of leveling rejection or threats of rejection at others. The dependent may express these negative attitudes by "putting down," downgrading, ridiculing, belittling, embarrassing, and demeaning others; by glaring, staring, frowning, and by verbalizing hatred; by snubbing, ignoring, not speaking to, and not responding to others. Hatred and aversion are also employed defensively (and justice is violated) by rumormongering, backbiting, defamation of character, calumny, and other forms of venomous or furtive attacks.

2. *Despair* or *desperation* is employed defensively by presenting it in the forms of compliance, agreement, timidity, conformity, dissolving into helplessness and inadequacy, withdrawing into silence, or even withdrawing physically. Or it may be applied as stalling, quibbling and arguing, appearing puzzled and confused, rambling, or verbalizing (talking a lot without coming to a point). Or it may come forth as humor, joking, grinning, laughing, or smiling. The main diagnostic clue to the defensive use of despair or desperation lies in recognizing that all of these devices "buy time" for dependents, who are in an ambiguous or ambivalent position from which they see no present escape.

3. *Fear* will appear defensively as evasion, avoidance, withdrawal, and silence.

4. *Anger* will appear defensively as sullen or open hostility, threats of violence, attacking, punishing, scowling, frowning; menacing or threatening looks, words and gestures; shouting, pounding, ranting, etc.

5. *Sadness* will appear defensively as manipulation for pity, sympathy, understanding, and protection.

6. *Insecurity* will appear defensively as defiance, challenging, arguing, disputing, and "stonewalling."

RIGID DEFENSE SYSTEM
SUMMARY OF ESSENTIAL SYMPTOMS

General Symptom: Defensiveness About Drug Involvement

Particular Symptoms:

1. Defensiveness about:
    a. Personal committed drug relationship.
    b. Drug-induced and drug-related attitudes and behavior.
    c. The pathology of the illness.
    d. The symptoms of the illness.
    e. The complications and consequences of the illness.
2. Denial of the above.
3. Minimizing the above.
4. Rationalizing the above and explaining, excusing, alibiing.
5. Intellectualizing the above; analyzing, speculating, theorizing.
6. Projecting onto others; blaming, accusing.
7. Justifying the above; generalizing, universalizing, switching, defying.
8. Repressing the above.

General Symptom: Negative Attitudes Employed as Defenses

Particular Symptoms:

1. Expressions of hatred, revulsion, aversion, rejection.
2. Expressions of discouragement, desperation, despair.
3. Expressions of fear, avoidance, withdrawal.
4. Expressions of anger, resentment, belligerence, hostility.
5. Expressions of sadness, especially "pity me."
6. Expressions of insecurity, inadequacy.
7. Expressions of defiance.

CHAPTER THIRTEEN

Chemically Dependent
Delusion

Everyone is deluded at times, in some ways and to some degree, and we all have personal experiences that reveal to us our delusion. We gradually — or suddenly — wake up to the fact that an opinion we have firmly held is false. We were not deliberately lying to ourselves or to others in holding or expressing our false opinion, although the fact is that we believed and stated falsehood when we did so. We were in error, but we did not know it. We were, in other words, deluded.

Delusion is to persistently believe things to be true that are not true, and conversely, to persistently believe things not to be true that are true. It is to affirm as real what is not real, and to deny as real what is in fact real. False is affirmed as true and true is affirmed as false. Opinions, positions, and attitudes are held that are not derived from reality and that cannot be verified in reality. In brief, delusion is denial of reality and affirmation of unreality. Another way to say it is "insane," in the proper meaning of that word, that is, unhealthy or unsound of mind. It is a form of mental ill health, a state of being out of touch with reality, of not having accurate mental contact with the real world.

Delusion is sincere — we do not deliberately or maliciously misrepresent reality to ourselves or to others. When we are mistaken in the way we see things, when we are in error or when our prejudices blind us to reality, it is not by any choice of ours and it is not a conscious thing. We do not intend any falsehood or deception. Even more than the defenses that produce it, delusion is subconscious. We sincerely believe that we are right, and we are so firmly convinced of it that we defend our delusions almost as vigorously as we defend our life itself. Unfortunately, in defending them, we make our false beliefs much stronger.

Now, before you go on with your reading, it might be helpful to "count to ten," that is, to recall to mind and list ten instances in which you have been deluded. You will probably understand chemically dependent delusion much more easily if you see it in comparison to your own. And if you believe that you have never been deluded, list that as number one.

Varieties of Delusion

Delusion varies in the forms it takes. It may be in regard to one area of reality only, or to several areas, or to all areas. It may be partial or total. It may be temporary or permanent. It may be "normal," that is, within an expected and generally accepted range for healthy human beings. Or it may be "abnormal," that is, beyond the natural limits or norms generally accepted for a healthy mental state.

Two Contributing Factors

Two factors are the main contributors to delusion: data distortion and data deficiency. Both of these can be caused by impairment of our cognitive or knowing powers and processes and by our psychological defenses.

Our intellect is our principal and properly human cognitive or knowing power. Our other cognitive powers — our external and internal senses — have as their ultimate function to feed reality data into our intellect for mental processing. Our intellect, in turn, must be open and ready to accurately receive this data, and it must be able to process it faithfully in order to arrive at correct conclusions about reality. Hence, if any of our sense-level cognitive powers are impaired in their functioning, they will provide our intellect with distorted or deficient data, that is, either partial data or perhaps none at all. In this case, our intellect lacks sufficient data for its processing function and therefore cannot arrive at correct conclusions. Furthermore, if our intellect is itself impaired in its functioning, its own processing operations will distort the data or leave some of it out, and so, again, it cannot come to correct conclusions.

Psychological defenses, as we saw in Chapter Twelve, are essentially cover-up devices. By their very nature they hide data; they keep it away from our intellect's awareness. So our intellect has only partial data or no data to work with and cannot come to sound conclusions about reality.

Definition

With this as background, we define **chemically dependent delusion** as essentially the mental state or condition of a person who, because of a committed love relationship to mood-altering chemicals, persistently and sincerely believes things to be false that are true and things to be true that are false. It is a form of insanity, of mental ill health or unsoundness of mind.

Deluded dependents affirm as real what is not real and deny as real what is real in regard to their drug relationship and all that it involves. They view as false what is true about their drug abuse and see as true what is false about it. They hold opinions, positions, and attitudes about their drug involvement that have no foundation in reality and that can in no way be verified in the reality of their actual condition. Their delusion is essentially a denial of reality and an affirmation of unreality. They have head problems; they are mixed up mentally.

Like all delusion, this delusion is sincere. Dependents' beliefs are total convictions. Whatever the defensive ploys they may consciously use to protect their drug relationship, their delusion is not a ploy — it is genuine.

This delusion is also persistent. It is not a temporary passing condition, but of its nature it is continuing and permanent. It will go with the dependents to their death if the illness runs its course. It is ultimately a total covering up of every aspect of the drug relationship and its effects and consequences. In its fully developed state, it is total denial. Dependents are aware of none of the realities of their sick condition and hence sincerely affirm that they are well and that they have no problems where drugs are concerned. Their self-deluding defenses conceal from them their relationship to drugs, their actual drug abuse, the pathology of the illness present within them, the symptoms manifested, the harmful consequences to themselves and to others, and any complications they may experience.

PROCESS OF DEVELOPMENT

THE PLEASURE STAGE

Even before a commitment to a personal drug relationship carries a person over the line into chemical dependency, delusion will probably be under way. Environmental, socio-cultural defenses are highly operative in a drug-oriented society. But "society" is not a substantial entity capable of having defenses of its own; rather, it is a community of individual persons. Hence, the defenses that are called "environmental," "social," or "socio-cultural" are in reality the collective defenses of *individuals* in the community.

Collective projection, as we have noted, is common, almost universal, among drug users, and so are rationalizations. Since these defenses, like all others, "put it where it isn't," they create collective delusion. A classic example is presented by much of so-called "social drinking," which completely disregards (and therefore in effect denies) the real nature of the alcoholic relationships and alcohol abuse. Instead, it focuses on the fact that a *group* is doing it or that "everybody does it" and so affirms that it is social drinking. This, of course, is not true. Similar collective delusion forms around other drugs as well. But whether or not projection, rationalization, and other defenses exist in a person before he makes his drug commitment, they take up their delusionary work in earnest once this initial stage dependency is entered.

Unwelcome Experiences

In their quest for pleasant mood-swings, dependents inevitably experience at least occasional unwelcome effects. Because these effects are unintended and unexpected, dependents are puzzled as to why they happen. They are genuinely curious and sincerely ask the question, "Why?" With rare exceptions, they fail to identify the real causes. It does not occur to them that their sick drug relationship has anything to do with these effects or that their drug abuse directly causes them. Instead, they find their answer in "the hot and stuffy room," "the lousy quality of the drugs," the "heavy tension" they were under.

Their "reason" is out there . . . somewhere . . . 180 degrees in the wrong direction. With no malice or deliberate dishonesty, they misjudge the cause of the happenings. And in one sense they are totally deluded immediately because they cannot get any farther off the track or farther away from the truth. Yet this is only a beginning.

Having focused their attention initially *away* from drugs, they will continue to explain additional unwelcome and even disastrous consequences in the same delusionary way. Without intending to and without knowing they have done so, they have surrounded the central aspects of their illness with walls of defense that prevent their recognition.

Delusionary Justification

During the pleasure stage, delusion progresses farther as dependents do things that are contrary to their personal values. Such things may be opposed to their social values, as with antisocial behaviors that damage interpersonal relations. Or they may be opposed to moral values, as with destructive and morally unacceptable conduct. In either case, deep embarrassment, shame, and guilt come into the picture, and the terrible conflict between values and conduct is under way. Repression comes in with full force at this point to ease the feelings of guilt by denying the immoral behavior or by denying that the behavior is immoral. And projection and rationalization do their bit when dependents explain their antisocial behavior by explaining it away.

To ease their uncomfortable consciences, dependents (like anyone else) need "justification." They need to restore the balance on the scales of justice that they have upset by their behavior. When we violate our values, it has the effect of putting us into a state of injustice. We have not "done right by" our values. We have not given "just value" according to our own standards of value. Hence, we experience guilt and feel the need to justify ourselves in order to rebalance our personal scales of justice.

We can set things straight by sincere remorse and by repairing the wrong through making due restitution. We can admit we are wrong and make amends. But when our defenses are primed and ready, we do not get that far. Repression denies, and projection shifts blame, and rationalizations explain it away. We thus "justify" ourselves through our defenses instead of through a reality process. We delude ourselves into believing that we are really justified, but we pay the price of insanity.

THE RELIEF STAGE

This second stage of delusion is at hand when the defense system focuses predominantly on covering up relief-seeking drug abuse rather than pleasure-seeking drug abuse.

Recall again that the four stages of the illness are characterized by shifts in the expected rewards of drug abuse, by the predominant motivation of the dependent at each stage. In the second stage, this is relief. Delusion, too, shifts its focus; its cover-up now centers mainly on drug abuse for relief, with its effects and consequences, rather than on drug abuse for pleasure. It remains essentially the same delusion throughout the illness, of course, but its content broadens as additional materials are in need of being covered up. Delusion's intensity deepens as it becomes more firmly rooted in the chemically dependent character, and its immediate focus changes from time to time to cover-up first for one aspect of the illness and then for another.

Three developments especially occur in the relief stage that extend delusion considerably:

- One is the dependent's transition from a drug-oriented to a rigidly drug-centered life style, which brings with it increasing resistance from significant other people.

- A second is the complications that usually begin to appear in the relief stage: auto accidents, telephonitis, driving while intoxicated, job problems, serious marriage and family problems, etc.

- A third is a notable and growing involvement of concerned persons in delusion of their own.

In regard to the first, the defense system builds new walls to conceal from sight the life style change, the negative reactions it generates, and the negative counter-reactions of the dependent. In regard to the second, defenses go to work to minimize and project the blame for complications, which are too evident to be denied, and to deny any connection between the drug relationship and the complications. And in regard to the third, the delusion of concerned persons only serves to support and reinforce the dependent's deluded conviction that they are the cause of all of his or her problems in the first place.

Thus, as quickly as new evidence appears and new crises come about that might get dependents into contact with reality, their defenses wipe them out and leave them more hopelessly victims of self-delusion. As the relief stage advances, some of the most astonishing delusionary defense patterns arise out of dependents' compulsive need to maintain their belief, and to convince others, that all is well.

More Blatant Lies, Less Likely Alibis

As the maintenance stage is approached, the defense system becomes conspicuous for its inconsistencies and disorganization, and the dependent grows still less aware of his or her condition. When lies are discovered and alibis are exposed, for example, the dependent "explains" by telling more blatant lies and producing less likely alibis. These are delivered with a sincerity that is both baffling and extremely exasperating to concerned persons.

Such delusionary innocence appears as arrogant denial in the eyes of those concerned persons who have been drawn into the illness along with the dependent. Their frustration, fuming, and fury are as much symptoms of their own illness as products of the dependent's illness. They do not see that the dependent is out of touch with reality, and they *cannot* see it because they, too, are out of touch with reality. It is their own delusion that sets them up to expect a deluded dependent to recognize his delusion and to be aware of the sick realities that are hidden by it.

There is something insane about expecting an insane person to know how insane he is . . .

THE MAINTENANCE STAGE

Delusion is just as successful in hiding from dependents their quest of maintenance through drug abuse as it is in hiding their earlier-stage motivations. It is also just as effective in continuing to conceal the drug relationship and its effects. However, the defense system breaks down noticeably in this stage. As it falls apart, delusion receives many hard blows from real crises. These blows are not hard enough ordinarily to penetrate delusion, much less to shatter it, but they are hard enough to threaten it severely at times.

In addition to the breakdown of defenses, and partly as a result of it, the gross physical and social complications that often show up in the maintenance stage create additional crises in reality. These crises, in essence, are brought about by dependents' state of conflict with reality, a state in which they continually wage war against what really is. They do so in compulsive efforts to make reality fit their drug-dependent needs. For them, all existential reality must be shaped by their manipulation to enable them to maintain their chemically dependent way of life.

Reality Fights Back

Crises, in effect, are reality fighting back, resisting this manipulation, and driving back upon dependents the consequences of their own assaults against it. They are thus "hit over the head" again and again in self-created and self-defeating crises. In one of them or in an accumulation of them, dependents may be brought up against reality with sufficient force to shake their delusion somewhat. Reality may confront them hard enough to penetrate the defense barriers and bring them into momentary contact with the real world. The dependent may even defiantly/compliantly assert, "Alright, so I am an alcoholic. It doesn't mean I need help." But such moments of truth ordinarily do no more than slightly crack the defense barrier; they seldom breach it. And defenses regroup quickly to misrepresent the nature and causes of the crises and thus to add on more delusion.

If in such moments of truth, concerned persons intervene to get dependents the help they need, recovery may be initiated. More often than not, however, concerned persons are so wrapped in delusion themselves that they are unable to recognize the opportunities that these crises present to them. And so they are immobilized. They cannot see, any more than dependents can see, that the complications are brought about by the drug involvement. Dependents' poor health, for example, will more likely be seen as a *cause* of drug abuse than as an *effect* of it. Thus, concerned persons continue in their enabling role and reinforce the dependents' own delusion that their physical ailments are the reason for their drug abuse and not vice versa.

Delusion Reinforced by Complications

Professionals, too, may be called upon for help with physical or social complications. If they are not aware of the drug relationship, they may add their reinforcement to such delusion by treating the complications in isolation, apart from their chemical dependency context, as though they were unrelated to the central problem. The net result of this enabling reinforcement is that complications, with the crises they create, rarely penetrate a dependent's delusion but only shore it up and drive it deeper. And opportunities for intervention are lost.

Another dimension is added to delusion when problems with physical health, family relations, or other complications seem to diminish somewhat from time to time, and a dependent's condition seems to improve. These are only appearances, not realities. But both dependents and concerned persons often mistake them for real and hence are led farther into the maze of delusion.

THE ESCAPE STAGE

The major feature of delusion in its final stage is the firm belief of dependents that continued and increased drug abuse is the most effective means of escape from the massive miseries of their drug-centered lives. Their faith in drugs and the committed relationship born of that faith are the supreme principles of their chemical credo. They once believed that the "instant" chemical pleasures of the initial stage of dependency were genuine peak experiences of joy. They went on to believe that the chemical comforts sought in the second stage were really "instant" relief. And they further believed that a more constant chemical ingestion would maintain their normalcy in the maintenance stage.

All of that faith was sheer delusion, as hard facts proved repeatedly, and anyone except the deluded would have seen it for what it was. Yet we find that escape stage dependents are still basically unshaken in their faith and continue looking to their "higher power" — mood-altering chemicals — to rescue them from their present plight.

Shared Delusion

In this final stage, as in the others, concerned persons share the delusion. It is expressed times without end: "If I had all the problems he has, I'd probably use drugs, too." "After all, what else does she have in life?" "Life has been so cruel to them! I can understand their wanting to blot it all out with booze or hash or pills or horse or meth or whatever . . ."

Every word of such "understanding sympathy" expresses pure delusion. Every word is like a placard carried aloft by enablers, with giant letters printed on it, "I AM DELUDED, TOO!"

Delusion is relentlessly preparing dependents for their last insane suicidal plunge. Nevertheless, in a sense, it holds their one remaining hope of life. For as long as their faith in drugs sustains their hope of deliverance by means of drugs, their quest for drug-induced oblivion is not seen for what it really is, that is, a mad pursuit of self-destruction. It is when reality finally comes crashing in to prove to them that their hope in drugs is vain, and that their long-held faith in drugs is but delusion, that the last thread binding them to the only way of life they know is broken. Then, with their faith in drugs destroyed and their hope of deliverance by drug-power abandoned, they make their final escape. They take their lives. And in this, too, they are deluded, since life eternal awaits them on the other side of death.

RESULTING CONDITIONS

When a toxic (i.e., poisonous) substance enters an organism, an emergency situation is created and the alarm goes out: "An enemy has invaded!" So the organism calls up its reserves and gathers its forces for battle. It "drops everything" and concentrates its efforts on fighting off the enemy and putting it to flight. Poisons upset the natural balance of an organism and impair its functioning. The organism's defensive reactions further impair functioning by drawing off energies from other vital powers to fight and get rid of the poison.

Direct Impairment of Feeling Powers

Feelings, both physical sensations and emotions, are directly affected by ingestion of chemicals. The toxic substance itself directly induces some physical sensations and alters others that arise from the contact of the senses with existential reality. The result is distortion. Filtered through poisoned sense powers, cognitive perception of tastes and odors, sights and sounds, textures and sizes, space and time, speed of movement, and so on are not faithful representations of the real world but damaged impressions derived from drug-distorted data.

Emotional feelings are similarly affected. Drugs induce directly some feelings of love and hate, joy and sorrow, anger and fear. Other emotions that are reality-induced are distorted or blocked because the emotional powers are impaired under chemical influence. Hence, cognitive perceptions of emotional states and responses are also damaged.

Direct Impairment of Mental Powers

The mental powers, the "data processors," are poisoned, too. If you drop a powerful acid into a computer, or give it a megavolt shock, you do not expect it to operate quite normally. You would be deluded if you did. Similarly, if you drop acid or take some other powerful drug like alcohol into your system, you cannot expect yourself to function normally either. You are deluded if you do expect it.

The mental power of memory is impaired by drugs, as we have already seen. Imagination is affected, too. Some images are blocked and others are distorted, so fantasy by turns runs riot or is laid to rest. The grandiosity of dependents and their delusions of enhanced creativity, for example, are actually products of impaired imaginative powers, not enhanced ones. And so is the rigid dullness of their monotonous monologues and their vacant staring into space.

Above all, and by far the most damaging to reality contact and relationships, are the effects of drug ingestion on the intellect itself, on a person's ultimate and central data processing power. With the brain and the central nervous system knocked out of proper functioning order, there is no way for intellectual processes to proceed normally. Hence, to the already partial and distorted data served up by other malfunctioning psychic powers, the intellect adds its own dysfunction and distortions. Intellectual perception, understanding, reasoning, deliberation, decision-making, and prudential judgments, as well as lesser intellectual processes, are severely impaired. Their product is ever widening and deepening chemically dependent delusion.

The Dawn of Delusion

At its outset, chemically dependent delusion is extremely difficult to recognize. Unless one is well-acquainted with the illness and in particular with the operations of the defense system, the delusionary element in chemical dependency will escape detection until the illness is well-advanced. This is largely because dependents, almost throughout their illness, *appear* to be rational and in touch with reality in many ways. They may be competent in many respects; they may be eminently successful in one or in many fields. Often the "good side" of them is so appealing that the drug-dependent "bad side" is tolerated, overlooked, and even supported and reinforced by family, friends, and associates.

The dawn of delusion, therefore, is so subtle that it practically defies recognition. Yet with the first defensive rationalizations and projections, delusion is initiated. And because the attention of the dependent and of others is thereby turned away from reality, the real cause of the dependent's condition is thrust out of sight at once. We cannot see a thing we are not looking at. In this case, we are not looking at either the relationship of the person to mood-altering chemicals or at its direct effects or essential symptoms.

The Nature of Defenses

Recall that it is in the very nature of defenses to cover up, to conceal realities from the person who employs them. Hence, as we have noted, a sincere attempt to explain why unwelcome consequences occurred when one was using drugs turns out to be the defensive rationalization and projection that puts one on the road to total delusion. And concerned persons both support the delusion and share in it when they concur in such "explanations" and perhaps suggest further "reasons" why unwelcome consequences occurred. One reason why concerned persons and associates often agree readily with deluded explanations is because they thereby cover up their uneasiness about their own drug relationship. This is a common example of the collective defensiveness and the collective delusion referred to earlier.

Once the delusionary process is under way, it quickly gathers new elements to reinforce it. Defense is added to defense, and so delusion is added to delusion. Delusion feeds on and reinforces defenses, and defenses feed on and reinforce delusion.

Delusion and Other Pathological Elements

All of the other pathological elements of the illness contribute to and are in turn aggravated and reinforced by delusion. Brief comments on each of the pathological elements will give some clues as to how this occurs:

- *Psychological Dependency* — The unhealthy psychological dependency or need, when processed through defenses, is presented to dependents' minds as perfectly normal. Then, when they are feeling satisfied that all is well, this sick need is set free to go its way unhindered.

- *Mental Obsession* — The drug-centered mental obsession is not seen as tied in with chemical dependency, but is "defensed" away. If any obsession is recognized at all, it is diverted to secondary obsessional materials such as family problems, emotional problems, etc. This leaves the drug obsession wrapped in delusion, and it goes on its way unhindered, too.

- *Emotional Compulsion* — The emotional compulsion that drives dependents to maintain their drug relationship and drug abuse is to them nonexistent, wiped out by delusionary denial. And again the effect is to leave the drug compulsion out of any mental picture dependents may have of their condition so that compulsion, too, proceeds unchecked.

- *Low Self-Image* — The low self-image of which dependents are at least partially and occasionally aware has no apparent connection with drugs. This leaves the cause of it unknown and thus adds to dependents' anxiety and further depresses their self-image. Their repeated drug-related behavior, too, continues to go unexplained. This adds new burdens that further sap their ego strength and fortify their delusion.

- *Rigid Negative Attitudes* — The rigid negative attitudes, with all the anguish they produce for dependents themselves and all the misery they create for others, are beyond dependents' awareness. At times these attitudes are admitted implicitly, of course, when dependents blame them on others and explain why they are so negative. In effect, dependents say, "Yes, I am negative, and it's all because of you!" They do not see that the very denial of negativism is itself a negation and as such is proof positive of the negative attitudes that are being denied. Dependents are unaware of the contradiction expressed in such statements.

- *Rigid Defense System* — The rigid defense system, which is essentially the cover-up process that causes delusion, is another object of delusion. Dependents rigidly defend themselves as non-defensive and grow more rigidly defensive as they do so. As is the case with negative attitudes, however, they implicitly admit they are defensive when they justify themselves by laying the blame on others: "Who wouldn't be defensive, being accused and attacked all the time? If you'd get off my back, I wouldn't have to be defensive!" They are rigidly defensive of their rigid defensiveness because, of course, "I have no reason to be defensive." It does not occur to them how completely inconsistent — and defensive — that is.

- *Delusion* — Delusion itself is a further matter of delusion. Within it is the entire content of the cover-up. It is the cover-up, in essence. "Sincerely deluded about one's sincere delusion" would seem to state it precisely. Dependents are as firmly convinced that they are as sane as any insane person can be.

- *Powerlessness* — Finally, dependents' powerlessness, their helplessness to recognize their condition or to do anything about it, is wrapped in delusion along with all the other elements in this pathology. They firmly believe they are fully in control of all their personal powers, of all areas of their lives and, of course, of what they view as their perfectly normal, healthy drug involvement.

Beyond the pathology are the symptoms it produces, and beyond the symptoms are physical and social complications. These, too, form part of the content of the delusionary cover-up.

The Greatest Delusion

In defining chemically dependent delusion, we stated that its cause is "a sick personal love relationship to mood-altering chemicals." We have variously referred to this as a "committed drug relationship," a "drug-dependent relationship," a "pathological relationship," etc. In whatever terms we refer to it, this is the key factor in chemical dependency and the essential clue to getting in touch with and unraveling its complexities. Therefore, to miss this point is to enter at once into delusion. This is the missed point that brings on chemically dependent delusion in the victims, and this is the missed point that brings on delusion about chemical dependency and its nature and causes in family members and others.

We have noted several times how easy it is and how common to point to "something else" as the central problem in alcoholism and the other drug dependencies. According to where one is and where one is coming from, one may assign (or assume) any number and variety of other factors as the essential problem or as the essential cause or causes of chemical dependency. In doing so, one brings on one's own delusion.

One deceives oneself by denying what is real and true (the committed love relationship to drugs as the central factor and key cause) and by affirming what is unreal and false ("something else" as the central factor and key cause). No doubt one does this sincerely. One genuinely believes that the drug relationship is not the essence of chemical dependency or its essential cause and that something else is. So also do dependents, in the utter sincerity of their faith. They are, as we have seen, completely genuine in their delusion. They are, in other words, *sincerely insane*.

SYMTPOMS OF DELUSION

Delusion is a mental state, a condition of mind, in which one persistently affirms as true and real what is untrue and unreal and persistently denies as untrue and unreal what is true and real. Dependents are *not aware* of what is real or unreal, true or false, where their drug involvement is concerned.

Chemically dependent delusion centers on the committed drug relationship and actual drug abuse, on the pathology that is their direct effect, on the symptoms caused by the pathology, and on consequences or complications. This delusion carries over into other areas of life, indeed, into the whole life of the dependent.

General Symptom: Unawareness Manifested by Sincere Denial

Dependents' unawareness of their drug-involved condition is manifested by the general symptom of denying what is true and real in regard to that condition.

Particular Symptoms of Unawareness Manifested by Sincere Denial

1. *Denial of the existence* of any personal drug problem. This symptom appears both as denial of the whole drug-involved condition and as denial of its various aspects: the sick drug relationship, actual drug abuse, the pathology, the symptoms, and the complications.

2. *Minimizing the extent and seriousness* of the problem. This symptom, too, appears both as minimizing the problem as a whole and as minimizing its various aspects, such as the frequency, quantities, costs, and consequences of actual drug ingestion; the depth and destructiveness of the drug relationship; the various pathological elements, etc.

3. *Denial of particular items of concrete data about antisocial, destructive effects* of drug abuse due to memory impairment (blackout, euphoric memory, repression). The reality data in such instances are available to others but are not available to the dependent for recall. Hence, denial will occur even in the face of massive data.

4. *Sincere conviction* that these denials are valid. This conviction, genuine as it is, may disarm a diagnostician unless it is borne in mind that the strength of a dependent's conviction is an indication of the depth of the delusion.

General Symptom: Unawareness Manifested by Sincere Affirmation

Dependents' unawareness of their drug-involved condition is shown by the general symptom of *affirming* as real and true in regard to their drug-involved condition what is in fact unreal and untrue.

Particular Symptoms of Unawareness Manifested by Sincere Affirmation

1. *Declarations* affirming that "everything is fine," that "nothing is any different than it ever was."

2. *Rationalizations* explaining that something other than drug involvement is the cause or causes of any personal, family, or other problems.

3. *Projections* attributing to others the responsibility and blame for personal problems and reading into others the dependent's own problems.

4. *Assertions* that drug ingestion is *completely under control* or that it is now under control despite clear evidence to the contrary: "I can take it or leave it." "I can quit any time I want to." "I can do without it." "I'll change the way I take drugs if you want me to."

5. *Assertions* that *others are mistaken* in their appraisals of the dependent's condition.

6. *Grandiose fantasies and undertakings* (delusions of grandeur) without realizing how unrealistic they are or how often they occur.

7. *Fantasies and suspicions of persecution* (paranoid delusions), assertions by dependents that others dislike them and are out to get them or are "hounding" them about their drug ingestion or their life style.

8. *Telephonitis*, that is, impulsive and often costly telephone calls while under drug influence without realizing how inappropriate the calls are.

9. *Expressions of indignation, hurt, self-pity, and resentment* when data are presented that demonstrate chemical dependency. These reactions are proof that a dependent is sincerely *unaware* of the truth of such data and of the reality of the events they report.

10. *Sincere conviction* of dependents that their affirmations are valid, that truth and reality are on their side. As with denials, the sincerity of this conviction may disarm the diagnostician. Actually, it is but an indication of the extent of the delusion.

CHEMICALLY DEPENDENT DELUSION
SUMMARY OF ESSENTIAL SYMPTOMS

General Symptom: Unawareness Manifested by Sincere Denial

Particular Symptoms:

1. Denial of the existence of a personal drug problem.
2. Minimizing the extent and/or seriousness of the personal drug problem.
3. Denial of particular items of data about antisocial, destructive effects of drug abuse.
4. Sincere conviction that denials are valid, objective, true.

General Symptom: Unawareness Manifested by Sincere Affirmation

Particular Symptoms:

1. Declarations affirming that "everything is fine."
2. Rationalizations explaining that something else is causing problems.
3. Projections attributing to others the responsibility for any problems.
4. Assertions that drug ingestion is "completely under control" or "now under control."
5. Assertions that others are mistaken about the drug involvement.

6. Grandiose fantasies and illusions.
7. Fantasies and suspicions of persecution.
8. Telephonitis.
9. Expressions of indignation, hurt, self-pity, and resentment in the face of data about their drug involvement.
10. Sincere conviction that these affirmations are valid.

CHAPTER FOURTEEN

Physical Pathology
of
Chemical Dependency

Chemical dependency, as should be evident by now, is a total person illness. The whole person is the subject in which the pathological relationship resides, and the whole person is affected adversely by this relationship — by its effects and by its consequences.

Primarily and essentially the illness is "psychological," with that term understood to mean the **human psyche** as

1. the animating or life-giving principle of the human psychophysical composite and the ultimate source of man's unique rationality, and

2. the ultimate source of all personal activity that is carried on more directly and immediately by our several psychic or life powers: intellect, will, emotions, etc.

Secondarily, and by consequence but not essentially, chemical dependency is a physical illness. The human being, note once more, is a psychosomatic composite of *psyche* (mind, soul, spirit) and *soma* (flesh, body). This unity is so intimate that what affects the psyche, or what occurs in the psyche, also affects the soma, and vice versa. Out of the continuous interaction of these substantial parts of the human composite arises the essential dynamic of human personality. Whenever psychological abnormalities develop, corresponding physical effects are produced. And whenever physical abnormalities develop, related psychological effects follow.

Physical Factors as Complications

The physical aspects of chemical dependency are not, in the *strictest sense*, essential elements in the pathology of the illness. They are more properly physical consequences or *complications* of what is essentially an illness involving the whole person and involving primarily the psychic powers of that person. The recuperative powers of the body are usually sufficient to ward off pathological physical developments for a considerable time after psychological dependency has set in. Hence, the physical elements in the illness are not pathological in the same sense as the elements we have thus far considered. They are more in the nature of secondary, derivative pathologies, or complications.

The significance of this to the diagnosis and treatment of chemical dependency, as well as to education, research, and training in the field, is obvious. Whatever physical factors may contribute to or result from the illness, they do not touch its essential nature. Biochemical "cures" for drug-dependent persons, for example, if such cures are ever discovered, will leave the essential pathology untreated and the person unrecovered, as much a victim of chemical dependency as before the "cures."

Each time drugs are ingested, of course, physiological effects are produced. Chemical or pharmacological reactions occur in the physical organism that result in alterations or changes of physical sensation and of psychological or psychophysical feelings and moods. But the mere ingestion and even the occasional excessive ingestion of drugs does not necessarily damage the organism in a way that can be called pathological in the usual meaning of the word — that is, no identifiable pattern of pathology is produced.

Each time psychoactive drugs are ingested, the body is placed in a potentially toxic condition, that is, the body may be poisoned to some extent by the introduction into it of a foreign substance. Excessive ingestion produces intoxication, which is a degree of poisoning sufficient to exceed, at least temporarily, the body's capacity to detoxify or to rid itself of the poison by exercising its recuperative powers. Obviously, a poisoned or toxic condition is not normal to the human body any more than such a condition is normal to any other organism. Hence, in this sense, we might speak of an abnormal or pathological condition resulting temporarily from even a single ingestion of mood-altering chemicals. In this sense, too, a drug overdose might produce death, which is clearly a pathological condition.

Pathology and Process

We have been using the term "pathological" in a more precise sense, namely, to signify an identifiable *pattern* or configuration of abnormal elements that progress through characteristic processes of development and that produce typical resulting conditions in the person who is sick. Implied is a permanence or a quasi-permanence of the pathology in its subject, the dependent, from the beginning to the end of the disease process. Clinically, we do not ordinarily see significant physical complications accompanying chemical dependency, as a rule, until the illness has already progressed at least into the late pleasure stage or early relief stage.

Meanwhile, the dependent has long since been the subject of the essential elements in the pathology of the illness. Physical abnormalities such as acute gastritis, pancreatitis, and severe liver and brain damage rarely develop until chemical dependency is already well-advanced. For that reason, these abnormalities are more properly classified as physical complications or as late-stage secondary physical symptoms of the illness instead of as essential elements in its pathology.

Earlier in this book, we noted that efforts to establish alcoholism as a disease within current or traditional definitions of physical medicine shifted the focus and emphasis away from the total-person relationship and the primary psychological involvement and onto the later-stage physical complications. Even at the present time, as we have noted, diagnosis is usually based on these and on social complications rather than on essential symptoms and pathology.

At this point, too, it may be opportune to recall that our purpose in this book is not to reinvent the wheel or simply to pass in review what has already been sufficiently stated elsewhere. Instead, we wish to provide a basis for understanding, diagnosing, and treating chemical dependency in terms of its essential aspects, starting with the existential reality of the committed personal pathological love relationship to drugs. Hence, our present limited consideration of its physical aspects is by design, not by oversight.

THREE PHYSICAL ASPECTS OF CHEMICAL DEPENDENCY

Three physical aspects of the illness are significant enough to warrant some special consideration since they appear frequently, if not always, in chemical dependency. They are physical addiction, physical tolerance, and memory blackout.

PHYSICAL ADDICTION

The term "drug addiction" is often used but seldom defined in chemical dependency discussions and literature, and, unfortunately, the meaning is not always made clear by the context. Confusion and uncertainty result. "Drug addiction" is sometimes, but rarely, used to mean "chemical dependency" as we have defined it, namely, a pathological relationship of a person to a mood-altering chemical substance or drug in expectation of a rewarding experience. At other times, and more often, it is used to distinguish other drug dependencies from alcoholism.

The most common current meaning of "drug addiction" is a pathological *physical* dependency on drugs. This is a narrow, technical meaning that signifies a condition wherein the body requires constant or frequent dosages of drugs in order to maintain a state of drug-dependent "normalcy," and wherein withdrawal reactions are "normal." It is in this sense that we use the term, and in this sense drug addiction is not chemical dependency.

"Addictive drug," like "drug addiction," is also frequently used but rarely defined. Again, confusion and misunderstanding result. The term "addictive drug" may mean what we have defined as a mood-altering chemical substance, that is, any drug that has the intrinsic capability or power to alter our moods or to change significantly the way we feel. More often, "addictive drug" is a term used to distinguish other drugs from alcohol. But usually, "addictive drug" is used in a narrower technical sense to mean a drug that characteristically induces a pathological *physical* dependency, so that constant or frequent dosages are required to maintain the body in a state of drug-dependent "normalcy." In this sense, it is commonly used as a correlative of "drug addiction." It is in this latter sense that we use the term. Thus, we define *physical addiction* to mood-altering chemicals as a state or condition of the human body in which the organism requires constant or frequent dosages of certain drugs in order to maintain it in a state of drug-dependent "normalcy."

The Development Process

This condition develops gradually through a process of physical adaptation of the organism as it adjusts to the presence of a toxic substance. The adaptation leads to habituation when the organism has achieved a new state of balance; it now depends on the presence of the toxic substance to maintain it in this state of balance. Habituation passes over into physical addiction when drug abuse has continued to the point where an essentially uncontrollable *physical* need for drugs has been generated. To have drugs in the system has now become the normal condition of the organism. If it is abruptly deprived of its accustomed dosages, reactions occur in the form of withdrawal symptoms. If the addiction is severe, the withdrawal symptoms will be acute and the organism may not survive.

Physical addiction ordinarily appears in the third or maintenance stage of chemical dependency. It is, in fact, a major distinguishing mark of this stage of physical dependency on *some* drugs. Constant or frequent dosages are now required to maintain the dependent at minimal levels of functioning and to avoid acute withdrawal symptoms.

That physical addiction is not essential to chemical dependency is clear from the fact that the illness begins and may continue indefinitely as a pathological relationship to drugs before physical addiction or dependency develops. And physical addiction apparently never develops in dependencies on certain drugs. Present evidence, at any rate, although insufficient to warrant a certain conclusion, seems to indicate that some drugs do not produce physical addiction. The danger in confusing "drug addiction," in the sense of "physical addiction," with "drug addiction" in the sense of "chemical dependency" or "drug dependency," is evident when one considers that a person may die of chemical dependency without ever becoming physically addicted.

Dangerous Misunderstandings

If there are dangers in the above-noted confusions, even more serious dangers grow out of misunderstandings of the terms "addictive" and "nonaddictive" drugs. For example, certain mood-altering chemicals are represented by drug companies and their representatives and are prescribed and administered by professionals as nonaddictive drugs. Patients assume that the label "nonaddictive" is a safety signal. So do advertisers and professionals who are unaware of the nature of chemical dependency. Patients then use the drugs as prescribed and become chemically dependent upon them. It is ironic, to say the least, that such patients should develop a pathology from their ingestion of "nonaddictive" drugs. They may go on to die of the pathology induced by prescriptions intended to relieve less serious pathologies.

Advertisers and professionals, in such cases, are obviously using "nonaddictive" in a narrow, technical sense to mean a drug that does not (or has not been demonstrated to) produce a pathological *physical* dependency, at least in early phases of its administration.

A serious by-product of "nonaddictive" drug administration turns up in clinical situations. We have found that one of the strongest and least penetrable of the delusionary defenses with which clients surround themselves is their subjective conviction that they *cannot* be chemically dependent because their physicians prescribed only "nonaddictive" drugs. In clinical experience, too, we find that some physicians insist on continuing or resuming their administration of such "nonaddictive" drugs to patients who are in treatment for chemical dependency and even to patients whose drugs of preference are the very drugs that the physicians wish to prescribe.

PHYSICAL TOLERANCE

A second physical element occurs often enough in chemical dependency to warrant comment. It is the phenomenon that is commonly referred to as the "physical tolerance factor." **Physical tolerance** is the ability of the human organism to absorb relatively large dosages of drugs without proportionate adverse effects. It appears clinically, as well as in common observation, as the ability of a person to ingest large quantities of drugs without apparently experiencing effects proportionate to the size of the dosages. As increased dosages are ingested, the drug user's capacity increases; larger quantities are then required to produce the same highs produced previously by smaller dosages.

Upon noting this phenomenon, drug users and those around them naively assume that there is no danger of getting into trouble with the drugs because they can "handle their highs" or "hold their liquor." The very opposite is true, of course. One of the surest signs of chemical dependency is an increase of tolerance for one's drug of preference, because the first appearance of the tolerance factor indicates that physical dependency or addiction is already present. By the time the tolerance factor shows up, therefore, chemical dependency is already present. There is then no room for debate about whether or not the person may become dependent. The diagnosis is already established and certain.

The Break and Reversal

At one point in the illness, this tolerance "breaks" and appears to go into reverse. It is believed by some that the break in tolerance marks the transition, in some dependents at least, from the relief stage to the maintenance stage of the illness. In any case, after the break dependents find that decreased drug dosages produce disproportionately increased adverse effects that are both unwelcome and destructive.

It has not been established conclusively that the tolerance factor is present in dependencies on all mood-altering chemicals. And since present research indicates that some dependencies may never include this factor, we have additional grounds at this time for questioning whether or not it belongs to the essential pathology of chemical dependency.

A puzzling aspect of the break and decrease in tolerance in the case of some drugs is the fact that tolerance can never be restored or recovered. Still more puzzling is the fact that after it breaks, the tolerance does not remain static. Instead, it steadily decreases whether or not the dependent continues to actually ingest drugs. If drug ingestion is resumed, even after many drug-free years, it is found that tolerance is at a lower level than it was when abstention began. It is as though one had been taking drugs all the while.

Psychological Effects of Tolerance

Although the tolerance factor is physical, its principal significance for dependents and for their enablers is psychological. Both believe, as a rule, that the capacity to handle large quantities of drugs without proportionate visible effects is an assurance that there is no danger of dependency. But the opposite is true, as we have seen. Thus, their delusion is reinforced and they feel assured that all is well.

Besides the delusion created and reinforced by the tolerance factor, there are other psychological and social effects. Persons who can handle their highs or hold their liquor accept this as a mark of distinction and subtly or openly claim recognition for it. They tend to gain the recognition they seek and to be set up as models of "social" drug use for others to imitate, while those who cannot match such prowess are rejected as models. By thus establishing the image of the "two-fisted" drinker or drugger as a cultural hero, the community unwittingly adopts chemically dependent drug abuse as its norm. We need not expand on the import of this for building and maintaining collective defenses around chemical dependency and drug abuse.

Ego Inflation and Tolerance

Another whole group of psychological effects gather around the inflated self-image or "big ego" of dependents. Big ego is actually overcompensation for a weak or shriveled ego, a low self-image. It feeds on trivia, which it magnifies to produce appearances of greatness. Hence, it is called "grandiosity" or "delusions of grandeur." If one has a large tolerance for drugs, it feeds into the ego inflation up to the point where the tolerance breaks. Then, with this basis for "greatness" removed, the blown-up ego is punctured and ego deflation begins to occur. This in turn plunges dependents into a twofold struggle, first, to recover "control," and second, to cover up the loss of tolerance, which dependents interpret as a personal weakness resulting in loss of control.

In the first struggle, dependents mistakenly assume that their great capacity to tolerate drugs was due to superior power of self-control. In their eyes, and in the eyes of others, it was a tribute to their extraordinary "will power." So now it seems to them and to others that they are relaxing their self-control too much too often and that they should put forth more will power to maintain or to regain their self-control. They try and try, but try to no avail. They are just as unaware of the drug compulsion that has long since neutralized will power as they are of the unrelatedness of tolerance and self-control. The second struggle — the efforts to conceal the loss of tolerance — is not quite as bitter, perhaps, because the defense system is already well-practiced in cover-up. It does add a considerable area to be covered up, however, since the adverse consequences of the break in tolerance are extensive.

MEMORY BLACKOUT

A third factor of significance in the physical symptomatology of chemical dependency is physical memory impairment by **blackout**. This is a chemically induced temporary memory failure caused by the blocking of memory reception centers in the brain and/or by the impairment of nerve centers or transmission routes for memory materials. This phenomenon, while common, is not necessarily universally present in every case of chemical dependency. When it does occur, it appears as total or partial amnesia.

As we have noted elsewhere, total blackout affects the memory while leaving other functional powers operational. In such a blackout, dependents may appear to be quite normal, may engage in coherent conversation, and even carry on many activities in what seems to be a normal way. Later, however, there will be no recollection of this. The memory materials that normally would have been produced by these personal experiences are not available for recall. Understandably, this becomes confusing to others who are not aware of the blacked-out condition and who therefore assume that dependents recall as well as they do what happened during a blackout episode. Dependents naturally deny knowledge of what happened and hence are likely to be judged liars, even though they give every appearance of sincerity.

Certain psychological effects of blackout have been discussed elsewhere, particularly in Chapter Ten. Note especially that blackouts create great anxiety for dependents and also contribute heavily to their delusion, because what occurs in blackouts is unknown to them and is therefore not a part of the reality with which they are in touch.

Other Physical Complications

Beyond these three factors, we do not see other physical elements as essential to chemical dependency. And these three are included conditionally and with reservations since we do not yet have conclusive evidence that they are always present in the pathology of every chemical dependency.

Other physical manifestations that have come to be associated or identified with chemical dependency and even to be widely used for diagnostic purposes are accidental complications that ordinarily do not appear until later stages, if they appear at all. To base diagnosis on liver and brain damage, acute gastritis, pancreatitis, circulatory dysfunctions, malnutrition, etc., is like diagnosing obesity when a person weighs five hundred pounds. And as for treatment of these complications, they have, in innumerable cases, been treated, alleviated, and in some cases healed, at least temporarily, without the slightest indication of the patient's recovery from chemical dependency.

PHYSICAL SYMPTOMS/COMPLICATIONS

Some physical symptoms are manifested with all particular episodes or incidents of drug abuse. Coming down from a high, or crashing, or suffering a hangover is characterized by physical reactions such as nervous excitation, accelerated heartbeat, mild tremors, gastrointestinal distress, headache, and so on. These are symptoms of *drug abuse*, but they are not necessarily symptoms of chemical dependency. Such symptoms may appear repeatedly with repeated drug abuse. But in such cases, it is the *repeated drug abuse itself* that is a symptom of dependency, not the bodily reactions to particular incidences of excessive drug ingestion.

In order to qualify as *essential* symptoms of chemical dependency, physical symptoms, like all the others, must appear consistently as parts of a pattern or syndrome that manifests the underlying illness or pathology. In other words, all the diagnostician can properly conclude from withdrawal symptoms as such is that a client has ingested drugs excessively and is now experiencing typical physical reactions. A diagnosis of chemical dependency would not be warranted on the basis of this data alone.

Physical symptoms appear as outgrowths of *physical tolerance*, of *physical addiction*, and of drug-induced *memory failure*. In presenting the following as symptoms, we do so tentatively and conditionally, since it has not been demonstrated conclusively that these three elements of physical pathology or their symptoms are present in every case of chemical dependency.

General Symptom: Increased Tolerance

A general physical symptom of chemical dependency is an increase of tolerance or capacity for drugs as ingestion is repeated over a period of time.

Particular Symptoms of Increased Tolerance

1. An *ability* to ingest increasing quantities of drugs without experiencing proportionate increased effects.

2. A *need* to ingest larger quantities of drugs in order to achieve the same effects formerly produced by smaller quantities.

3. An ability to *hold* one's liquor or to *handle* one's highs. This demonstrates that a high tolerance has already developed and hence is a symptom of late pleasure stage or of relief stage dependency. This is one of the symptoms most easily recognized by others and is often the object of admiration and envy by those whose capacity is more limited.

4. A capacity to absorb large quantities of *anesthetic* without proportionate effects. This is observed in surgical settings.

General Symptom: Break and Decrease in Tolerance

Physical dependency is manifested by the general symptom of a break, followed by a decrease, in tolerance.

Particular Symptoms of Break and Decrease in Tolerance

1. Increased *adverse effects* with decreased drug dosages: "I can't handle it like I used to."

2. Adverse effects notably *disproportionate* to the decreased drug dosages. Because this occurs after the illness is well

advanced and because the progression sometimes takes many years, it is often attributed to age factors. However, the fact that it occurs among youth as well as among those approaching or into middle age shows that factors other than aging are productive of this symptom.

3. Decreasing tolerance during periods (even many years) of *total abstinence.* This becomes evident if and when ingestion is resumed.

General Symptom: Inability To Function "Normally"

A general symptom of physical addiction is the inability of dependents to function "normally" without frequent dosages of drugs. This symptom appears when dependents reach an advanced stage of the illness — the maintenance stage — characterized by a "drug-dependent normalcy."

Particular Symptoms of Inability To Function "Normally"

1. *Physical agitation* when drug ingestion is delayed beyond customary intervals. This is not the mental and emotional anxiety that is a symptom of psychological dependency, obsession, and compulsion; it is a state of physical agitation that precedes physical withdrawal.

2. *Loss of motor coordination* and disordered and incoherent speech when drug dosages are considerably reduced.

3. *Nerve and muscular spasms* of the face, arms, hands, and legs (severe tremors or "shakes") when drug dosages are considerably reduced or terminated.

4. *Acute withdrawal symptoms* such as visual and auditory hallucinations, convulsions, and delirium tremens when ingestion is terminated.

General Symptom: Blackout

A general symptom of drug-related memory failure is *blackout*, that is, a total inability to recall events, conversations, and personal behaviors that occurred during a drug-abuse episode.

Particular Symptoms of Blackout

1. *Surprise, confusion, and puzzlement* when presented with data about what happened during a drug-abuse episode.

2. *Disbelief and denial* when presented with such data.

3. *Leading questions, cautious inquiries* about what happened during such episodes. A dependent attempts to cover up blackouts while gathering information from others to fill in the memory gaps.

4. *Furtive searches and inspections* in attempts to piece together what happened. For example, looking out the window or going to the family garage the "morning after" to see if the car is there and in one piece because the dependent cannot remember coming home or how he or she got home; searching for "misplaced" items (keys, checkbook, money, drug supplies, etc.) that disappeared during blackouts.

5. Cautious, tentative responses to questions asked or comments made about what happened during a drug-abuse episode. This is another way of trying to conceal blackouts while piecing together what actually occurred.

General Symptom: Euphoric Memory Recall

A general symptom of drug-related memory failure is euphoric memory recall, that is, vivid recall of euphoric or "high" feelings, but only partial and distorted recall of events, conversations, and personal behaviors that occurred during a drug-abuse episode.

Particular Symptoms of Euphoric Memory Recall

1. The same five particular symptoms that are produced by blackout, noted above, may also be symptoms of euphoric memory impairment.

2. *Vivid recall of euphoric feelings,* of how good one felt during a drug-abuse episode, with only partial recall of what actually went on.

3. *Partial recall* of events, conversations, and behaviors, but inability to recall details or the manner in which things took place, for example, slurred and incoherent speech, staggering, etc.

4. *Distorted recall*, confused recollections of circumstances and disorientation regarding times, places, and sequences of events.

5. *Laughing it off*, making a joke or a game of any references to inappropriate behaviors to cover up one's memory impairment.

PHYSICAL ELEMENTS IN CHEMICAL DEPENDENCY SUMMARY OF SYMPTOMS

General Symptom of Physical Tolerance: Increased Tolerance

Particular Symptoms:

1. Ability to ingest large quantities of drugs without proportionate effects.
2. Need for larger quantities to produce same effects.
3. Ability to "hold one's liquor" or to "handle one's highs."
4. Ability to absorb large quantities of anesthetic without proportionate effects.

General Symptom of Physical Tolerance: Break and Decrease in Tolerance

Particular Symptoms:

1. Increased adverse effects with decreased drug dosages.
2. Adverse effects notably disproportionate to decreased drug dosages.
3. Decreasing tolerance even during periods of total abstinence.

General Symptom of Physical Addiction: Inability To Function "Normally" Without Drugs

Particular Symptoms:

1. Physical agitation when ingestion is delayed beyond accustomed intervals.
2. Loss of motor coordination, etc., when dosages are considerably reduced.
3. Nerve and muscular spasms when dosages are considerably reduced or terminated.
4. Sub-acute withdrawal symptoms: hangovers, spacing out, crashing.
5. Acute withdrawal symptoms: hallucinations, convulsions, delirium tremens.

General Symptom of Memory Failure: Blackouts

Particular Symptoms:

1. Surprise, confusion, and puzzlement when presented with data about drug-abuse episode.
2. Disbelief and denial of such data.
3. Leading questions, cautious inquiries about what happened during drug-abuse episode.
4. Furtive searches and inspections.
5. Cautious, tentative responses to questions about drug-abuse episodes.

General Symptom of Memory Failure: Euphoric Memory Recall

Particular Symptoms:

1. The same five particular symptoms produced by blackout.
2. Vivid recall of euphoric feelings, with only partial recall of what happened and how it happened.
3. Partial recall of events, conversations, and behavior without recall of details.
4. Distorted and confused recall; disorientation regarding times, places, and sequence of events.
5. "Laughing it off" to cover up memory impairment.

PART THREE

The
Essential Causes
of
Chemical Dependency

CHAPTER FIFTEEN

The Problem
of
Causes

The Many "Whys" of Chemical Dependency

The fact that millions of dollars and work-hours are spent each year on research into the causes of drug ingestion, drug misuse, drug abuse, and chemical dependency is persuasive evidence of the importance we attach to discovering the "whys" of these phenomena.

Chemical dependency is a major national health and social problem; it is in fact a major problem internationally. *Why?*

Many people of all ages, of all personality types, with every background of opportunity, education, and experience, on every social and economic level and in every profession, occupation, and walk of life, are pathologically dependent on mood-altering chemicals. *Why?*

Drug misuse and drug abuse are increasing rapidly among children and adolescents. *Why?*

By any standard of measurement, the consequences of chemical dependency are enormously destructive to individuals, to families, to businesses and industries, to communities, and to nations. *Why?*

The illness, chemical dependency, is far beyond epidemic proportions, it is pandemic. *Why?*

These are but a few of the endless questions we keep asking about chemical dependency. Why do we persist in asking "why"? Because we know there are answers to the questions, "Why do people ingest drugs?", "Why do they misuse drugs?", "Why do they abuse drugs?", and "Why do they become chemically dependent?"

We know there are answers from the fact that there are reasons or causes for everything. Whether or not we ever *discover* the reasons, we are nonetheless aware that nothing, including drug problems, would or could exist *without* causes. We are cause-seeking beings, and our constant quest of causes is the prompter of our incessant "whys," from the dawn of reason to the dark of the grave.

It is not a mere matter of convenience, but often a matter of survival, that as rational human beings we learn the causes of things and events. In fact, learning cause-and-effect relationships is what reason and rationality are all about. We exercise our rationality and fulfill our rational nature when we probe, discover, and understand the **rationales** of things and events, that is, their causes, the reasons why they are as they are, or why they came about, or why they act or operate as they do. We know *that* things are when we perceive them directly in their existential reality. But our minds do not rest with knowing only that things are; we are not mentally comfortable until we come to know *why* things are. Our need to know the causes of things is so deep that our mental health depends on it. We become mentally unsound, unhealthy in mind, when our need to know causes is seriously frustrated.

Pragmatically, too, and right to the point in our context, we need to know the causes of drug problems. If their causes escape us, their solutions also escape us. But if their causes can be identified, if our "whys" about drug problems can be answered with certainty, we can educate to prevent them, recognize them when they are present, and go on to solve them successfully.

"Why" Is a Complex Question

Before attempting to answer the question, "What is (or what causes) chemical dependency?" by identifying its various causes, some preliminary clarifications are in order.

"Why" is a simple three-letter word. But the content of this word is vast. To expect an easy, simple answer to the question "why?" is to invite frustration, disappointment, and confusion. And to adopt a single factor causality approach in exploring the whys of chemical dependency — or of any existential reality — is the height of naiveté. Probably the greatest block to our understanding of reality is our universal human tendency to oversimplify, to ask "why?" and then to feed our minds on mere bits and pieces of "because." We are impatient to have our answers before we ourselves know the meaning of our questions.

If you ask me "why?" about *anything*, I cannot answer your question until I know at least the sense in which you ask it. "Why?" is always a confusing question unless and until both you, the questioner, and I, the one questioned, are certain about the kind of causality implied in your question.

One Question, Many Possible Answers

For example, you may notice a new car in my garage and ask me, "Why the car?" I may answer, "For transportation," interpreting your question as a search for the ultimate purpose of the machine in my garage. Or I might reply to your query, "Because X Company manufactured it," thinking that you are asking for the reason it is in existence at all, or who made it.

Another perfectly reasonable answer (not knowing what *specific* information you are seeking with your "why" question) could be, "Because it's not a boat or a snowmobile or a motorbike." That would be a general but accurate answer if I interpreted your question to mean, "Why is it a car instead of something else?" In this case, my answer would tell you that it is specifically and precisely a car and not another kind of a machine, because it is structured or designed to be a car.

Or, again, I might respond by saying that it is a car because it is a collection of nuts, bolts, steel, glass, chrome, plastic, rubber, and other assorted bits and pieces. The same materials might have been put together in the form of some other machine, but in this case they were assembled to make a car.

Categories of Causality

Each of my answers is given in a different category of causality. Before a satisfactory reply can be made, both you and I must know the category in which you are asking your question. So when you ask, "What is (or what causes) chemical dependency?" do you mean:

- What *motivates* people or *attracts* them to ingest mood-altering chemicals?

- Or, what is the *purpose* or *goal* of ingesting drugs?

- Or, whose actions produce chemical dependency?

- Or, what is the *intrinsic* pattern of chemical dependency?

- Or, what *form* does its pathology take?

- Or, what is the *subject* in which chemical dependency exists, resides, or is embedded — that is, *where* is it essentially?

Actually, when you ask, "What is (or what causes) chemical dependency?" you are asking a very complex question because chemical dependency has many causes. To answer that question, each of three areas of contributing factors — the *person*, the *agent* or *drug*, and the *environment* — must be explored. The causal input of each of the three factors must be identified first in terms of the four basic kinds of causality, and then in terms of various contributing causal influences included under each kind of causality.

What Do I Want To Know?

One way to sort out for myself the *kind* of causation I am inquiring about is to stop and ask myself, "What do I want to know?"

- Do I want to know the *purpose* for which something exists, the *goal* or *objective* of it? If so, I am asking my question and expecting my answer in terms of "finality," that is, the end purpose of it. The kind or category of causation I want to know about is **final cause.**

- Do I want to know what *brought it about* or who or what *produced it or brought it into being or moved it* along the way? If so, I am asking my question and expecting my answer in terms of "efficiency," that is, the maker or mover or producer of the thing in question. Then the kind of causation I want to know about is **efficient cause.**

- Do I want to know what *shape* or *form* or *plan* or *structure* or *design* it has within it? If so, my question and its answer will be in terms of "formality," that is, the particular specific form of it that makes it this thing instead of that, for example, a tree and not a cow. Here the kind of causation is **formal cause.**

- Or do I want to know what it is *made out of*, what *materials went into it*, or *in what form it exists*, or in what *subject* does this particular form reside? If so, my question and its answer will be in terms of "materiality," that is, the matter or stuff out of which it is made and in which its form exists. In this case, the kind of causation is **material cause.**

- Or, do I really want to know any of these causes at all? Perhaps I want to know only about *circumstances*, such as time or place or space or quantity or measurements, that is, perhaps I am only asking "when?" or "where?" or "how far?" or "how much?" or "how big?" Or, finally, do I want to know only about the conditions under which something happened or came into being, or the occasion on which it took place? In all of these cases, I am not asking about true causes but only about incidentals and accidentals.

Turning our attention directly to chemical dependency, what is it you want to know when you ask about the causes or the "whys" of this illness?

WHAT DO YOU WANT TO KNOW ABOUT CHEMICAL DEPENDENCY?

Final Cause?

When you ask, "What causes people to be chemically dependent?" do you want to know what *goal* they are seeking to achieve, what *purpose* they pursue in their ingestion of mood-altering chemicals? If so, you are asking your question in terms of the *finality*, the final cause or the "end-purpose causation" of chemical dependency. And the answer is: they are seeking the *rewarding experiences* that drugs can give them. Their purpose, their goal, in ingesting drugs is to achieve pleasure or relief, or to maintain their drug dependent "normalcy," or to escape to oblivion. What causes chemical dependency (in terms of final cause) is their ingestion of drugs in pursuit of rewarding experiences.

Efficient Cause?

Do you want to know what it is or who it is that *acts* or *moves* or *takes action to produce* chemical dependency in people? If so, you are asking your question in terms of the "effector," the efficient cause, the direct producer of the illness. And the answer is the *persons themselves*, the individuals who at first decide and choose and take personal action to ingest drugs into their bodies, who go on to make a personal commitment to getting high on drugs and thereby set up their personal pathological relationship to drugs, and who then lose control of their drug relationship and go on to ingest drugs compulsively. What causes chemical dependency (as efficient causes) are the persons who ingest mood-altering chemicals.

Motivational Cause?

Do you want to know more particularly what it is that *prompts* people to become chemically dependent, what stirs them up, whets their appetite for good, and triggers their actual ingestion and induces them to make their committed drug relationship? If so, you are asking about their motivation, and that is a double question. First, you are asking what they have in mind that gets them moving, what *decides* them to move. And secondly, you are asking what inclination or impulse stimulates them to action, what makes them *choose* to move. The answer is: their *expectation of rewarding experiences* by means of drug ingestion. This same motivation is the push behind their commitment to a permanent drug relationship. And this expectation remains as their motivation even after they become obsessed and can no longer make rational decisions. It remains even after compulsion has destroyed their power to make free choices in matters concerning drugs. The motivational cause of chemical dependency, therefore, is a person's *expectation* of rewarding experiences.

Formal Cause?

When you ask, "What causes people to be chemically dependent?" do you want to know what it is that makes them sick, why they are in the shape they're in? If so, you are asking what form or kind of illness they have, what is the specific illness that is making them sick. Your inquiry now is about formal causality, about the particular *pattern of elements* that make it this illness instead of another. Your answer is: a *pathological love relationship*, a personal, committed, sick love relationship to mood-altering chemicals. What causes chemical dependency in the category of formal causality is the pattern of pathology that originates in and develops around a person's *committed love relationship* to drugs.

Material Cause?

Finally, do you want to know the cause of chemical dependency in the sense of "what is it in?" or "who is it in?" or "where is it?" — that is, what or who is the subject in which this pathological relationship exists, the *subject* or *substance* in which this form exists? You are now inquiring about *material causality*, the matter or stuff or receptacle in which the sickness resides or inheres. The answer is: this sick relationship is *in a person* as its subject of inherence. The cause of chemical dependency in the category of material causality is the person who is its subject of inherence.

Drugs as a Cause?

Do you want to know how drugs cause chemical dependency? If so, you are asking several questions. You are asking first, "What is there about or in certain drugs that cause this illness?" And, "Why are they so attractive to people?" Or, "Why do people find them so desirable?" The answer to all three questions is: their *psychoactive power*, that is, their inherent capacity to alter moods and minds, to significantly change the way one feels. Hence, they are called "mood-altering chemicals."

You are also asking, "How do these drugs make people sick?" The answer is: people *ingest* them and get *rewards*. Then, when they have experienced drug rewards, they set up a personal ongoing relationship having drugs as its object; they make a *commitment to getting high on drugs*. This committed drug relationship then *directly* causes the pathology of chemical dependency.

Finally, you are asking, "What kind of causation do drugs exercise?" The answer is: a kind of *efficient causality*. They are instruments or means used by persons to produce an effect, like tools used by mechanics to produce effects. The mechanic is a principal efficient cause; his tools are instrumental efficient causes. So also a person is the *principal efficient* cause of drug ingestion and drugs are the *instrumental efficient* causes. The person uses the drugs as means to produce the desired highs.

Environments as a Cause?

Do you want to know how environments cause chemical dependency? Here you are asking at least two questions. First, "What do environments do to persons to cause them to get into drugs?" The answer is: environments *dispose* or *incline* or *prepare* people to take drugs. They exert the influence of environmental pressures and examples. Secondly, you are asking, "What kinds of causation do environments exercise?" The answer is: two kinds, both dispositive.

Pressures are a kind of efficient or producer causality; they dispose us by pushing or pressuring us toward using drugs and toward using them in certain ways.

Examples are a kind of formal causality; they dispose us by presenting "how-to-do-it" pictures, patterns, or plans of action, models or forms of conduct that attract or draw us toward imitation. We internalize these examples, make them our own, and then act them out in our own behavior. In other words, we reproduce in our own behavior the examples set before us for imitation.

Circumstances, Conditions, and Occasions?

Do you want to know the circumstances that surround and accompany chemical dependency? Now you are no longer asking about proper causes, but about other factors that may or may not be present and that may or may not be relevant if they are present. The only possible answers to questions about circumstances must come from individual cases and from the individual circumstances of each case. Circumstances, in other words, are *not directly or properly* causative; they just happen to be around.

Finally, do you want to know the conditions under which people become chemically dependent or the occasions of their dependencies? If so, then again you are no longer asking about causes in the proper sense, but about other incidental factors that have no direct connection at all with chemical dependency. It is, for example, a condition of chemical dependency that some drugs are available to ingest. But the mere condition of availability does not *cause* you to use them. Again, occasions for drug ingestion are around us almost all the time. But the mere existence of occasions never *causes* anyone to take drugs. Conditions, occasions, and circumstances, in other words, may be *correlative*, but they are *not causative* in the proper sense.

For the convenience of students of chemical dependency and of professionals in the field, we offer in the following chapters two schematic outlines to summarize the foregoing exploration of the causes of this illness. In doing so, we employ as framework the four basic kinds or categories of causality examined above — namely *final, efficient, formal,* and *material causes* — and indicate the aspects of the illness that identify the causal input of each.

CHAPTER SIXTEEN

Causal Input
of
Contributing Factors

The purpose of the following outline is to identify in summary form the precise kind of causality (causation) exercised by each factor that contributes to chemical dependency.

I. **In the category of final cause,** that is, the essential *purpose* for which mood-altering chemicals are ingested and which leads a person into chemical dependency:

    A. What is *the ultimate purpose*, that is, what is it the person seeks as the ultimate goal-to-be-achieved? It is the rewarding experience or a welcome change of feeling or mood or mind. The rewarding experience sought varies in the successive stages of the illness, starting with pleasure or pleasant moods and moving on to relief, then to maintenance, and finally to escape to oblivion.

    B. What is *the immediate or proximate purpose*, that is, what is the here-and-now goal-to-be-achieved, the first or necessary goal to be accomplished as a necessary step toward or as a means of achieving the ultimate goal? It is the *actual ingestion* of mood-altering chemicals.

    C. What is *the motive*, that is, what is it that gets a person going on the way to actually seeking that ultimate rewarding experience? It is an *expectation* or anticipation of the ultimate rewarding experience. Thinking about it, recalling past experiences of it, and fantasizing about it stir up an inclination to seek it again. One is thus motivated or moved to go after it again, to ingest the drug in order to experience again its welcome effects.

II. **In the category of efficient cause,** that is, the essential *mover* or *producer* whose personal action of ingesting drugs puts one on the road to chemical dependency:

A. What is *the principal or primary mover or producer (the principal efficient cause)?* It is the person who acts to ingest drugs and who makes a personal commitment to getting high on drugs and thereby establishes a permanent pathological relationship to drugs or a committed drug relationship.

B. The drug itself is a *passive instrument* (an instrumental efficient cause) that depends upon being used by another, a principal mover, to be activated and thus to produce its effects.

C. The *external environment* (the socio-cultural environment) surrounding both the person and the agent (the drug), and especially the people in the external environment, influence persons by exerting pressures to ingest drugs, to do so in particular ways, and to continue or to terminate their ingestion. These influences induce dispositions within the person and therefore exercise *dispositive efficient causality* toward (or away from) chemical dependency.

D. Similarly, the *internal environment* of a person (the psychophysical environment) may apply pressures and induce dispositions toward (or away from) chemical dependency. This, too, is *dispositive efficient causality*. But note well that these dispositions are at most only a susceptibility or readiness; they do not and cannot in and of themselves directly cause chemical dependency. The *person must act* as the principal and direct efficient cause to ingest drugs and to become pathologically dependent on them.

III. **In the category of formal cause,** that is, the essential specific *form* or *pattern* of chemical dependency that makes it this particular illness instead of another:

A. The *pathological love relationship* of the person to mood-altering chemicals is the *essential intrinsic* form or "formality" that gives specificity to chemical dependency — that is, chemical dependency is essentially, intrinsically, formally, and precisely this committed pathological love relationship. This design, form, or characteristic pattern of chemical dependency is within the actual drug relationship that exists within the person. The essential pathological elements or components that go into and make up this design or pattern are formal aspects of the illness and proper to chemical dependency as such; they form a characteristic pattern that is present wherever chemical dependency exists. In fact, for chemical dependency to exist, these formal or "formative" elements necessarily *must* be present. The essential *symptoms*, too, are formal aspects of the illness. These symptoms taken together form the pattern that is the chemical dependency *syndrome*.

B. The *external environment* surrounding a person exercises a type of formal causality by presenting examples or models of drug ingestion. These examples whet our appetites for good. They influence us by their attractiveness and draw us or dispose us toward imitation. When the examples are internalized, they become patterns for our personal drug ingestion and our drug-related behaviors and thus dispose us in our *internal environment* toward acting out these patterns. This is *dispositive formal causality* toward (or away from) chemical dependency.

IV. **In the category of material cause,** that is, the "matter" out of which a thing is made or in which it exists.

Note that when the material causality of a relationship is explored, the focus is directed toward the *point of origin and continuation* and the *point of termination* of the relationship. A relationship, properly speaking, is not a material thing; it does not have true matter like a stone or a tree; it is a transcendental reality. To identify the material cause of a relationship, therefore, we regard the relation as if it were informing or embedded in some matter. The question we ask is: "In what, or where, does this relationship reside?" To put the question in another way: "What is the material *subject* and what is the material *object* of this relationship?" In chemical dependency, the point of origin and continuation, or the "material" subject in which the relationship inheres, is the *person* who is chemically dependent. The point toward which the relationship is directed and in which it terminates, or the "material" object of the relationship, is the agent, the *mood-altering chemical.*

CHAPTER SEVENTEEN

Causes
in the
Essential Definition

The purpose of this outline is to indicate clearly how the causality (causation) exercised by each factor contributing to chemical dependency is included in the essential definition of the illness.

I. **Essential Definition**

Chemical dependency is essentially a committed pathological love relationship of a person to a mood-altering chemical substance, a psychoactive drug, in expectation of a rewarding experience.

II. **General Causal Factors**

- The *person* who is chemically dependent.

- The *agent* or drug that is ingested by the person.

- The *environments* surrounding the person and the drug ingestion: the environment outside the person (socio-cultural or external environment) and the environment inside the person (psychophysical or internal environment).

III. **Particular Causal Inputs** of these three factors as expressed in the essential definition.

A. Final Causes:

1. *The Ultimate Reason Why*: "Rewarding experience" states the ultimate *goal* or end-purpose cause for ingesting mood-altering chemicals and for making one's committed drug relationship. This is the ultimate "reason why" a person becomes chemically dependent.

2. *The Motive of Expectation*: "In expectation of" states the motive. It is the "goal-in-anticipation" or the "goal-in-one's-intention," that is, the goal as it attracts and induces one to move toward achievement of it by taking the necessary intermediate steps.

3. *The Proximate Goal*: The *actual ingestion* of drugs is an immediate or proximate *goal* insofar as it is a necessary intermediate step toward achieving the rewarding experience that is the ultimate goal. With repeated drug ingestion, chemical dependency develops, and once the illness sets in, it remains whether or not actual ingestion is taking place.

B. Efficient Causes

1. "A person" is the *principal efficient cause* of chemical dependency. It is a person who expects the rewarding experience and who therefore moves or acts to ingest drugs and who makes a commitment to getting high on drugs. The person's repeated acts of drug ingestion and the person's continuing commitment to drugs causes chemical dependency within that person.

2. "To a mood-altering chemical substance, a psychoactive drug." This is the *instrumental efficient cause* of chemical dependency. The person (the principal efficient cause) uses the drug as an instrument in order to achieve the rewarding experience of drug highs.

3. The *environment* (external and internal) exerts pressures that influence a person by disposing him or her toward (or away from) drug ingestion, drug abuse, and a committed drug relationship. Environmental *pressures* are *dispositive efficient causes* of chemical dependency. Whether the pressures are from outside a person or from within a person, their effect or product is to dispose the person toward, not to directly cause, drug abuse and/or chemical dependency.

C. Formal Causes

1. "A pathological or sick love relationship" states the specific, *intrinsic form*, the precise formality that is chemical dependency essentially. This relationship of

the person to a mood-altering chemical, as it actually exists within the person, is the *intrinsic formal cause* that gives to chemical dependency its *specificity*, its uniqueness as an illness.

2. "Pathological or sick" states the *quality* of the relationship. It is unhealthy. The relationship as it exists within a person is characterized by a typical pattern, design, structure, or configuration of pathological elements. The pathological elements, in other words, give the *form* to this relationship and manifest it by a typical pattern of *symptoms* and a specific chemical dependency syndrome made up of these symptoms taken collectively.

3. "Pathological relationship" also states a *kind* of relationship to drugs that can be seen and imitated by people other than dependents. Dependents, in other words, show others one way of relating to drugs; they exhibit or exemplify one form of drug relationship — a sick one. Others may internalize this example and thereby become disposed to imitate it by acting it out in their own drug relationship. This *example*, as it is presented in one's external environment and as it becomes a part of one's internal environment, is an "exemplary" or *formal dispositive cause*.

D. Material Causes

1. "A person" is the "matter," that is, the subject in which the chemical dependency relationship resides or inheres, as in its point of origin and continuation. The relationship is in the person as a form is in matter. Without a person as its subject, the relationship would not and could not exist. The person therefore is the material subject that causes chemical dependency.

2. "A mood-altering chemical substance, a psychoactive drug" is also the "matter," that is, the *object* toward which the drug relationship is directed and in which it terminates. Without such a drug as its object, the relationship would not and could not exist. The drug, therefore, is the material object that causes chemical dependency.

233

PART FOUR

Chemical Dependency
Diagnosis and Evaluation

CHAPTER EIGHTEEN

An Overview of Chemical Dependency Diagnosis and Evaluation

The urgent need for early diagnosis of chemical dependency — alcoholism and the other drug dependencies — is clear to all who are concerned with drug problems. On every side we hear voices calling for a higher level of public awareness of the early symptoms of this illness and for a higher quality of professional expertise in diagnosing it, especially in its initial stages. Yet despite the increasing calls for early recognition, and despite all that has been learned in the past half century, diagnosis still generally remains at chronic later-stage levels because the common current focus of diagnosis remains on *complications* and not on *essential symptoms*.

Alcoholics Anonymous originated with acute terminal-stage alcoholics, with those who had "hit bottom." Its first members were "hopeless cases," at skid-row, hard rock bottoms. Experience proved that it is not necessary to wait until one has hit this "low bottom" before intervention and recovery are possible. For that reason, A.A. has moved its focus upward from the terminal escape stage, through the maintenance stage, and into the relief stage. A similar upward shift of focus has taken place throughout the field, followed at some considerable distance by an upward trend in the general level of public awareness.

Much of the material that follows in this section has appeared in some detail earlier in this book. We present that information here in a new context, to show its practical application in a diagnostic setting. In doing so, our hope is that this material will serve as a valuable, reasonably brief, and sharply focused reference guide for persons in the helping professions who are faced with determining the presence of chemical dependency in a patient or client. This section may also prove helpful to family members concerned about the presence of chemical dependency in a loved one, and it may even be of some help to chemically dependent persons themselves as they come to grips with their addiction.

Obstacles to Early Diagnosis

The movement toward earlier recognition and intervention has been slowed by the difficulty we have in identifying early indicators of alcoholism and the other drug dependencies.

Another, and serious, obstacle to early diagnosis based on essential symptoms is our compulsive urge to *oversimplify*. If there is one inherent fault from which we all appear to suffer, it would seem to be a congenital haste to have our answers before we know (or pause to ask) exactly what we are asking. We press quick-answer buttons and expect neat fixes to come popping out in tidy mini-packages. Essential symptoms of chemical dependency are so massive that they practically defy enumeration. Therefore, if we try to simplify the diagnostic process by limiting our focus to a few of our favorite symptoms, we close the door to early recognition and to accurate and objective diagnosis and evaluation.

It is not so much that essential symptoms are not known or knowable, but that they often are not recognized for what they are. No doubt a part of our difficulty in recognizing them is our tendency to look too exclusively for *physical* symptoms and thus to overlook both the presence and the abundance of personality, character, life-style, attitudinal, and behavioral symptoms of this *relational* illness.

Other obstacles, of course, are the widespread social defensiveness surrounding early-stage dependency and the moralistic attitudes with which the illness continues to be regarded. If, for example, I myself am dependent on my drug ingestion and my drug relationship for the pay-offs that they yield to me, I am not easily persuaded to take a careful look at the symptoms I exhibit. These symptoms include the following:

1. the drug-oriented personality and life style changes that I am undergoing;
2. the drug-related character deterioration that I am experiencing;
3. the drug-protective negative and defensive attitudes that I am developing;
4. and the inappropriate drug-induced and drug-related behavior that I am repeating.

All of these are early and essential symptoms, but my case, multiplied by millions, sets up formidable social barriers against their recognition. And further, if I mistakenly believe that by diagnosing chemical dependency I am thereby passing moral judgment on my loved ones, friends, or clients — or myself — as weak-willed moral degenerates or morally evil persons, then understandably, I — and they — will be reluctant to recognize the early symptoms of our common illness.

In order to move the focus toward the early stages and even to the beginnings of chemical dependency, we must probe beyond complications into proper symptoms, and beyond symptoms into the underlying chemical dependency pathology that causes the symptoms.

To do this is a major objective of this book and the rationale for approaching chemical dependency with our focus on its essential aspects. If this book accomplishes nothing else, it may perhaps continue to encourage the move toward early diagnosis, intervention, and treatment.

Co-occurring Disorders

The examination of personality and behavioral symptoms can potentially become complicated by the fact that many people have co-occurring chemical dependency and mental health disorders. It is well documented that people with diagnosable psychiatric disorders are at a higher risk for substance abuse than the general population. This occurs, in part, because of attempts by individuals to "self-medicate" an emotional or psychiatric problem. The flip side of this is that persons with severe substance abuse problems may display symptoms of psychiatric disorders, such as severe depression, anxiety, rage, and suicidal behavior. In many cases, these individuals have no history of mental health problems prior to their becoming chemically dependent.

Despite the interactions and complications that occur between the two conditions, chemical dependency and an emotional/psychiatric condition are two separate, independent problems, and they must be identified as such, when they exist, for an individual to fully recover. A dual diagnosis by both a qualified chemical dependency professional and a trained mental health clinician may be required to ensure that the individual receives accurate, comprehensive diagnosis.

In the past, a person with a co-occurring disorder often came into chemical dependency treatment with a psychiatric diagnosis that never changed. Today, chemical dependency and mental health professionals recognize the need to re-evaluate the psychiatric diagnosis as a patient moves through recovery. Kenneth Minkoff, M.D., a nationally recognized expert on co-occurring disorders, has noted that treatment usually begins when neither the chemical dependency nor the mental health disorder are at baseline, which means that most initial diagnoses are based in patient history. For this reason, Dr. Minkoff cautions that "initial diagnoses are often presumptive, and the initial goal of assessment is to engage the individual in an ongoing process of continual reassessment as treatment progresses, during which diagnoses may be continually revised as new data emerge." (From the *Service Planning Guidelines for Co-occurring Psychiatric and Substance Disorders* developed by Dr. Kenneth Minkoff for the Behavioral Health Recovery Management project funded by the Illinois Department of Human Services' Office of Alcoholism and Substance Abuse, 2001.)

The Purpose of Diagnosis

Diagnosis is one of the specialties required of chemical dependency professionals. In their preparation for this function, and in carrying it out, diagnosticians will do well to keep in mind the limited scope of their specific function. Diagnosis is *diagnosis*, not confrontation, counseling, therapy, or any other service. Diagnostic interviews have a special and limited purpose, namely, to determine, on the basis of symptoms, whether or not chemical dependency is present in a client, and if it is, to evaluate what stage the illness appears to have reached.

This purpose is achieved when the diagnostician is satisfied with his or her conclusion on the basis of objective data, not when a client is convinced that the conclusion is correct. Whether or not clients and/or concerned persons (or others) *agree* is totally irrelevant, and diagnosticians as such have no obligation or responsibility to bring about agreement but only to report their diagnoses as supported by the available data.

In some situations, of course, chemical dependency specialists may wear two hats or even several hats. They may be called upon for counseling, referral, confrontation, therapy, and so on, in addition to diagnosis. But it should be clear, at least in their own minds, which of these several services they are performing as they wear their different hats because each special service has its own special goals and its own proper processes. To intermingle and confuse them is to run the risk of undermining and destroying the effectiveness of all.

A Team Process

Because dependent's self-assessment is unreliable, concerned and meaningful persons, "significant others," must participate in diagnosis. Chemical dependency diagnosis, therefore, is essentially (and ideally) a *team* process involving diagnosticians, dependents, concerned persons, and other professionals authorized by the dependent to disclose pertinent information. Concerned persons, particularly family members, are themselves so locked into delusion, negative and defensive attitudes, and life styles and behavior patterns centered on and revolving around drugs that they are seldom helpful at the beginning of the diagnostic process. Even when they are willing, they are usually uninformed about the nature and symptoms of chemical dependency and feel extremely fearful, insecure, and inadequate. In most actual real-life situations, therefore, the diagnostician's first task is to prepare and dispose spouses, family members, and other concerned persons to cooperate effectively in the diagnostic process.

We have found that a brief educational session consisting of selected content from Parts One and Two, and adapted to the level of the concerned persons, provides a basic introduction of chemical dependency: its nature, pathology, progression, and symptoms. This basic information helps to set concerned persons more at ease; gives them an opportunity to ask questions; enables them to more accurately recall and identify essential symptoms; and motivates them to cooperate more effectively in the diagnosis and evaluation process. A simple chalk talk is an effective way to convey this information.

CHAPTER NINETEEN

Diagnosis
by
Essential Symptoms

A Definition of Diagnosis

To *diagnose* means to perform an examination in order to identify or determine the nature of a disease or illness that appears to be present in a subject (in this context, in a person).

Diagnosis involves three things:

1. A *purpose*, namely, to discover whether or not a particular disease or illness is present, and if it is present, to evaluate the stage of progression or advancement it has reached in the person.

2. A *process*, namely, a systematic examination of the person to identify symptoms of the illness.

3. *Diagnostic skill*, namely, an ability on the part of the diagnostician to apply the examination process effectively in order to identify symptoms accurately and thereby to discover the nature of the underlying illness and evaluate its stage of progression.

Chemical dependency diagnosis is the examination of a person who appears to be chemically dependent in order to discover whether or not this illness is in fact present, and if it is present, to evaluate the stage of its progression. The examination or diagnostic process is directed primarily to identifying the *symptoms of chemical dependency* manifested by the person.

Diagnostic Symptoms

A **symptom**, broadly, is any circumstance or phenomenon regarded as an indicator or characteristic of a condition or event. It is an *evident* sign of a fact, condition, or quality that is not itself immediately evident. Smoke, for example, is a symptom of fire. Although a fire may not be visible, we know it is present when we see smoke.

A **diagnostic symptom** is any observable or apparent sign that serves to indicate the presence of a disease or illness and is therefore used in diagnosis.

Essential diagnostic symptoms are those that are caused directly by the underlying illness itself. Such symptoms *demonstrate* the existence of the illness because they are its *direct effects*. (As smoke is a direct effect of the fire that causes it.)

Other remote consequences or **complications** may also be used in diagnosis, of course, but these are much less effective because they are accidental, that is, there are no necessary cause-and-effect relationships between the illness and such complications. Therefore, these complications may or may not appear at all, and if they are apparent it will ordinarily be in the later stages of an illness. At best, such complications only yield an uncertain diagnosis because they may be caused by something other than the suspected illness.

Diagnostic symptoms of chemical dependency are defined as those observable or apparent signs that serve to indicate the presence of chemical dependency in a person and are therefore used in diagnosis of this illness.

Essential diagnostic symptoms of chemical dependency are defined as those outward, perceivable signs or indications, observable by someone other than the dependent, that are *caused directly* by the pathological elements of the illness and that therefore *demonstrate* the presence of chemical dependency and serve as aids in its diagnosis.

In this last definition, note that the essential symptoms of chemical dependency, like the symptoms of any illness, are *outward* signs that are available for observation. Thus, the general symptom "defensiveness" is a personal attitude that is apparent to others, and the particular defenses that are symptoms, such as denial, projection, and rationalization, are likewise externally observable.

These symptoms are *direct effects* of the elements in the chemical dependency pathology, which, in turn, are direct effects of the personal love relationship to chemicals, or the committed drug relationship. In sequence, therefore, "number one" is the drug relationship; "number two" is the pathology it causes; and "number three" is the chemical dependency syndrome, or collection of symptoms, caused by the pathology.

The existence of these symptoms *demonstrates* — that is, proves conclusively — that the illness is present in a person. The symptoms produce a *certain* diagnosis of chemical dependency. For example, the drug-oriented life style that is a general symptom of the initial or pleasure stage of psychological dependency is a clear and quiet (or sometimes not so quiet) fact. It is not an obscure mystery or a heated opinion or a mere conjecture. It is simply there, objectively, like the rest of reality, to be recognized (or disregarded), but not to be denied. A drug-oriented life style has only one direct, essential cause: a person's psychological need to orient his or her life around chemicals. Therefore, the presence of such a life style *proves* the existence in that person of psychological dependency.

Furthermore, this psychological dependency itself has only one direct, essential cause: a committed personal love relationship to mood-altering chemicals. Hence, since the cause-and-effect relationship operates directly in this sequence, we have proof positive that the person is chemically dependent. This is a matter of certainty, not of guesswork, opinion, or tentative conjecture. And it is not a moral judgment any more than is affirming the existence of tree roots when you see a redwood forest or affirming the law of gravity as you fall from a redwood tree.

Note also that these symptoms are observable by *someone other than the dependent*. Dependents and uninformed concerned persons who are themselves deeply involved in the pathology are incapable of recognizing their own condition. In this respect, they are little different from patients suffering from other diseases. Self-diagnosis is, in any case, a risky matter: "A physician who is his own diagnostician is the patient of a fool." In light of this, the common saying that "only a dependent can say that he or she is a dependent" needs careful qualification. It may mean that until I become personally aware of my chemical dependency and accept it, nothing on earth or in heaven can motivate me to seek recovery. In this sense, it is true that only I can say, "I am chemically dependent," that is, "I accept my illness." But if it is taken to mean that only I can recognize my symptoms and *diagnose* my own dependency, it is patently false. Such an assumption does nothing more than provide another defense to enable the dependent's continued drug abuse.

These symptoms serve as *aids in diagnosis*. They are objective diagnostic criteria evident to those who are trained to diagnose chemical dependency. These symptoms are evident, too, to anyone who knows what to look for in attempting to decide whether or not a person is chemically dependent. The symptoms of this illness are just as evident and far more numerous than the symptoms of the common cold.

We must emphasize here that this definition says nothing about complications or consequences. These may be used as diagnostic aids, of course, most commonly when the illness has progressed into its later stages, and assuming that they do, in fact, appear at all.

In summary, *essential* or primary diagnostic symptoms are those observable general and particular effects that are caused directly by the underlying chemical dependency pathology and that therefore demonstrate (prove conclusively) the existence of chemical dependency.

The complications that may appear in later stages of the illness may also serve as secondary diagnostic symptoms *if* a history of drug abuse is clearly established. Marriage and family problems, job problems, psychological problems, physical problems, etc., may be caused by many things other than chemical dependency, hence the need to establish a *history* of drug abuse before these can serve as secondary diagnostic symptoms.

General and Particular Symptoms

In this section, we distinguish between "general" and "particular" symptoms. Both are direct symptoms caused by the chemical dependency pathology and therefore they are *equally essential symptoms.*

General symptoms are the broad signs or indications that are caused by one or another of the eight pathological elements of the illness and that appear as *personal characteristics* or general *personal attitudes* of dependents. Thus, for example, dependents appear to be "negative persons." "Negativism" is a general symptom of chemical dependency caused directly by the pathological element "rigid negative attitudes," and this symptom affects the total person, the whole personality of the dependent.

Particular symptoms, by contrast, are the more limited signs or indications that are caused by the pathological elements and that appear as *concrete behaviors* and *behavior patterns* or as individual outward manifestations of a dependent's interior dispositions. They are the particularized ways in which general symptoms are expressed or manifested, the "integral parts" of the general symptoms. A negative person, for example, shows this negativism by being touchy, hypersensitive, hypercritical, gloomy, pessimistic, discouraged, depressed, or fearful. These are all particular symptoms of rigid negative attitudes, just as personal negativism is its general symptom.

Three Diagnostic Guidelines

In attempting diagnosis, it is well to keep in mind, first, that many symptoms of this illness also appear as symptoms of other illnesses. Some of these symptoms, at first glance, may not seem to be symptoms at all because they are exhibited by persons who appear to be quite normal. In fact, they may be exhibited by almost everyone in some respect and to some degree. In all such doubts, the key question is: "Are mood-altering chemicals involved?" or, "Does this person ingest drugs?" The presence of these symptoms *and* a personal drug involvement are the central clues leading to an accurate diagnosis.

It should be borne in mind, secondly, that the symptoms of chemical dependency are massive; they are many and varied because the illness affects the whole person and every aspect of his or her life. Unlike many diseases that affect only a part or a few parts of the human organism and one or a few life areas, this is a *total* illness. Hence, it produces a great number and variety of symptoms, literally a *mass* of symptoms.

Two things follow from this that are significant in diagnosis. One, it is relatively easy to identify the presence of the illness by an accumulation or collection of symptoms — a syndrome — even though one or even several of the symptoms do not appear to be present or do not appear as prominently as the others at the time of diagnosis. Another consequence of the multiplicity of symptoms manifested may be feelings of self-doubt on the part of the diagnostician. This self-doubt arises because, on the basis of symptoms manifested, so very many people appear to be chemically dependent. Almost everyone who goes through the personal experience of the illness and is on the road to recovery finds himself or herself "seeing the problem everywhere" and has difficulty believing what is seen. The same thing happens to professionals and trainees — and to others — when they first become acquainted with the essential symptoms of the illness. Almost reluctantly, they come to realize that chemical dependency is everywhere and that they are seeing the *real magnitude of the problem* for the first time. Self-doubts always vanish as clinical and everyday experiences prove over and over again the validity of their diagnoses and observations. Then the reaction is apt to be: "How could I have been so blind for so long!"

Thirdly, it will be noted that the same symptoms sometimes appear as manifestations of *different elements* in the pathology. This is because all the pathological elements are equally rooted in the same dynamic human composite and are therefore united together as one total reality, that is, as one specific pathology or illness entity within the person. In a sense, therefore, the whole pathology causes all the symptoms, the whole chemical dependency syndrome, and the presence of even one essential symptom is proof of the presence of the illness in its entirety. Moreover, since the same symptoms are in some instances produced conjointly by different pathological elements, their presence provides direct evidence of the underlying presence of those different elements. This, of course, adds to the certainty of a chemical dependency diagnosis.

CHAPTER TWENTY

Target of Diagnosis and Evaluation

Origin and Nature of Chemical Dependency

Chemical dependency is essentially a pathological love relationship of a person to a mood-altering chemical substance, a psychoactive drug, in expectation of a rewarding experience. It is initiated by a personal commitment to getting high on drugs, that is, by setting up within oneself a committed drug relationship based on the expectation of achieving repeated drug highs (feeling, mood, and mind changes) by means of drug ingestion.

Mood-altering chemicals, that is, psychoactive or psychotropic drugs that have the inherent power to change significantly the way one feels, are the *object* of this relationship. Broadly, these include all sedatives, stimulants, narcotics, hallucinogens, and many volatile substances.

Progression of Chemical Dependency

Chemical dependency progresses steadily through four successive stages, with each stage characterized and distinguishable by its own predominant (but not exclusive) motivation or expectation. They are as follows:

1. *the pleasure stage,* with pleasure (pleasant mood-swings) as the predominant motivation;

2. *the relief stage,* with relief from discomforts as the predominant motivation;

3. *the maintenance stage,* with maintenance of drug-dependent "normalcy" as the predominant motivation; and

4. *the escape stage,* with escape to oblivion as the predominant motivation.

Once a diagnostician has identified chemical dependency as present in a client, the stage of the illness will be evaluated according to the motivation that appears to be predominant.

Diagnostic Evaluation

Beyond the diagnostician's identification of the presence of chemical dependency in clients, diagnosticians have a further function of evaluating the stage of progression of the illness.

It must be kept in mind that a dependent's motives in a pathological love relationship to mood altering chemicals are dynamic and usually mixed. Motives appear to change back and forth very quickly from one expectation to another. Diagnosticians, therefore, need to observe more than a discrete "snapshot" of motivation at a given point in time. Rather, they need a "moving picture" of motivation over time to evaluate the client's motivational stage.

This "moving picture" is best obtained through drug ingestion history matched with developing essential symptoms of pathological elements. Drug ingestion history reveals a pattern of motivational expectations that must be distinguished from the shorter-term shifts continually taking place. It is important to note here that these stages of predominant motivation are not discrete, and that a dependent will shift back and forth between stages very quickly from one motivation to another so that at any one time the most obvious present motive may not be the one that is predominant. This shift is often due to the dependent's exercise of "marginal control." Having some degree of awareness that the drug ingestion is getting out of control and either spoiling or preventing the desired "high," dependents' attempt to prove to themselves, and usually to others, that they are "in control" and "really can handle it." Marginal control will generally work for a time, but it is ultimately destined to give out.

It is also worth noting that some kind and degree of pleasure is experienced at all stages of the illness. For example, a person who has moved well into the relief stage will experience some degree of pleasure even after the predominant relief motivation has shifted from predominant pleasure to predominant relief. Therefore, in each case, the diagnostician must examine various essential pathological symptoms for evidence that can support and confirm the evaluation.

As the following diagram shows, once the disease begins progressing through the various stages, the highs are never as high as they once were, and the lows are always lower. All the while, the sick relationship to drugs steadily and directly descends through each successive stage. In the absence of effective intervention, the disease will ultimately end in insanity or early untimely death, either through accident, injury, drug-induced physical complications, overdose, or suicide.

A Moving Picture of Motivation
in Chemical Dependency Progression

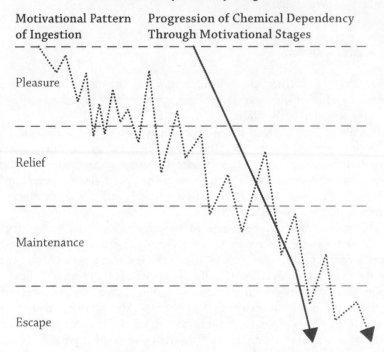

Motivational Pattern
of Ingestion

Progression of Chemical Dependency
Through Motivational Stages

Pleasure

Relief

Maintenance

Escape

Essential Pathology of Chemical Dependency

Diagnosis is made by means of symptoms. Symptoms are caused by, and hence manifest, an underlying chemical dependency pathology. Therefore, acquaintance with the essential pathology of chemical dependency is helpful in its diagnosis. Note, however, that although a thorough understanding is highly desirable, it is not absolutely necessary for accurate diagnosis of the pathology. One need not know all about fire to know that smoke is an essential symptom of it. For a professional diagnostician, of course, a thorough understanding of both pathology and symptoms is required.

"Pathology," in one sense, is a scientific study of the nature of diseases, of their causes, processes, development, and consequences. Taken in this sense, pathology is a branch of medical or biological research that deals with diseases and especially with organic, structural, or functional changes caused by or accompanying diseases.

"Pathology," in another sense, refers to the disease entity as a whole, the illness itself, including the following:

1. the various *elements* that constitute the disease/illness entity;

2. the *structure* or *pattern* of these elements, that is, their interrelationships and typical configuration;

3. the *origin* and *progression* of these elements and of the disease/illness entity as a whole through successive stages of advancement; and

4. the *resulting changes* (functional, behavioral, organic) that result in the organism (in this context, in the chemically dependent person).

This is the meaning of **pathology** as the word is used here in reference to chemical dependency. It is the disease/illness entity, the underlying *diseased condition* within a person that is caused by the person's drug relationship, that directly causes the essential symptoms and that, in its later stages, results in complications.

Following is a summary of the **essential pathology of chemical dependency** (or chemical dependency as a disease/illness entity). It includes the following pathological elements, each of which directly causes a number of essential general and particular symptoms:

1. *Psychological dependency:* an irrational need, caused by a person's committed drug relationship, to rely on the ingestion of mood-altering chemicals in expectation of achieving rewarding psychophysical experiences, or more concretely, in order to achieve welcome changes of feelings, moods, and mind. It is an unhealthy need, involving the whole person and extending directly and destructively to all psychic powers.

2. *Powerlessness:* the state or condition of a person who, as a direct and immediate result of a committed drug relationship to mood-altering chemicals, is without the ability in and of himself or herself to recognize or to remedy this drug-involved condition or to appropriately manage his or her life. As with psychological dependency, powerlessness is an element that affects the whole person, undermining all areas of his or her life and being.

3. *Mental obsession:* an intense, uncontrollable, and largely subconscious mental preoccupation with mood-altering chemicals and their rewards, caused by a person's committed drug relationship. Secondarily, this obsession extends to the drug-related and drug-induced adverse effects and consequences of the committed drug relationship.

4. *Emotional compulsion:* an intense, uncontrollable, and largely subconscious emotional impulsiveness or urgency, caused by a person's committed drug relationship, to ingest mood-altering chemicals excessively and to experience their rewards. Secondarily, this compulsiveness extends to the dependent's whole personality and to all areas of life activity.

5. *Low self-image:* a state or condition of persistently or habitually regarding oneself as of little value or personal worth and of having little self-esteem and self-respect as a direct result of one's relationship to mood-altering chemicals. It is a condition of weak ego, of low ego strength resulting from one's committed drug relationship and from the values-behavior conflicts that this relationship causes.

6. *Rigid negative attitudes:* firmly set negative positions or attitudinal postures caused by a person's relationship to mood-altering chemicals and directed against self, against other people, against God, and against anything that threatens the person's committed drug relationship. These attitudes are complex, including knowledge, feeling, and behavioral components. They affect the whole personality and extend to all areas of a dependent's life.

7. *Rigid defense system:* a complex pattern of psychological defenses that are compulsively and subconsciously used to conceal from oneself and from others one's pathological relationship to mood-altering chemicals and the destructive effects caused to oneself and others by that drug relationship. Secondarily, this defense system extends to a dependent's whole personality and manner of life.

8. *Delusion:* the mental state or condition of a person who, because of a committed relationship to mood-altering chemicals, persistently and sincerely believes things to be true that are false and believes things to be false that are true. It is a form of insanity in the proper sense, that is, mental ill-health or unsoundness of mind. It is being mentally out of touch with reality.

9. *Physical tolerance:* the ability of the human organism to absorb increasingly large dosages of drugs without exhibiting proportionate adverse effects. With increasing dosages, tolerance increases and larger quantities are required to produce the same effects that smaller quantities formerly produced. Tolerance reaches a breakpoint after which it steadily decreases so that smaller quantities of drugs produce disproportionately increasing adverse effects.

10. *Physical addiction:* the condition of the human organism in which it requires constant or frequent dosages of a drug in order to maintain itself in a state of drug-dependent "normalcy" and to avoid severe withdrawal reactions.

11. *Memory failure:* a drug-induced memory block that renders a person unable to recall what happened during a drug abuse episode. This may be *blackout,* which is a total memory failure, or *euphoric memory,* which is partial, leaving a person able to recall drug-induced euphoria or "high" feelings and general aspects of a drug abuse episode but unable to recall details.

CHAPTER TWENTY-ONE

Qualifications
for
Diagnosticians

Anyone Can Diagnose

In general, anyone who knows the symptoms and who can recognize them when they are present in a chemically dependent person can diagnose the illness. Symptoms are so obvious and so many that a dependent stands out like a screaming siren in a string quartet *if* one knows the symptoms. Perhaps the most promising of all prospects for gaining ground against drug problems is the abundance of their symptoms and the ease with which these are recognized once they are known for what they are. Every man, woman, and child, in other words, can become a diagnostician of sorts by learning to recognize the symptoms of this illness. More, of course, is required of chemical dependency professionals.

Chemical Dependency Professionals

Chemical dependency professionals, like all other professionals, must be qualified for their tasks. For this they must possess adequate knowledge, appropriate attitudes, and special competencies or skills. For a diagnostician,

Adequate knowledge includes:

1. An understanding of the essential nature of chemical dependency, of its origin, pathology, and progression.

2. An understanding of its symptoms and of the causal relationship between pathology and symptoms.

3. A knowledge of its common complications.

4. A knowledge of the essential nature and functional powers of the human being and of the life areas in which these powers enable the person to carry on activities.

5. A knowledge of available community resources to which dependents can be referred for help.

6. Self-knowledge of one's personal abilities and limitations, of one's personal values, of one's behavior in relation to one's values, of one's attitudes, special knowledge, and competencies.

7. Self-knowledge, verified by chemical dependency professionals, of the quality and extent of one's own personal relationship to mood-altering chemicals.

Appropriate attitudes include:

1. Above all, a deep personal and professional *commitment* to the service of chemically dependent persons and their families.

2. *Love*, that is, genuine affection for chemical dependents expressed in sincere concern for their personal well-being and hence for their recovery.

3. *Empathy*, that is, an ability to feel what another is feeling, when he or she is feeling it, to "walk in another's shoes," unhindered by one's prejudices, biases, preconceived assumptions, or personal defenses.

4. *Objectivity*, that is, an ability to concentrate total attention on the dependent's condition, to perceive the dependent as he or she really is, without becoming ego-involved, that is, without allowing personal interests or considerations or a dependent's manipulation to influence one's perceptions or conclusions.

5. *Courage*, that is, firmness, toughness, or "guts" in dealing with dependents in the face of their hostility, resentments, rejection, and threats and in spite of one's own fears, hurts, anger, and other negative feelings.

6. *Hope*, that is, an unshakable conviction that no dependent is a hopeless case and a genuine expectation that every dependent can recover.

7. *Self-acceptance*, that is, a total acceptance of the reality of oneself as one is here and now with all of one's positive and negative qualities.

"Humility" is another word for it, and "ego strength" is its immediate effect. This is the only personal attitude that can prevent or rid one of the self-rejection that impairs or destroys all of the above appropriate attitudes. A self-rejecting person has a pathological fear of rejection by others and is therefore easy prey to their manipulations. Such a person is incapable of truly supporting a dependent personally while dealing with his or her chemical dependency with "tough love." Invariably, a self-rejecting person becomes an enabler, supporting the dependency instead of the dependent person.

Special competencies or skills include:

1. *Recognition* of symptoms, that is, an ability to discern accurately the essential symptoms of chemical dependency in a person who appears to be chemically dependent.

2. *Identification* of the underlying pathological elements that cause the symptoms.

3. *Evaluation* of the stage the illness has reached in its progression.

4. *Recommendation for referral*, that is, the ability to decide and to suggest, on the basis of the diagnosis and other factors, the most appropriate community resource or resources to which to refer a dependent for further help. This involves consideration of the dependent's illness itself, his or her personal attitudes and resources, the attitudes and resources of concerned persons, the availability of community resources, and any other pertinent circumstances.

5. *Reporting of data*, that is, the ability to communicate to a dependent and to concerned persons in an honest, non-moralistic manner the evidence of symptoms manifested and to explain clearly the significance of this data.

6. *Recording of data*, that is, the ability to state briefly and clearly in writing the diagnostic conclusion, the symptomatic data on which it is based and the recommendations for referral.

CHAPTER TWENTY-TWO

Some Obstacles
to
Diagnosis

Professional chemical dependency diagnosticians face special obstacles stemming from (1) dependents; (2) concerned persons, especially family members; and (3) themselves.

Obstacles Arising from Dependents

1. The *illness itself* is complex, involving the total person. The pathology affects all psychic powers and produces such a number and variety of symptoms that several disorders or kinds of disorders may appear to be indicated, for example, mental or emotional disorders, psychopathy or sociopathy, etc. This can lead an unskilled diagnostician into error.

2. Dependents are *defensive* about their drug involvement. Diagnosticians pose direct and immediate threats to further drug ingestion and to the continuation of the drug relationship. A dependent's rigid defense system therefore operates with its fullest force to conceal the drug involvement and to ward off and neutralize the diagnostician's threats against it. Denial, rationalization, minimizing, attacking, belligerence, etc., are at peak performance levels.

3. Dependents are *negative* against those who threaten interference with their drug relationship and/or interruption of their drug ingestion. Diagnosticians seriously threaten this drug involvement and are therefore targets of hatred, aversion, rejection, fear, anger, hostility, resentment, manipulation, etc.

4. Dependents are *deluded*, unable to recognize their true condition or its cause: their sick love relationship to mood-altering chemicals. Hence, their self-reporting is of little or no value. Any information they offer is filtered through their defense systems and is therefore

badly distorted. Denial, repression, memory impairment, etc., deprive them of much reality data.

5. Dependents are *sincere* in their delusion. Their obvious sincerity and deep subjective conviction can be very persuasive, inviting the diagnostician's belief that their self-reporting can be trusted.

6. Dependents are given to *self-diagnosis*. Sincerely convinced of their own insights, they diagnose their own cases with complete subjective certitude. Invariably, their diagnosis is that some problem other than drugs is their real problem.

7. Dependents are subconsciously and compulsively *manipulative*. Only two roles are possible for them: their own as chemical dependents and the reciprocal role of enabler. Hence, their every word and action is an automatic manipulation to place and to keep the diagnostician in the enabler role.

8. Dependents may display relative *integrity of life* in the earlier stages of their illness, that is, no serious family, social, employment, physical, financial, or other complications may be evident. This they allege as proof that they are not chemically dependent. An unskilled diagnostician who bases diagnosis on complications instead of essential symptoms is an easy victim of this ploy.

Obstacles Arising from Concerned Persons, Especially Family Members

1. *Their own illness* closely parallels that of dependents. Hence, they, too, exhibit many and various symptoms that may appear to indicate a wide range of disorders.

2. They, too, are *defensive* about their own enabler role and about the dependent's drug involvement.

3. They, too, are *negative* against threats of interference with their sick relationship to the dependent and of interruption of their enabler role.

4. They, too, are *deluded* about both their own and the dependent's conditions. Hence, their reporting is not totally reliable and must be carefully sifted.

5. They, too, are *sincere* in their delusion, thus inviting the diagnostician's complete trust in what they say.

6. They, too, are given to *self-diagnosis* and to *misdiagnosis* of dependents. When they are locked into the enabler's role, as is often the case even when they are sincerely seeking help, they readily support their own misdiagnoses by offering many "reasons" for the problems the dependent is having. The "reasons" assigned are seldom relevant.

7. Concerned persons and especially family members compulsively *manipulate* to get the diagnostician to agree with their own diagnoses of what is wrong with the dependent and with their own prescriptions of what should be done about it.

Obstacles Arising from Diagnosticians Themselves

1. *Personal drug involvement.* Diagnosticians who ingest mood-altering chemicals may themselves be chemically dependent. If so, they are self-deceived, personally deluded. Their diagnoses are filtered through their own defense systems and are therefore badly distorted. In effect, they manipulate their professional position to be both self-enablers and enablers for their clients. A typical diagnostic criterion will be *horizontal comparison*: "If my client's drug ingestion is like my own, then there is no chemical dependency."

2. *Misdirected focus.* Because dependents present many complications that are consequences of chemical dependency, but which may or might be produced by other causes or problems, diagnosticians may misdirect the focus of their attention to the complications as such or to the "other causes" or "other problems" that could produce such complications. This leaves the chemical dependency problem unregarded and leads to misdiagnosis.

3. *False assumptions.* Diagnosticians may harbor false assumptions about the nature and symptoms of chemical dependency. For example, chemical dependency may be regarded as a symptom of some other illness or problem; as a manifestation of some under-lying psychological, personality, or character disorder; or as a neurosis, psychosis, emotional, or mental disturbance, etc. All such assumptions destroy the objectivity necessary for accurate diagnosis and preclude the possibility of a proper chemical dependency diagnosis.

4. *Ignorance of essential symptoms.* Without a thorough knowledge of these, early diagnosis is impossible and late-stage diagnosis will not be based on the diagnostician's personal verification of direct symptoms, but on gross complications and hearsay reports. More particularly, such a diagnostician will (a) be personally threatened by

257

the defensiveness, negativism, and low self-image of clients; (b) be personally drawn into clients' defenses; (c) miss the significance of clients' defenses as proper diagnostic symptoms; and (d) regard such symptoms as obstacles to diagnosis instead of as its essential bases.

5. *Inappropriate personal attitudes.*

    a. *Moralism.* A moralistic diagnostician is unable to view clients and their symptoms objectively but sits in judgment. Instead of drawing factual conclusions based on objective data, he or she will pass moral judgments of right or wrong, good or bad, and will condemn the person instead of examining the illness.

    b. *Fear.* A timid diagnostician will retreat from a firm diagnosis when threatened by the defensive hostility and belligerence of dependents and concerned persons and when contradicted or attacked by other would-be diagnosticians, especially other professionals.

    c. *Hostility.* An angry diagnostician will easily lose objectivity and become punitive, dumping his or her own load of anger onto clients.

    d. *Ego involvement.* An insecure diagnostician is easily manipulated into destructive personal relationships with clients: "love" affairs, parental protectiveness, and other enabling relationships.

    e. *Self- rejection, low ego strength.* A self-rejecting diagnostician with a sick need for approval will avoid the rejection directed against him or her by clients by backing away from objective diagnosis or will counter such rejection by rejection of clients.

    f. *Personal defensiveness.* This impairs both perception and clinical judgment and blocks effective relationships and communication with clients.

    g. *Personal negativism* both directly repels clients and renders the diagnostician incapable of conveying to clients the hope they need to generate motivation for recovery.

6. *Incompetence.* Lack of skill in any of the competency areas noted above seriously impairs diagnostic work. Inaccurate, ambiguous, or dishonest reporting of data (feedback) to clients is especially destructive of the diagnostic relationship. Incompetence, like

ignorance of the nature and symptoms of chemical dependency, destroys the confidence of clients and prevents self-confidence on the part of diagnosticians. Fear prevails when confidence is lacking, and effective diagnosis is impossible.

Some Final Thoughts

As we stated in the Foreword to this book, chemical dependency affects people from every walk of life, without exception. It follows, then, that the individuals — both professional and lay, addicted and non-addicted — who might benefit from this book will inevitably represent the widest range of philosophical, religious, and spiritual beliefs one could imagine. Given that reality, we do not expect every single reader to share our philosophical and spiritual beliefs.

At the same time, we must note again that from the start those beliefs played a major part in our investigations into chemical dependency. It was clear to us in the late 1960s that a unifying theory or organizing principle of some sort was missing from our society's descriptions and definitions of addiction. We resolved to pursue this burning question until we could arrive at an answer. The major outcome of our pursuit was to identify the unifying factor of addiction as a *relational disease*, which we did in 1975.

We always believed that our study of that relationship — as well as the treatment of the illness that develops from it — would greatly benefit from the perspectives of philosophy and theology, as well as from science. As mentioned in the opening pages of this book, the transcendental aspects of human experience, as well as *being* itself, have long been the realm of philosophy and theology, while science properly concerns itself with matter, with the measurable things of the material world. These transcendental aspects of human experience include those powers, activities, and *relationships* that transcend matter and defy quantification, and yet are very real.

In our examination of the essential nature of chemical dependency, we utilized the philosophical principles of faculty psychology to provide us with a structure for examining the nature and function of the whole person, *soma* and *psyche*, body and soul. In other words, faculty psychology allowed us to take into account both the material and the transcendental nature of the human person wherein addiction exists. These explorations of the whole person led us to the conclusion that the key to understanding addiction, as we have been saying throughout this book, is in the person's committed pathological love *relationship* to mood-altering chemicals. This relationship affects every aspect of a person's being. Any efforts intended to help a chemically dependent person, then, must address the needs of the whole person if a true recovery is to be effected.

Today, we still see a continuing need to integrate the application of the disciplines of philosophy and theology into the study of addiction in order to effectively address all aspects of the human person. We have revisited this issue in our closing pages to emphasize how important we think it is that treatment programs and recovery plans offer opportunities to heal the whole person.

In light of this whole-person approach to understanding the nature of addiction, we believe that the Twelve Steps of Alcoholics Anonymous provide the most effective guidelines developed to date for the whole person healing of chemical dependency. Historically and clinically, theoretically and practically, empirically and pragmatically, the Steps are well established. The superabundant fruits of the Twelve Steps demonstrate their power as healing principles.

Since the founding of Alcoholics Anonymous in 1935, it has been the experience of millions of people worldwide that the Twelve Steps speak directly, firmly, and compassionately to the heart of the illness, to its symptoms, and to the damage it has caused in their own lives and the lives of others.

Many treatment centers do integrate the principles of the Twelve Steps with other therapeutic program components. Still others categorically reject the Steps altogether. They may employ treatment modalities that are so focused on a single aspect of the whole person or on other problems related to the disease that the Twelve Steps prove to be completely incompatible with their approach. It may also be the case that some reject the Steps because of differing philosophical and spiritual beliefs.

There is little question that differences in personal beliefs present a challenge in any treatment or counseling setting. There also is no question that chemically dependent persons comprise a cross-section of the general population and will likely hold a wide range of different beliefs.

In general, though, the belief in "a Power greater than ourselves," to use a term from the Twelve Steps, is something a great many people can subscribe to. Recent polling of the general public conducted by the Pew Research Center for the People and the Press and the Pew Forum on Religion and Public Life (2006) found that 96% of the public in the United States say they believe in God or some form of Supreme Being. The Harris Interactive Poll (2006) conducted an on-line poll of an all-adult base and found that 73% believe in God and 58% said they were absolutely certain that there is a God.

In light of these results, one can conclude that millions of Americans believe in God, and of these, thousands are likely to make their way along diverse paths into addiction treatment, or counseling. These people deserve to be provided with, not deprived of, the knowledge and tools to effect *whole person* recovery. It is our hope that helping professionals, in spite of differing personal beliefs, will meet the challenge of addressing the essential, whole-person nature of addiction in those with whom they work, and that they will be open to seeking creative and effective ways to introduce them to the healing principles of the Twelve Steps. Some addicts, of course, will hold differing beliefs and reject the Steps. Those who are already searching for the One, the Other, the More, the Mystery in their lives may find what they are looking for in the Twelve Steps and experience a sought-after spiritual healing.

Application of the Essentials Approach

In Chapter One, we stated that we leave the *application* of the essentials approach to chemical dependency educators, diagnosticians, counselors, therapists, trainers, researchers, and other professionals who, directly or indirectly, serve addicted persons. These professionals adapt the content and structure found in this work to their own methods and processes, which are designed to meet the specialized needs of their particular disciplines and the clientele they serve.

As one might expect, over the course of our professional practice, we applied the essentials approach in all areas of service that we engaged in, including diagnosis, intervention, counseling, treatment, public education, training, and consultation. We present below just one example of applied "essentials" content and structure that we developed in the delivery of therapeutic education in treatment.

Therapeutic Education Component of Primary Treatment

The Essentials of Chemical Dependency provides a common, simple language with which to convey to clients a basic understanding of the essential nature of their relational illness and the process of recovery.

We have found that the most effective clinical approach to whole person treatment and whole person recovery is an integrated essentials approach. Toward this end, we developed an effective, integrated, two-component, or "two-track," system of daily therapeutic education, which provided a sound knowledge base and a clear focus of peer group therapy.

The *first track* consists of a coordinated sequence of developmental education focused on the illness entity of addiction, the pathological love relationship, its causes, nature, progression, pathology, and symptoms; the nature of the human person; and the faculties that enable us to function as fully human.

The primary goal of this track is to convey to dependents an integrated body of knowledge about chemical dependency that will lead to an understanding and acceptance of the illness and, ultimately, to surrender to the reality of addiction.

The focus of the *second track* is on the healing principles of the Twelve Steps, including the termination of the sick love relationship, the healing of pathology, and the healing and restoration of the functional powers of the whole person. Each presentation of a particular element of pathology is followed by a presentation of the Step(s) that have a special power to advance the healing of that particular element of pathology.

The goal of the Twelve Step track is to assist persons in acquiring knowledge of the guidelines for healing and for full personal recovery — a process that leads to a stable, solid reintegration of the whole personality. Another goal is to assist persons in developing the motivation to recover and in practically applying the guidelines that will help them in this process. A third goal is to assist them in addressing complications, issues, and related problems, and in learning to act responsibly and with accountability.

The Twelve Steps of Alcoholic Anonymous

1. We admitted we were powerless over alcohol — that our lives had become unmanageable.
2. Came to believe that a Power greater than ourselves could restore us to sanity.
3. Made a decision to turn our will and our lives over to the care of God as we understood Him.
4. Made a searching and fearless moral inventory of ourselves.
5. Admitted to God, to ourselves, and to another human being the exact nature of our wrongs.
6. Were entirely ready to have God remove all these defects of character.
7. Humbly asked Him to remove our shortcomings.
8. Made a list of all persons we had harmed and became willing to make amends to them all.
9. Made direct amends to such people wherever possible, except when to do so would injure them or others.
10. Continued to take personal inventory and when we were wrong promptly admitted it.
11. Sought through prayer and meditation to improve our conscious contact with God as we understood Him, praying only for knowledge of His will for us and the power to carry that out.
12. Having had a spiritual awakening as the result of these steps, we tried to carry this message to alcoholics and to practice these principles in all our affairs

All the steps help to heal all of the pathology in our whole person and in all of our functional life powers. But some Steps are more powerful than others in healing a particular pathology at work in specific life powers. The chart below shows the inter-relationship among pathology, life powers, and the Steps.

Essential Elements of Pathology Matched to Life Powers and the Twelve Steps

Essential Element of Pathology	Life Powers Directly Impaired	Step That Especially Heals This Pathology
Psychological Dependency	All	Steps Eleven, Twelve
Mental Obsession	Mental	Step Seven
Emotional Compulsion	Emotional	Step Five
Low Self-Image	Spiritual	Step Four
Rigid Negative Attitudes	Emotional	Step Six
Rigid Defense System	Mental	Steps Three, Eleven
Delusion	Mental	Step Two
Powerlessness	Volitional	Step One
Desocialization	Social	Steps Eight, Nine, Ten

The chart below shows individual Steps in relation to particular Life Powers and the element of pathology healed by the Step.

**The Twelve Steps Matched to Life Powers
and Essential Elements of Pathology**

The Healing Steps	Life Powers Healed	Pathology Healed
Step One	Volitional	Powerlessness
Step Two	Mental	Delusion
Step Three	Mental	Rigid Defense System
Step Four	Spiritual	Low Self-Image
Step Five	Emotional	Emotional Compulsion
Step Six	Emotional	Rigid Negative Attitudes
Step Seven	Mental	Mental Obsession
Step Eight	Social	Rigid Defense System, Desocialization
Step Nine	Social	Rigid Defense System, Desocialization
Step Ten	Social	Rigid Negative Attitudes
Step Eleven	All	Relationship to Mood-Altering Chemicals
Step Twelve	All	Psychological Dependency

The chart on the next page describes in more detail how each of the Steps advances healing and the recovery process.

Focus of Special Healing Powers of Particular Steps

Steps	Special Power to Advance Healing
1	**Step One** heals powerlessness by one's identifying and accepting the reality of one's current helpless condition as the starting point for any real change.
2	**Step Two** heals delusion by pointing to and providing access in faith to God's healing power beyond one's current human insanity.
3	**Step Three** heals the rigid defense system by opening in total vulnerability to God's loving care (God's will/love to heal) exactly where one is at right now with God, and thus undermines/implodes/"blasts" the entire defense system from the inside out.
4	**Step Four** heals low self-image at its principal source, the massive moral anxiety (depressing guilt) that results from the repeated behavior in conflict with one's personal value system.
5	**Step Five** heals emotional compulsion by 1) surfacing, pinpointing, accepting, and surrendering it as a major influence in compelling immoral behavior; and 2) by making nonjudgmental forgiveness easier to accept, in view of the impact of compulsion on one's behavior.
6	**Step Six** heals rigid negative attitudes by opening a person totally and at depth for inner healing, especially of the characteristic avoidance (negative) attitudes central in sick love relationships.
7	**Step Seven** heals rigid mental obsession by directing the mind to God in prayer, thus initiating and fostering mental attention to God, thinking about, imagining, and remembering God; cultivating a healthy mental preoccupation quite different from and opposite to mental obsession with a creature love object.
8, 9, 10	**Steps Eight, Nine, and Ten** heal interpersonal relationships by removing obstacles from the person, the origin of such relationships: making amends for harm done; forgiving all who have harmed us; reaching out to restore, cultivate, and maintain healthy relationships.
11	**Step Eleven** heals the sick relationship itself by directly cultivating a love relationship with God, the principal healer, the source of life, health, wholeness, holiness, and happiness. In other steps the gifts of God are sought; in this step the Giver of the gifts is directly sought.
12	**Step Twelve** heals psychological dependency in/through the spiritual awakening that is the result of these steps—whole person healing of whole person sickness. The good of one's personal healing prompts personal sharing with its diffusion among those sisters and brothers still suffering in sick love relationships.

Peer Group Therapy

The purpose of peer group therapy as an essential component of a chemical dependency (addiction) treatment program is to harness the healing power of the addicts themselves in a dynamic group process that enables them to help each other. This process is highly effective when all addicts engaged in peer group therapy are equipped, through Essentials therapeutic education, with an in-depth understanding of the essential nature of their illness, of whole person pathology, and tools for recovery. Their common goal is to help one another uncover, discover, and recover in the following ways.

1. *To consistently focus their primary attention on their sick love relationship.* This is their central problem and the reason they are in treatment. All addicts compulsively focus on other problems. To keep them on track is a huge challenge to group facilitators as well as all the group members.

2. *To gain conscious awareness of the sick love relationship present within them.* The defense (denial) system of the addicts puts them out of touch with and blinds them to the reality of the disease entity present within themselves. By having others in the group point out symptoms of the addict's pathology as they appear here and now, the addict is able to identify and to become gut-level convinced that the illness is present within.

3. *To gain self-acceptance of themselves as persons having the illness.* Addiction is a fatal illness. It kills not only physically, but also psychologically and spiritually, by destroying one's self-esteem and one's love relationships with God, neighbor, and universe. This is an overwhelming, depressing, and discouraging burden to bear. The loving acceptance and support of the other addicts in a therapy group eases the burden, greatly facilitates self-acceptance, and goes a long way toward the healing of disrupted relationships.

4. *To gain actual here and now experiences of freedom,* which become strongly motivational foretastes of the great release into freedom that recovery holds out in promise.

Peer group therapy chips away at addiction pathology by identifying it through symptoms that are here and now present and observable. As each bit is chipped away, addicts feel a bit of relief. Their burden is lightened a little. They experience little releases into freedom.

In effective peer group therapy, these experiences multiply and are cumulatively so rewarding that freedom from mood-altering chemicals and freedom to exercise their God-given powers to live and act as normal, healthy human persons displaces and replaces their sick love relationship to mood altering chemicals.

Most dependents accept the view that their illness is a pathological love relationship because the concept speaks directly and authentically to their own life experiences. Typically, dependents involved in a process of thorough, thoughtful study of the content and structure of chemical dependency as presented in this two-track system of therapeutic education experience a lowering of delusion as their denial system is penetrated more and more deeply by the truth of what they discover about themselves in relation to the object of their addiction. They spontaneously engage in a process of self-diagnosis. They tend to come out of the process much less resistant to the diagnosis of others. They have been directly involved in discovering the truth of their condition, which subsequently opens them up and prepares the way for recognizing and dealing with the pathological effects of the disease, especially their devastated feeling/emotional life and their badly battered low self-image

Therapeutic Education in Aftercare Treatment

Two major goals of aftercare are ongoing support in the recovery process, and positive growth and development. For our purposes, in the context of applied therapeutic education, we address here only the positive growth and development goal.

To assist clients in growth and development in recovery, we created a therapeutic approach focused on the recovery of life power functions.

Throughout the course of a one-year aftercare program, participants focus on a different life power every two months. Each person identifies a particular recovery goal and lists steps to achieve it. Goals and steps toward achievement of goals should be specific, clear, measurable, realistic, relevant, meaningful, and attainable within two months. Group members assist each other with goal setting. They also support and encourage one another as they take steps toward achieving their goals.

A report session at the end of two months proves to be a celebratory event. An accomplished pianist shares how her creative life power has come alive again. She had feared that her ability to play at a concert level was lost forever. A father tells of two steps forward and one back in the process of rebuilding his relationship with his teenage son. Another makes a difficult amends that previously never seemed possible. An elderly woman begins to take responsibility for her diabetic condition. A young adult leaves a gang he belongs to. A husband and wife attend a retreat for couples in troubled marriages. A man returns to the practice of religion. Not all are completely successful in achieving their intended goals; but all are touched and motivated by the witness of others to continue to pursue them. Each is stronger in his or her recovery for having taken these concrete actions. Total person reintegration is underway.

The Adventure of Recovery

Perhaps the greatest thrill of recovery is to experience the rebirth of the life powers.

To know in one's deepest self that your mind is alive and sharp, decisive, creative and spontaneous is a self-affirming, exciting experience.

To feel physical health returning and to experience a physical sense of well-being as a result of healthy living; that is, eating, exercising and rest, etc., stimulates one's whole person. Simply experiencing a strong, supple, healthy body-tone provides energy and enthusiasm for living.

When emotions begin to flow spontaneously and are expressed appropriately, there is a strong sense of inner "one-ness" with self. You begin to feel congruent or like you really do "fit" inside yourself. Then the feeling of being fully human and fully alive becomes a reality. Now the whole range of emotions become available through which to experience life. New depths of feelings provide a richness of response to the little as well as to the big events of day-to-day living.

As your values become clearer to you and your will recovers its freedom to choose once again, the ability to follow through on those choices also reemerges. Behaviors naturally begin to fall in line with your choices and with your intentions to live up to your values. A reassuring sense of "measuring up" brings back a sense of self-respect and self-acceptance. It feels good to like yourself.

The joy of human friendship, intimacy and committed healthy love relationships become possible as the ability to engage in satisfying interpersonal relationships returns. Nourishing and nurturing relationships restore a sense of "family." Loving and being loved becomes a reality. Both are warming, comforting, and strengthening.

The most deeply reaffirming personal relationship open to you in recovery, however, is with your God. God is at once the beginning and the end of your healing. God is the Power to replace your powerlessness. God removes the insanity and restores to sanity. God's loving care fills the void left by empty attempts to control. With your newly restored freedom of will, surrender to God's loving care is possible. True surrender at last opens the way to experience God's total and unconditional love for you. You become empowered to receive God's compassionate touch of healing love. What God began in you he brings to fulfillment in a spiritual awakening of each life power and thus of your whole person.

In closing, our hope is that all chemically dependent persons and their families experience the adventure of recovery and find their way to new and true freedom and peace.

CPSIA information can be obtained at www.ICGtesting.com
Printed in the USA
LVOW041715090812

293688LV00008B/59/P